Jackie
Nefdt
Jan '08

D0520009

# Project**WILD**®Aquatic

## K–12 Curriculum & Activity Guide

## Principal Sponsors

Project WILD is administered by the Council for Environmental Education and is cosponsored with the Western Association of Fish and Wildlife Agencies.

The views and conclusions contained in this document are those of the authors and should not be interpreted as representing the opinions or policies of the U.S. Government. Mention of trade names or commercial products does not constitute their endorsement by the U.S. Government.

Cover photos of large-mouth bass and swordfish courtesy of Bass Pro Shops.

## Awards and Recognition

Project WILD, its sponsors, and many of its participants—including students and educators—have received a variety of awards and recognition. Project WILD was honored at the White House in 1991 as one of the first recipients of the Gold Medal for Education and Communications in the President's Environment and Conservation Challenge Award program. This award was bestowed "for excellence in developing innovative solutions to the nation's environmental challenges." Project WILD has also received the Conservation Education Award from The Wildlife Society. Additionally, the National Environmental Education and Training Foundation in Washington, D.C. recognized the Council for Environmental Education with the 1997 National Environmental Education Achievement Award for leadership in conservation education. Project WILD materials have been endorsed by the National Council for Social Studies and are consistent with recommendations of the National Science Teachers Association.

These materials were originally developed in 1987 with the U.S. Fish and Wildlife Service. In 2000, the Council for Environmental Education revised these materials in response to a comprehensive Project WILD program evaluation and national education reform efforts. Funding for the development of the original materials was provided from monies made possible through the Wallop-Breaux Amendment to the Sport Fish Restoration Act. This federal legislation provides support for aquatic resources education to increase public understanding of, and responsibility toward, the nation's water resources and aquatic life forms.

CEE
COUNCIL FOR
ENVIRONMENTAL
EDUCATION

Project WILD National Office
5555 Morningside Drive, Suite 212
Houston, TX 77005
Phone: (713) 520-1936   Fax: (713) 520-8008
E-mail: info@projectwild.org
Web: www.projectwild.org

5555 Morningside Drive, Suite 212
Houston, TX 77005
Phone: (713) 520-1936   Fax: (713) 520-8008
E-mail: info@councilforee.org
Web: www.councilforee.org

© Copyright 2006, 2005, 2004, 2003, 2002, 2001, 2000, 1992, 1985 and 1983 by the Council for Environmental Education. Nothing in this volume may be copied or reproduced by any means without the written permission of the Council for Environmental Education, in accordance with copyright policy established by the Council for Environmental Education, except pages indicated for student use, which may be reproduced without permission for educational use in conjunction with the activities contained herein.
All rights reserved.
Revised Edition. Printed in the U.S.A. on recycled paper using soy ink. ♲

# Table of Contents

*continued*

# Project WILD Sponsors

## Project WILD State Sponsors

Alabama Department of Conservation
and Natural Resources

Alaska Department of Fish and Game

Arkansas Game and Fish Commission

California Department of Fish and Game

Colorado Division of Wildlife

Connecticut Department of
Environmental Protection

Delaware Department of Natural Resources
and Environmental Control

District of Columbia Environmental
Health Administration

Florida Fish and Wildlife
Conservation Commission

Georgia Department of Natural Resources

Hawaii Department of Land
and Natural Resources

Idaho Department of Fish and Game

Illinois Department of Natural Resources

Indiana Department of Natural Resources

Iowa Department of Natural Resources

Kansas Department of Wildlife and Parks

Kentucky Department of Fish and
Wildlife Resources

Louisiana Department of Wildlife and Fisheries

Maine Department of Inland Fisheries
and Wildlife

Maryland Department of Natural Resources

Mass Audubon

Massachusetts Division of Fisheries and Wildlife

Michigan State University
Department of Community, Agriculture,
Recreation and Resource Studies

Minnesota Department of Natural Resources

Mississippi Department of Wildlife,
Fisheries and Parks

Missouri Department of Conservation

Montana Department of Fish, Wildlife and Parks

Nebraska Game and Parks Commission

Nevada Department of Wildlife

New Hampshire Fish and Game Department

New Jersey Division of Fish and Wildlife

New Mexico Department of Game and Fish

*continued*

New York State Department of
Environmental Conservation

North Carolina Wildlife Resources Commission

North Dakota Department of Game and Fish

Ohio Division of Wildlife

Oklahoma Department of Wildlife Conservation

Oregon Department of Fish and Wildlife

Oregon State University Extension 4-H

Pennsylvania Fish and Boat Commission

Pennsylvania Game Commission

Puerto Rico Department of Natural and
Environmental Resources

Rhode Island Division of Fish and Wildlife

South Carolina Department of
Natural Resources

South Dakota Department of Game, Fish,
and Parks

Tennessee Wildlife Federation

Texas Parks and Wildlife Department

Utah Division of Wildlife Resources

Vermont Department of Fish and Wildlife

Virginia Department of Game and
Inland Fisheries

Virginia Division—Izaak Walton League
of America

Washington Department of Fish and Wildlife

West Virginia Division of Natural Resources

Wisconsin Department of Natural Resources

Wyoming Game and Fish Department

## Contributing Sponsors

National Fish and Wildlife Foundation

ConocoPhillips

## Associate Sponsors

American Fisheries Society

Defenders of Wildlife

National Wildlife Federation

U.S. Environmental Protection Agency

U.S. Fish and Wildlife Service

## International Sponsors

Canadian Wildlife Federation

Centre for Environment Education,
Ahmedabad, India

Czech Junak, Czech Republic

National Centre for Educational Materials,
Iceland

Parks and Recreation Foundation of Japan

Umea University, Sweden

# Preface

Project WILD is an interdisciplinary conservation and environmental education program emphasizing wildlife. The goal of Project WILD is to assist learners of any age in developing awareness, knowledge, skills, and commitment resulting in informed decisions, responsible behavior, and constructive actions concerning wildlife and the environment.

The waters of the earth, in some form, are within walking distance from anywhere on the planet. The *Project WILD Aquatic K–12 Curriculum and Activity Guide* serves as an invitation to explore and understand the fascinating world of water and the aquatic habitats it supports.

Water in all its forms is one of the most dramatic of today's arenas in which informed, responsible, and constructive actions are needed. Water is one of the basic components of habitat for people and for wildlife—it is essential to all life. Aquatic species and aquatic ecosystems give humans early and clear warning about the quality of the water environment upon which we all depend.

For instructional purposes in Project WILD, wildlife is defined as any nondomesticated animal. Wildlife may be as small as a microscopic organism or as large as a blue whale. Wildlife includes but is not limited to insects, spiders, birds, reptiles, fish, amphibians, and mammals, if nondomesticated. For instructional purposes in the *Project WILD Aquatic K–12 Curriculum and Activity Guide*, aquatic wildlife refers to any wild animals that depend upon aquatic environments for survival.

Project WILD originated as a joint project of the Council for Environmental Education (CEE) (formerly Western Regional Environmental Education Council, Inc. [WREEC]) and the Western Association of Fish and Wildlife Agencies (WAFWA) in the 13 western states. WREEC was founded in 1970 in a unique and visionary effort to create a partnership between education and natural resource professionals. WAFWA is comprised of the directors of the public agencies in 13 western states that are responsible for management of wildlife in their respective states.

In 1996, WREEC officially changed its name to the Council for Environmental Education (CEE) to reflect its national network of state department of education and natural resource agency professionals. CEE's mission is to provide environmental education programs and services that promote stewardship of the environment and further the capacity of learners to make informed decisions. To accomplish its mission, CEE supports programs and partnerships for environmental education.

## One Million Educators Gone WILD!

Since Project WILD was introduced in 1983, more than 1,000,000 educators in the United States have participated in Project WILD workshops. Those educators, in turn, will have provided instruction using Project WILD to more than 53 million youth since the program was first introduced. (See **www.projectwild.org** for more information.) This success, which has made Project WILD one of the largest wildlife education programs in the world, is possible only through the enthusiastic support of Project WILD's extensive and talented network of Project WILD Sponsors, Coordinators, and Facilitators. Project WILD is endorsed by both the National Council for Social Studies and the Association of Fish and Wildlife Agencies.

*continued*

Project WILD's primary audience is educators of kindergarten through high school students. This approach does not limit the usefulness of Project WILD to formal educational settings, however. Volunteers working with students in pre-school and after-school programs; representatives of private conservation, industry, and other community groups; and personnel involved in preparation of future educators are all among those who effectively use the instructional resources of this program.

Project WILD is sponsored throughout the United States, the District of Columbia, Puerto Rico, and six countries in addition to the United States. Project WILD enjoys additional support through contributions and grants.

Project WILD's educational materials are provided to educators through practical, interactive workshops conducted by representatives of sponsoring state wildlife, natural resources, and educational agencies. The dedication and commitment of teachers, wildlife biologists, interested citizens, school administrators, and other ecological enthusiasts who volunteer hours of time and effort make Project WILD possible at the state and local levels.

The Board and staff of the Council for Environmental Education; Project WILD Program Committee; WAFWA and IAFWA members and all the organizational, state, and international sponsors; and others associated with the program are dedicated to achieving the highest possible standards of professional quality, factual accuracy, and objectivity in all programs, activities, and materials bearing the Project WILD name. Project WILD has adopted policies and guidelines that state the program's commitment to neutrality on controversial issues, treating such issues fairly and honestly without advocating any one particular point of view and recognizing that people need information from a variety of sources to make their own informed decisions. Project WILD programs, activities, and materials are not to be used to promote agency or organizational policies or political points of view.

The views and conclusions contained in this document are those of the authors and should not be interpreted as representing the opinions or policies of the U.S. Government. Mention of trade names or commercial products does not constitute their endorsement by the U.S. Government.

## For Additional Information

For additional information about participation in Project WILD as an associate or international sponsor, please contact the following:

Project WILD National Office
Council for Environmental Education
5555 Morningside Drive, Suite 212
Houston, TX 77005
Phone: (713) 520-1936
E-mail: **info@projectwild.org**
Web: **www.projectwild.org**

## Other Programs Administered by CEE

The Council for Environmental Education has launched a new migratory bird education program, *Flying WILD. WET in the City* and *Team WET Schools* are urban water education efforts also administered by CEE. For more information contact:

Flying WILD
Council for Environmental Education
5555 Morningside Drive, Suite 212
Houston, Texas 77005
Phone: (713) 520-1936
Web: www.flyingwild.org

WET in the City and Team WET Schools
Council for Environmental Education
5555 Morningside Drive, Suite 212
Houston, Texas 77005
Phone: (713) 520-1936
Web: www.wetcity.org

## Council for Environmental Education Staff

Josetta Hawthorne
Executive Director

Bill Andrews
Director, Project WILD

Mary Ford
Sr. Manager, Project WILD

Jennifer Paschke
Manager, Program Communications

Marc LeFebre
Sr. Coordinator, Flying WILD

Jeff Dornbos
Coordinator, Water Education Programs

Beshka Candelaria
Coordinator, Water Education Programs

Angee Austin
Business Administrator

Lanese Bush
Administrative Assistant, CEE

Leslie Sun
Intern

Sara Yerger
Intern

# Introduction

A concern for the land, its resources, and its continuing viability is basic to our survival and well-being—as individuals, as a nation, and as members of the world community. Two groups within society play important roles in shaping future environments: resource management professionals and educators. Educators have the responsibility for equipping learners with the skills and knowledge necessary to access and evaluate information upon which sound judgments can be made. Resource management professionals provide us with the information and technology necessary to achieve our goals.

Project WILD was created by the Western Regional Environmental Education Council (WREEC), which was founded in 1970 to bring together state-level resource management professionals and education administrators from 13 western states to work on environmental education programs of regional and, ultimately, national importance. Funding and support were provided by the Western Association of Fish and Wildlife Agencies (WAFWA).

Based on WREEC's successful Project Learning Tree model, the Project WILD conceptual outline was developed with input from educators, preservationists, conservationists, wildlife managers, business and industry representatives, and others. Learning activities in a variety of subject matter and skill areas were written by classroom teachers in regional writing workshops, and their work was tested extensively by other educators before being edited and assembled in final form. WREEC did not seek to produce a course of study, but aimed to develop a collection of good learning activities that could be used in many settings and content areas.

As with all good educational materials, Project WILD is concerned with providing information,

as well as helping students to evaluate choices and to make responsible decisions. In short, Project WILD's mission is to help students learn *how* to think, not *what* to think.

This revised edition of Project WILD adheres to those strict efforts for balance and objectivity, backed by sound educational practices and theory. It also represents the work of many within the fields of education and natural resource management from across the country. The materials are available to those who attend instructional workshops offered by certified leaders and supported by a network of sponsoring state, national, and international agencies.

We are pleased to bring you Project WILD in an easy-to-use format that organizes activities by thematic topic, subject matter, and grade level. If you have used Project WILD before, you will find much that is familiar, as well as some new activities designed to more effectively teach core concepts. If you are new to Project WILD, we hope that this curriculum guide will become a most valued educational resource.

Personally, I take great pride in being part of the Council for Environmental Education and the great Project WILD family that has done so much for literally millions of students over the years. For those who are just now joining us, a hearty and sincere welcome. Yes, working together we can make a difference!


Rudolph J. H. Schafer

Founder
Western Regional Environmental Education Council

Board Member
Council for Environmental Education

# How to Use the Project WILD K–12 Curriculum and Activity Guides

Project WILD was designed to be an instructional resource for educators who want to introduce students to hands-on activities that encourage problem-solving and decision-making skills about the environment they share with wildlife.

## Supporting Academic Concepts Required in the Classroom

The activities found in Project WILD are intended for use in both classroom and non-formal settings. The instructional materials are designed to support state and national academic standards appropriate for grades K–12. The activities can easily be adapted to meet the learning requirements for academic disciplines ranging from science and environmental education to social studies, math, and language arts. Educators may choose one or numerous Project WILD activities to teach a concept or skill. The activities may be integrated into existing courses of study, or an entire set of activities may serve as the basis for a specific course.

## Updates and Revisions

The *Project WILD* and *Aquatic K–12 Curriculum and Activity Guides* were updated in 2000 in keeping with national education reform efforts. Both the conceptual framework and individual activities were revised to help meet national education standards and assessment criteria. The background information found in the activities also was revised (1) to provide current statistics and updated factual information and (2) to highlight successful conservation efforts.

## Organization of Materials

The Project WILD curriculum is organized into three sections (1) Ecological Knowledge, (2) Social and Political Knowledge, and (3) Sustaining Fish and Wildlife Resources. Each of those sections is divided into topic areas that correspond directly to the conceptual framework found in the back of the guide. The activities within each topic are ordered by complexity, moving the student from basic conceptual understanding to application. Therefore, educators may find activities in the beginning of a topic area more applicable to elementary classrooms, while those at the end may be more suited for higher grade levels.

### Section One:
### Ecological Knowledge

Activities found in this section are generally introductory lessons that focus on awareness. They are designed to establish a foundation for most of the activities that follow, to develop a basis of understanding for the characteristics of environments, and to comprehend how they function. There are five areas of study: (1) *wildlife populations*, addressing characteristics and population dynamics; (2) *habitats, ecosystems and niches*, addressing distribution and importance of these concepts; (3) *interdependence*, addressing commonalties and interactions among living things; (4) *changes and adaptations*, addressing environmental changes and organism adaptations; and (5) *biodiversity*, addressing types of biodiversity, human influence, and the importance of habitat.

### Section Two:
### Social and Political Knowledge

This section builds on awareness and moves the students toward understanding. Students examine the way human cultures, economics, and politics have affected people's attitudes toward natural resources. There are four areas of study: (1) *cultural perspectives*, addressing cultural development, expressions, and appreciation of wildlife and natural resources; (2) *economic, commercial, and recreational considerations*; (3) *historical and geographic development*, addressing the development of society and commerce as related to natural resources; and (4) *political and legislative frameworks*, both domestic and international.

### Section Three:
### Sustaining Fish and Wildlife Resources

Activities found in this final section of the book are generally higher level lessons that take the students from understanding to action. The activities are designed to serve as a way for students to recognize, evaluate, and make responsible choices in their own lives regarding natural resources while reflecting on the knowledge and skills they have acquired in earlier activities. There are five areas of study: (1) *attitudes and awareness*, including human perspectives and values; (2) *human impacts*, both positive and negative; (3) *issues and trends* in global perspectives, land use, consumptive and nonconsumptive uses of wildlife, and wildlife populations; (4) *wildlife management*, addressing basic concepts related to management considerations and practices; and (5) *responsible action and service*, focusing on how students and others can take action on behalf of wildlife and the environment.

## Organization of Each Activity

Each activity includes a statement of the instructional objective, a brief description of the instructional method used, a list of materials, educator background, step-by-step procedures, extensions or additions to the activity, and several evaluation ideas. Several activities also include variations or alternate procedures. In the small box at the bottom of the first page of the activity, educators will find a summary of the suggested appropriateness based on the grade level, duration, group size and location (indoors or outdoors). It is important to note that the grade level reference is based on a correlation to national subject standards, not on the ability of students to perform the activity. Activities may

be adjusted by educators for use with broader grade levels, as appropriate. Subject areas listed in the box indicate that the activity meets specific national learning standards for that discipline. This reference box also includes key terms relating to the activity, appendices to note, and a list of concepts taught from the conceptual framework found on page 203. The conceptual framework topic reference codes in the box are specific only to the topic area under which the activity falls. The first two letters of the code indicate the topic section.

## Appendices

The Appendices include a glossary of terms, a metric conversion chart, and a list of agencies and organizations that are referenced in one or more Project WILD activities. Other useful appendices include a brief guide to the concept of ecosystems, tips for using the outdoors as a classroom, a guide to keeping an aquarium in the classroom, guidelines for the study of live animals in the classroom, and tables that cross-reference skills and topics to the activities.

Also listed in the Appendices is the conceptual framework in outline form. The conceptual framework is part of an overall "learning framework," a matrix that organizes all the Project WILD concepts and major subject area learning standards for each activity. The matrix cross-references all Project WILD activities by topic, grade level, activity type and assessment type. Both a summary of each activity and literature books appropriate for each activity are presented. The complete learning framework is available on the Project WILD website at **www.projectwild.org**.

NOTE: At the time of printing, all website addresses referenced in this guide were up-to-date. However, due to the dynamic nature of this media, these sites may no longer be functioning. Furthermore, views expressed on these sites do not necessarily reflect those of Project WILD or its sponsors, nor does Project WILD endorse the factual accuracy of the information presented.

# Project WILD: Connecting with No Child Left Behind

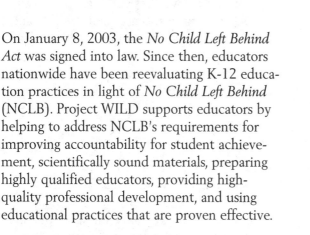

On January 8, 2003, the *No Child Left Behind Act* was signed into law. Since then, educators nationwide have been reevaluating K-12 education practices in light of *No Child Left Behind* (NCLB). Project WILD supports educators by helping to address NCLB's requirements for improving accountability for student achievement, scientifically sound materials, preparing highly qualified educators, providing high-quality professional development, and using educational practices that are proven effective.

## Project WILD Supports Accountability for Student Achievement with Scientifically Sound Materials

Academic standards and annual testing anchor our country's effort to improve every student's opportunity for success. Standards set clear expectations for teaching and student performance. The *No Child Left Behind Act* puts state standards and annual assessments on center stage and targets federal support at programs and practices that are proven effective through rigorous scientific research.

Explicit links between educational standards and the Project WILD curriculum guides make it easy for instructors to use Project WILD activities as part of a standards-based curriculum. In most states, Project WILD instuctional materials have been correlated with state educational standards in discipline areas such as science and social studies. Project WILD materials are correlated to national standards in science and environmental education and provide a guidepost for these state standard-setting efforts. (See www.projectwild.org for more information.)

Project WILD materials are grounded in scientifically proven instructional approaches. Activities emphasize hands-on inquiry-based, and cooperative learning strategies with demonstrated classroom effectiveness.[1] These strategies are included among research-based instructional practices approved by schools and districts across the country. Project WILD also relies on well-proven techniques such as simulations, non-linguistic representations, and learning activities that encourage higher-order reasoning skills such as comparison and classification.[2]

Project WILD materials follow a conceptual framework that was developed through a rigorous process to ensure its accuracy, balance, and educational validity. Over 500 professionals critiqued and reviewed the *Project WILD K-12 Curriculum and Activity Guide* and the *Project WILD Aquatic K-12 Curriculum and Activity Guide*. Project WILD curriculum and activity guides are updated regularly to incorporate new information and respond to educator feedback.

## Project WILD Helps Prepare Highly Qualified Teachers

The *No Child Left Behind Act* holds that well-prepared teachers are the most important link to student success in school. The Act demands that teachers know what to teach, how to teach and

---

[1] These strategies have been the subject of hundreds of scientifically rigorous studies, as reviewed and reported in Marzano, R.J. (2003). What Works in Schools: Translating Research into Action. Alexandria, VA: Association for Supervision and Curriculum Development, 78-87. See also Hattie, J. (1992). Measuring the Effects of Schooling. Australian Journal of Education, 36(2), 99-136 and Wenglinksy, H. 2000.

[2] See Marzano 2003, and Hattie 1992.

have a command of subject matter being taught. Teachers' classroom practices are directly linked with student achievement. The research suggests that teachers who emphasize higher-order thinking skills and hands-on learning activities help boost their student's prerformance significantly.

Project WILD's education materials rely strongly on these hands-on, minds-on instructional techniques. Our training programs help educators apply these techniques in the classroom to teach subject matter and skills pertinent to a range of discipline areas. Teacher evaluations tell us that teachers learn new teaching skills and practices through Project WILD that translate into more effective teaching.

Project WILD increases teachers' knowledge of academic subjects, particularly in the sciences and social studies. Project WILD training, advanced courses, and extended pre-service training programs in addition to the classroom materials enhance educators' content base, especially as it relates to wildlife and conservation.

## Project WILD Offers Effective Professional Development

Like our activities, our workshops are committed to addressing K-12 classroom priorities. Results from workshop surveys indicate that educators consistently give Project WILD high marks for content, quality, and usefulness. Project WILD workshops and educator institutes are offered thoughout the year in most states. Many of the Project WILD training workshops are offered in conjunction with university teacher training programs or university-affiliated museums and nature centers. In most states, a teacher's first Project WILD workshop introduces them to the state fish and wildfie agency, a unique partner that provides resources, support, and advanced training in special topics and classroom techniques. Ongoing contact with the state Project WILD Coordinator is the primary link to an active network that provides quality resources and professional development.

Project WILD workshops and training programs meet key characteristics of high-quality professional development specified in the No Child Left Behind Act—sustained, intensive, classroom-focused, and rich in academic subject content.

## Project WILD is Proven Effective

Project WILD training programs and educational materials are proven effective, fair and balanced, and engaging for instructors and students alike. Over 40 studies at the national and state level have evaluated Project WILD activities, materials, and professional development offerings. Visit www.projectwild.org to download "Project WILD: A Summary of Research Findings 1983-1995 and 1996-2003."

The *Project WILD K-12 Curriculum and Activity Guide* and the *Project WILD Aquatic K-12 Curriculum and Activity Guide* are widely respected supplemental curricula with a proven track record. The program's success is due in large part to emphasis on classroom testing and experience, input from subject matter and education experts, teacher feedback, extensive evaluation, and quality training programs. Educators can feel confident that Project WILD materials are classroom tested for grade-level appropriateness, effectiveness, attainment of instructional objectives, and quality of the activity and student involvement.

Project WILD knows that education reform is an ongoing process. Over the years, Project WILD has responded to changes in education reform with correlations to state and national curriculum standards; development of pre-service training to complement our in-service training programs; instructional focus on hands-on, learner-centered, and cooperative learning strategies to involve students; and collaborating with state education departments to develop more intensive, sustained trainings to meet your needs for NCLB-qualified professional development.

# Section One
## Ecological Knowledge

# Are You Me?

## Objective

Students will recognize various young stages of aquatic animals and match them with corresponding adult stages.

## Method

Using picture cards, students match pairs of juvenile and adult aquatic animals.

## Materials

Cardboard for making cards, art supplies

## Background

Many animals look significantly different in their earliest stages of development when compared to adulthood.

This difference is obviously true for some aquatic insects. Many aquatic insects undergo metamorphosis, which means change during growth. Some insects experience simple metamorphosis while others undergo complete metamorphosis. In simple metamorphosis, the insect egg develops into a nymph. Nymphs resemble adults, but they still vary considerably from their adult form. Eggs that develop into larvae characterize insects that experience complete metamorphosis. The larvae grow through several stages and then change into pupae. Pupae are usually encased in a protective cover for their next stage of growth. From the pupae emerge the soft-bodied, often pale-colored adults. They differ remarkably in appearance from their earlier forms but are not yet completely formed. Gradually the soft pale bodies develop firmness and color. In complete metamorphosis, there is little resemblance between adult and earlier forms.

There are also remarkable similarities and differences between other aquatic animals in different life stages. The eggs of many animals hide their eventual form (alligators, turtles, birds). Pelican hatchlings, for example, may be the closest image of miniature dinosaurs to be found on the planet. Aquatic mammals often are easy to recognize. They frequently do not change as dramatically as some other animals in overall appearance as they grow from young to adult stages.

The major purpose of this activity is for students to recognize that there are differences in the life stages of aquatic animals. The students will increase their appreciation of the diversity of wildlife as well as their understanding of growth and change in animals.

**Grade Level:** K–4

**Subject Areas:** Science, Environmental Education

**Duration:** one or two 20-minute sessions, preparation time for students to bring family pictures to class

**Group Size:** small groups of three or four students each

**Setting:** indoors

**Conceptual Framework Topic Reference:** WPIB

**Key Terms:** aquatic animals, grow, change, adult, young

**Appendices:** none

## Procedure

1. Make pairs of cards of aquatic animals such as a pair of beavers, a pair of pelicans, and so forth. One animal in the pair should be an adult; the other should be at a younger stage of development. The pairs might include adult, larva, nymph, hatchling, juvenile, infant, or egg forms of aquatic animals. Educators may use the masters provided on pages 4–7.

2. Ask the students to bring two pictures from home: one of an adult, the other of a child. The pictures should be pictures of the same person as an adult and as a child.

3. Divide the class into small groups of three or four students, and have them stand around a table. Have the students at each table place the adult-child pictures on the table and mix them randomly. Once the adult-child pictures are mixed at each table, have the entire group shift to another table so there will not be anyone at the table where his or her own pictures are placed.

4. At the new table, have group members attempt to match pairs of adult-child or student-infant photos.

5. When the students at each table have completed their efforts to match the pairs, ask all of the groups to return to the table where they started this activity. Are the matches correct? Ask the students to change any pairs that are not correctly matched. Talk about how difficult or easy it was to correctly match pairs. Introduce the idea that many animals look remarkably different as adults from how they appeared in younger forms. Tell the students that they are about to learn how to match young and adult forms of many different kinds of aquatic animals.

6. Introduce the aquatic animal cards, and divide the class into groups. Designate one group as "adults" and the other half as "young animals." Give each student in the adult group an adult animal image. Give each student in the young animal group a young animal image. Make sure there is a corresponding match, adult or juvenile, for each card given. Instruct the students to look for their match by pairing the appropriate adult and juvenile forms.

7. When all the students have made their choices, let the group ensure that the matches are correct. Educators may show the students the matched images on the master.

8. Have all of the students examine the correctly matched pairs. Look for the similarities and differences in how aquatic animals grow and change.

NOTE: This activity can be repeated several times by shuffling the adult and young images so that each student becomes familiar with a wider array of animals.

## Extensions

1. Research some of the habitats in which these animals live.

2. If possible, visit some of the habitats where the animals are actually found.

3. Pick a pair of images, and find out more about the life cycles of the animals shown.

4. Discuss and/or pantomime the concept of metamorphosis.

## Evaluation

Choose two aquatic animals. Draw a picture of each animal as an adult and another picture of each animal as it looks when it is young.

*continued*

Whirling Beetle

Whirling Larva

Caddisfly

Caddisfly Larvae

Dragonfly

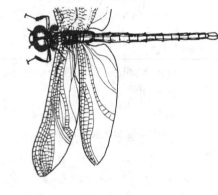

Dragonfly Nymph

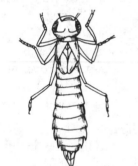

Stonefly

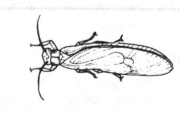

Stonefly Nymph

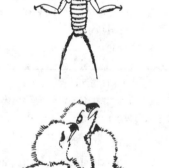

Osprey

Osprey Hatchlings

**Ecological Knowledge** .........................................................................................................................

............................................................................................................................ **Are You Me?**

Mayfly

Mayfly Nymph

Pelican

Pelican Nest and Eggs

Butterfly

Butterfly Larvae

Duck

Ducklings

Frog

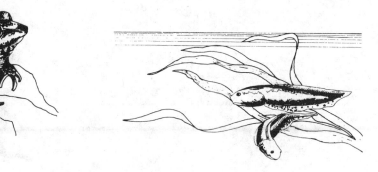

Tadpoles

*continued*

Sea Turtle

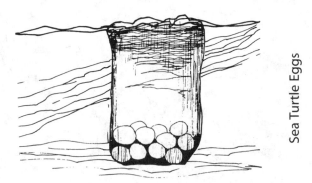
Sea Turtle Eggs

Sea Otter
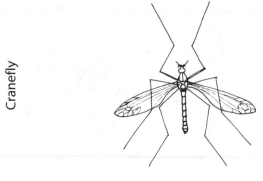

Young Sea Otters

Cranefly

Cranefly Larva

Manatee

Young Manatee

Skate

Skate Egg Cases

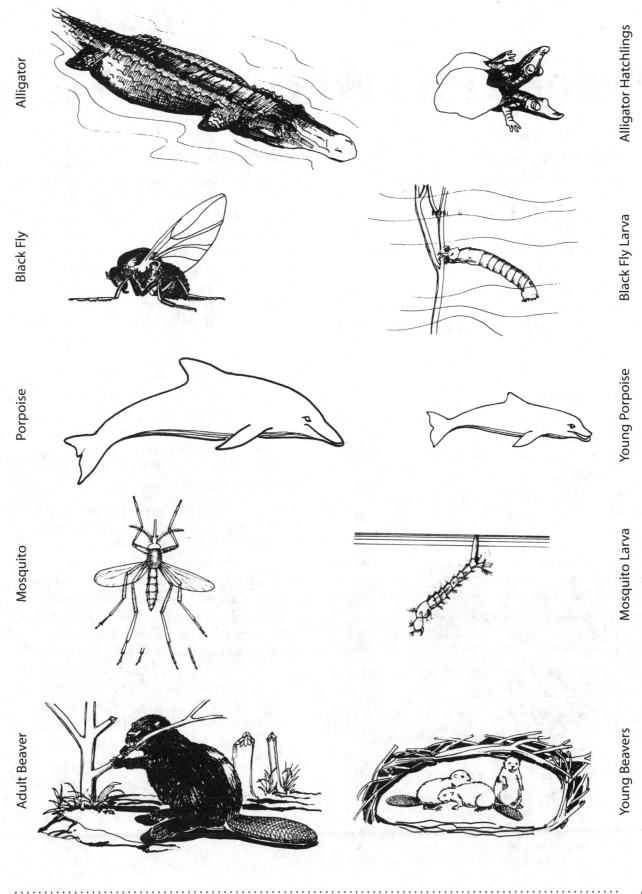

Alligator

Alligator Hatchlings

Black Fly

Black Fly Larva

Porpoise

Young Porpoise

Mosquito

Mosquito Larva

Adult Beaver

Young Beavers

# Fishy Who's Who

## Objectives

Students will (1) recognize and identify the major species of freshwater or saltwater fish that live in their area, (2) describe various values of fish species in some aquatic communities, and (3) locate places where the fish species occur.

## Method

Students complete an inventory of fish habitats that exist in their area, obtain information about the various fish species that occur in these habitats, and locate the fish species on a map.

## Materials

Paper, pencils, large piece of paper for wall map, map of the state, overhead projector, painting or drawing materials for illustrations, colored string or yarn, tape, thumbtacks or pushpins

---

**Grade Level:** 5–8

**Subject Areas:** Science, Language Arts, Expressive Arts, Social Studies, Environmental Education

**Duration:** three 45-minute sessions

**Group Size:** small groups

**Setting:** indoors

**Conceptual Framework Topic Reference:** WPID

**Key Terms:** biography, habitat, fish

**Appendices:** Using Local Resources, Agencies and Organizations, Aquarium, Animals in the Classroom

---

## Background

Fish play a variety of roles in aquatic ecosystems. Some are predators on other aquatic life, while others feed on plant material. Still others scavenge or feed on detritus. Some species deposit eggs in special nests; some have live young. Fish also exhibit a wide range of behaviors and have many different characteristics and adaptations. While some fish species are better known or seen more often, all fish species play important roles in freshwater and saltwater ecosystems.

## Procedure

1. Ask the students what fish species they think inhabit the waters in their community, state, or region. What different fish species have they seen, caught, heard of, or read about? Make a list of these different kinds of fish, and post it in the room.

2. Obtain a large map of the area or region. Make sure the map identifies landforms as well as such major bodies of water as lakes, rivers, large streams, bays, and oceans. Identify each major kind of aquatic habitat located on the map as fresh water or salt water. Identify a certain area to be studied more closely by the class. A simple way of making a large wall map is to (1) place a map on an overhead projector, projecting the image onto a wall where a piece of paper is taped to the wall; or (2) trace around the part of the map to be studied.

3. Divide the class into teams. Have each team identify possible sources of information about fish and fish habitats in the community, state, or region and then develop plans for obtaining the information. State wildlife

agency personnel, water-quality specialists, and marine and aquatic biologists may be of assistance. Also contact state and federal agencies to obtain materials. Local wildlife clubs, state wildlife agencies, and private groups and organizations often have useful publications. Other sources might include the school or public library and the Internet. Have each team use its sources and develop "biographies" for as many of the fish that occur in its study area as possible.

NOTE: Each "biography" could include what the fish's name (common and scientific) is, where it lives, and what its habits are. It could also include specific information about the kind of habitat (freshwater, estuarine, or marine) the fish needs to survive. In addition to biological information about the fish and its habitat, the "biographies" could include information about ecological, scientific, recreational, economic, political, cultural, aesthetic, and intrinsic reasons for which fish are valuable.

4. Ask each team's members to create a set of paintings, sketches, or other illustrations of the fish they have written about in their biographies, as well as an illustration of the fish's habitats. These drawings should be large enough to be seen easily in a wall display.

5. Have the teams meet and compare the research information from different sources. In some cases, the information they have found may not agree. If so, the students might try to determine why. Through this process of comparing research notes, the students might be able to improve the accuracy and comprehensiveness of their descriptions of various fish and habitats.

6. Returning to the large wall map, ask the teams to post the biographies (on cards or other suitable format) and the artwork depictions of the fish and the habitats on the map near the locations where the fish occur. If the fish biographies begin to overlap, post the cards on the outer edges of the map and extend colored string or yarn from the cards

and sketches to the areas where the various fish species live. Use tape, thumbtacks, or pushpins to attach the yarn to the artwork and map.

7. Finally, have the students compare their original list of fish from Step 1 with the current information on the map.

## Extensions

1. Research why some fish species occur widely, in various habitats, while others are more restricted or specialized. What special needs do some fish have, or what special abilities do they have?

2. Invite a local fish biologist to come and speak to the class about fish and fish habitat in the state.

3. Locate any local hatcheries, fish research stations, or other places doing research with fish and fish habitats. If possible, arrange a tour of one of these facilities for the class or group.

4. Are there any special fish habitat "hot spots" in your state—places where fish are in danger because of human or natural actions? Note these on your wall map, and describe the nature of the problem.

5. Conduct a "creel survey," which involves conducting interviews of people whom you find fishing (e.g., along streams and rivers, in lakes, at the ocean shore, even at urban parks).

## Evaluation

1. Identify five species of fish that live in your state.

2. Describe where in the state each of these fish is most apt to live and in what types of habitat.

3. List and describe a variety of reasons that fish are important.

# Whale of a Tail

## Objective

Students will describe the sizes of different whales compared to their own body size.

## Method

Students use computational, graphing, and measuring techniques to draw or sculpture life-size replicas of whales.

## Materials

Large sheets of paper (flip chart or butcher paper), 1-inch grid paper, 200–300 feet (60–90 meters) of twine; writing materials, measuring devices (meter sticks, yardsticks, tape measures), chalk (preferably sidewalk chalk); OPTIONAL: carpenter's chalk line (extremely useful)

## Background

Whales, or any of the marine mammals constituting the order Cetacea, are unique among mammals in that they live their entire lives in the water. The term "Cetacean" encompasses all 78 known species of whales, dolphins, and porpoises.

Most smaller whales and all dolphins and porpoises belong to the toothed whale suborder. Toothed whales have teeth that are uniform in size and shape or are toothless; they feed on fish and invertebrates such as squid and crustaceans. Most larger whales belong to the baleen whale suborder. Instead of teeth, whales in this group have large baleen plates that hang from the upper jaw and filter the plankton or krill on which the animals subsist. Probably the largest animal ever to have lived is a baleen whale, the blue whale, which has been measured up to 100 feet (30 m) in length, with a weight of more than 220 tons (200 metric tons).

The whale's body is enveloped in a layer of blubber that aids in buoyancy, preserves body heat, and serves as a source of stored energy. Whales breathe air through one or two nostrils on the top of the head, and they can dive deeply.

Reproduction in whales is essentially the same as in other mammals. The pregnant female carries her unborn young for 9 to 16 months; usually a single calf is born underwater. A healthy calf can swim from the instant it is born. Soon after, it begins to nurse. A whale reaches sexual maturity at 6 to 13 years of age. The life span ranges from about 30 years for small toothed whales to as long as 80 years for baleen whales.

Typical lengths and weights for mature whales are listed in the table at the bottom of the next page.

**Grade Level:** 5–8

**Subject Areas:** Mathematics, Expressive Arts

**Duration:** three or four 20- to 60-minute sessions

**Group Size:** teams of five students each

**Setting:** indoors and outdoors

**Conceptual Framework Topic Reference:** WPIA2

**Key Terms:** whale, scale, grid

**Appendices:** Outdoors, Agencies and Organizations, Metric Conversion Chart

The most difficult part of this activity for the students may be transferring the smaller grid to the larger grid. Although it may appear to be somewhat formidable, the process is rich and rewarding. Students use mathematics, art, and measurement skills. The process is also invaluable in providing the students with a lasting awareness of these huge marine creatures.

## Procedure

1. This activity requires the students to draw life-size whales. For this activity, students will need to know the average size of several species of whales. Divide the class into groups of five, and assign a different whale species to each group.

2. Have the students research the length of the different whale species. Students can also gather information about the life history of the whale to report to the class. Research topics include what characteristics the whale has, what it eats, how it reproduces and cares for its young, what its migration routes are, what its history is in terms of whaling, and what its current status is.

3. Once the size and natural history information have been compiled, students can learn how to use grids to draw the whale to scale. Provide the students with grid paper. Tell them to make a drawing of the outline of their hand as shown in Diagram A.

4. Once they have finished drawing the outline of their hand, have students make a grid on a much larger paper (i.e., flip chart paper or butcher paper). The grid squares on the large

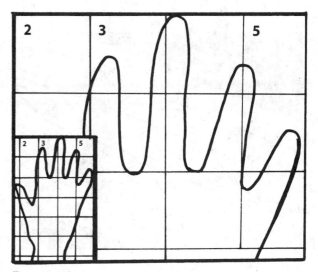

*Diagram A*

paper should be three to five times bigger than the squares on the smaller grid paper. Once the students have a larger grid made, have them transfer the small drawing of their hand to the larger paper. See Diagram A.

NOTE: It helps to number the squares on both pieces of paper. Matching the numbers of the squares on the two pieces of paper helps to transfer the drawing.

5. Students will use the same method to draw life-size whales. First, have the students make a drawing of a whale on a clean sheet of 1-inch grid paper. For this drawing, 1-inch squares represent 10 feet on each side. For example, a blue whale is 90 feet long. On the 1-inch grid paper, the drawing will be nine squares long. See Diagram B on the following page.

| Type of Whale | Length | | Weight | |
|---|---|---|---|---|
| | Feet | Meters | Tons | Metric Tons |
| Humpback whale | 50 | 15.0 | 50 | 45.0 |
| Sperm whale | 55 | 16.5 | 47 | 42.3 |
| Finback whale | 70 | 21.0 | 50 | 45.0 |
| Gray whale | 40 | 12.0 | 35 | 31.5 |
| Right whale | 55 | 16.5 | 47 | 42.3 |
| Blue whale | 90 | 27.0 | 75 | 67.5 |

*continued*

**Diagram B**

6. Using chalk, students next create a large grid on a parking lot or other open site. The site should be large enough to accommodate the full size of a whale. Make each of the grid squares at the site 10 feet on each side. Transferring the whale image from the 1-inch grid to the 10-foot grid may be made easier by the following:

- Use two or three long strings with markers every 10 feet. (Knots, short strings tied to the main string, or magic marker spots at 12-inch intervals all work well.)

- If available, use a carpenter's chalk line.

- Make sure to number the squares on the drawing and have them numbered the same on the site.

- The site grid does not have to be exactly square, so don't let this part of the process become too burdensome.

NOTE: Whales can also be created using the metric scale. On 1-centimeter grid paper a blue whale, for example, would be 27 squares long (see table on page 11). Make the large squares at the site 1 meter on each side.

7. After the grid is transferred to the study site, the students can begin drawing the whale. Depending on how large the study site is, the class may be able to do only one whale

at a time. If this is the case, make enough copies of the 1-inch grid drawing of the selected whale so that each group can have its own copy. Each of the groups can then select a portion of the whale and transfer a section. Collectively, the groups will accomplish the transfer.

8. Have the class gather around the image of the whale. Invite the students to join hands to see if the class can make a continuous chain that surrounds the whale. Ask them to stand inside of the outline of the whale. How many students fit inside? How many students could fit inside the whale drawing? How many cars could park on the drawing of the whale?

9. Next, have the groups report on the whale species they have researched. If more than one whale was drawn, repeat the process with each whale group.

10. Summarize by asking students how this activity has broadened their awareness and appreciation of the variety and size of the different species of whales.

## Extensions

1. Draw the actual size outline of an African elephant or a brachiosaurus among the whales.

2. Research the current status of all species of whales. Find out about the work of the International Whaling Commission.

3. Pretend that you are a pod of whales in a great court of oceanic law. Prepare a bill of rights for all whales.

4. Make a life-size whale out of heavy-weight plastic according to the pattern provided at the end of this activity.

## Evaluation

Draw the outline of a person and the outline of several whales researched in this activity. Draw the sketches according to scale. Place the sketches in order from smallest to largest.

# Pattern for Life-Size Whale

## List of Materials

1. Black plastic, 4 mil, 24 feet (7.2 m) by 100 feet (30 m)
2. Clear/White plastic, 4 mil, 16 feet by 100 feet (4.8 m by 30 m)
3. Clear 2 inch (5 cm) wide plastic tape—20 rolls

## Tools Needed

1. Tape measures, 100 feet (30 m) and 26 feet (8 m)
2. Scissors to cut the plastic and tape
3. High-speed fan

## Steps

1. Lay plastic on 10-foot (1 m) grid.
2. Cut out all parts; cut out some of the flippers or tail flukes from the cutout sections of the whale body.
3. Tape together the flippers and tail flukes (remember the right and left sides for both), and tape together the top dorsal fin. Do not tape the body (straight side) connection.
4. After taping the "fins," turn inside out, placing the tape seam inside.
5. Tape together the cutout sections of the whale's top section as indicated on the plan.
6. Tape together the cutout sections of the whale's bottom section as indicated on the plan.
7. Place the tail flukes and flippers on the bottom section of the whale at their locations.

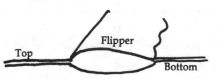

8. Start taping the top section to the bottom section, using the tail flukes as side walls where they connect to the body; start at the tail section on each side and work toward the mouth area.
9. Do not tape the end of the tail section together.
10. Mouth area—the clear/white plastic will have to be pleated to meet the side area taping; start in the center of the mouth and work out the sides—about 2 inches (5 m) for each pleat.
11. Once the whale is fully taped, place the fan in the tail opening and inflate the whale. One person will go into the whale to the nose section and pull the nose section out through the tail opening, inverting the seams and letting the flippers and tail flukes to the outside.
12. Mount the top dorsal fin on the black top section in the center of the tail section about 58 feet (17.4 m) from the front of the whale.
13. Place the-9 inch (22 cm) eye drawings on the top section, just in front of the flippers.

14. Inflate the model with the high-speed fan; step back and give it room.

## Tail Flukes

2 black and 2 clear/white pieces
(Will create right and left tail sections)

6' (1.8 m)

12' (3.6 m)

## Top Dorsal Fin

2 black pieces

3' (1 m)

5' (1.5 m)
(This side attaches to body of whale)

## Flippers

2 black and clear/white pieces
(Will create right and left flipper sections)

6' (1.8 m)

16' (4.8 m)

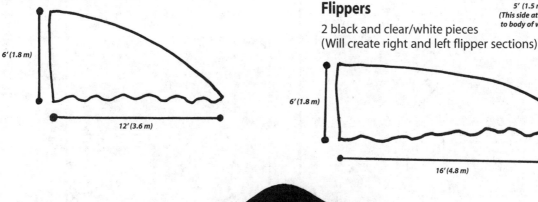

Activity courtesy of Needham Science Center, Needham, Mass.

*continued*

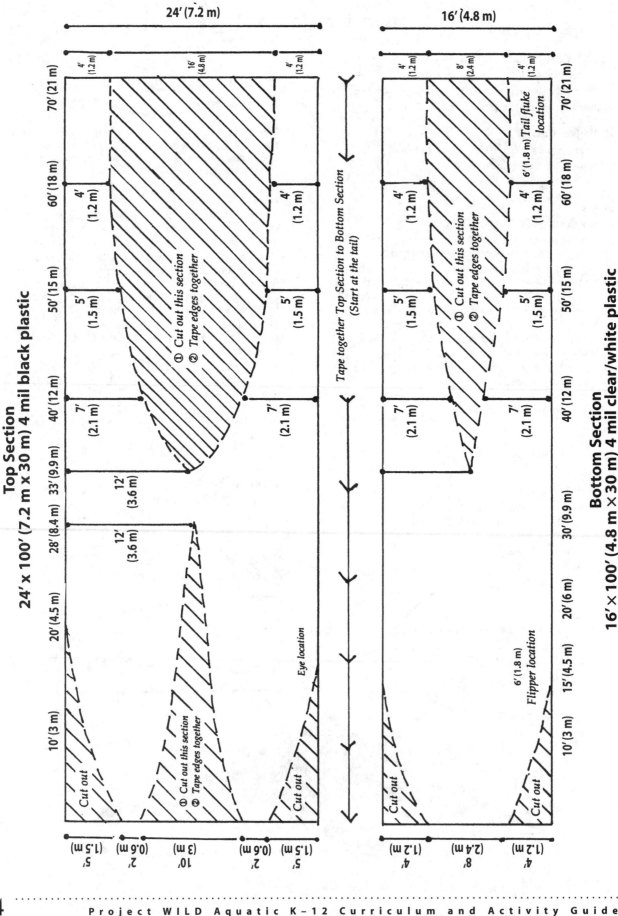

## Top Section
## 24' × 100' (7.2 m × 30 m) 4 mil black plastic

24' (7.2 m)

## Bottom Section
## 16' × 100' (4.8 m × 30 m) 4 mil clear/white plastic

16' (4.8 m)

Tape together Top Section to Bottom Section
(Start at the tail)

① Cut out this section
② Tape edges together

Eye location

Flipper location

Tail fluke location

Cut out

# Migration Headache

## Objectives

Students will (1) list limiting factors affecting habitats and populations of migrating water birds, (2) predict the effects of such limiting factors, (3) describe the effects of habitat loss and degradation on populations of migrating water birds, and (4) make inferences about the importance of suitable habitat for migrating water birds.

## Method

Students portray migrating water birds traveling between nesting habitats and wintering grounds.

## Materials

Large playing field or gymnasium, two bases (paper plates or carpet squares, for example) for every two or three students

## Background

Birds that migrate depend not just on having one suitable habitat, but two and often three habitats. For example, some birds nest and raise their young in the northern limits of their ranges. The same birds may also require suitable habitats in the southern limits of their range to live during winter. Because migrating birds travel hundreds or thousands of miles between nesting and wintering grounds, resting and feeding sites (known as stopovers) are crucial.

A variety of remarkable migrating shorebirds and waterfowl inhabit the skies and waters of the United States. Many migrating birds—ducks, geese, cranes, herons, rails, terns, and plovers, for example—require wetlands in their breeding, stopover, and wintering grounds. Without wetlands, dozens of species of water birds face loss of necessary habitat.

Over the past 150 years, water bird populations have been threatened by the alteration of habitats and direct mortality of birds. Numerous populations of water birds have declined, some significantly. The disappearance and degradation of wetlands are major threats to the survival of migratory water birds. Destruction of wetland habitats reduces the quantity of suitable nesting, feeding, and resting areas. Alteration of wetland habitats often reduces the quality of habitats, making them unsuitable for water birds. Wetland habitats, usually found in low, fertile plains along watercourses, were historically prized for conversion to farmland and settlements. Agriculture and development, both residential and industrial, have reduced the number and quality of natural wetlands.

Direct mortality of water birds occurs in various ways. The migration routes of North American water birds are well known. Before the passage of regulations regarding the hunting of water birds, market hunters of the 19th century and very early 20th century decimated the flocks by

*continued*

---

**Grade Level:** 5–8

**Subject Areas:** Science, Environmental Education, Expressive Arts

**Duration:** one 45-minute session

**Group Size:** 20 to 40 students or more

**Setting:** outdoors or large indoor area

**Conceptual Framework Topic Reference:** WPIIA2b2, WPIIA2a2a

**Key Terms:** migration, limiting factors, habitat, wetlands, water birds, shore birds

**Appendices:** none

taking advantage of the vast numbers of water birds that concentrated at strategic points along these routes. Pollution, through insecticides and herbicides for example, has also taken a toll. The birds ingest the poisons through the food chain, sometimes with lethal effects. In some cases, pesticides also kill the birds' food, reducing their food supply.

Many international, federal, state, and private groups recognize the importance of wetland habitats to wildlife preservation. In the early 1900s, several laws and treaties were enacted that regulated the hunting of water birds and protected the habitat on which they depended. Laws that conserve and enhance wetland habitats have slowed the alteration of these habitats. The Clean Water Act of 1977 and the Farm Bill of 1985 are two major pieces of such legislation. In addition, techniques have been developed to build new wetlands as well as enhance the quality of existing wetlands. The U.S. Fish and Wildlife Service (USFWS) has principal legal responsibility in the United States for managing migratory wildlife at the federal level. State wildlife agencies share some responsibilities with the USFWS in conserving migratory water birds.

The effects of natural occurrences and human management efforts during the 1990s have produced mixed results. The North American Waterfowl Management Plan, coordinated by the USFWS, has worked through private-public partnerships to conserve and enhance waterfowl habitat in Canada and the United States. This effort, aided by several years of plentiful rain and snow, has allowed populations of many species of waterfowl (ducks, geese, and swans) to rebound from near record lows in the 1980s and early 1990s to near historic high numbers. Conversely, shore birds like plovers, terns, and the red knot continue to suffer losses because of habitat loss and alteration along coastal regions.

In this activity, each student (assuming a class of 30) represents thousands, if not tens of thousands, of water birds. Thus, occasional losses to predation and other events of relatively minor magnitude during the course of migration are not emphasized in the simulation. The major

purpose of this activity is for students to dynamically experience some important factors that affect habitat quality and the associated survival of migratory water bird populations.

## Procedure

1. Select a large playing area about 70 feet in length. Place an equal number of bases in three areas on the playing field as shown below:

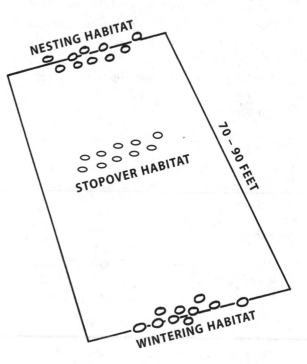

Choose the number of bases so that there is one base for each two or three students at each of the three areas on the field. Designate one of the end areas the "wintering habitat," the other end as the "nesting habitat," and the area in the middle as "stopover habitat."

2. Explain to the students that they are water birds and will migrate between these three areas at your signal. Tell the students that the bases represent wetlands. These wetlands provide suitable habitat for water birds. At the end of each migration, the students will have to have one foot on a base in order to be allowed to continue (survive). Tell the students that only two (or three as decided in Step 1) water birds can occupy a habitat

(base) at one time. If they can't find a habitat that isn't "filled," that means they have not found any suitable habitat. They "pass away," and have to move, at least temporarily, to the sidelines. During migration, the students may want to "flap their wings," moving their arms like birds in flight.

3. Explain to the students that many factors will limit the survival of populations of migrating water birds. Some involve changes in the wintering, stopover, and nesting habitats. There will be periods of time where food, water, shelter, and space are suitably arranged to meet the habitat requirements of the birds. There will be other times when the habitat is stressed, with many factors limiting the potential for the birds' survival.

4. Begin the activity with all students at the wintering habitat. Announce the start of the first migration. Have the students migrate slowly until they become familiar with the process. Then they can speed up. On the first try, all the birds will successfully migrate to the stopover habitat.

5. Explain that most water birds need these areas to rest and eat before continuing the migratory journey. Then have them migrate from the stopover habitat to the nesting habitat. Explain that there has been no loss in the area of available high-quality habitat. Thus, a successful nesting season is at hand.

6. Before the students migrate back "south," remove one base from the stopover habitat. Explain that a developer has received a permit to drain a wetland to build a mall. Repeat the instruction to migrate, and send the birds to the stopover habitat. Have the students who could not find available habitat stand on the sideline. Tell the students that these birds died as a result of habitat loss. Remind any "deceased" birds that they will have a chance to get back into the activity. They can come back as surviving hatchlings when favorable conditions prevail and there is habitat available in the nesting ground.

NOTE: the migrations can be graphed as shown below.

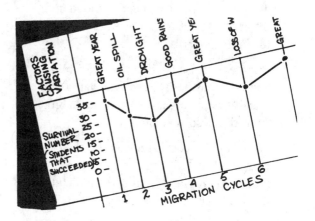

7. Continue the migrations by reading the Habitat Scenarios on this page. Educators may want to appoint two students as monitors to remove and add bases (habitats) as required on the cards.

8. After the activity, ask the students to identify factors that caused water bird populations to decline or increase. What are the short- and long-term effects of the decline or increase? Which factors are human-caused? Which are natural? Which factors reduced or enhanced the quality of the habitat? What are the benefits and liabilities related to these factors for the community?

## Habitat Scenarios

*(Educators may want to photocopy these pages before beginning the activity.)*

These scenarios can be used during the activity to assist educators with the factors that may reduce or enhance a wetland habitat.

• A marsh has been dredged to allow a marina to be built. Remove one habitat from the stopover habitat.

• A landowner has agreed to re-flood fields after harvesting, increasing acreage for wintering birds. Add one habitat to the wintering habitat.

*continued*

- A joint federal and state wetland restoration project involved removing drain tiles, allowing a former wetland to flood and return to its natural state. Add one habitat to the stopover habitat.

- A large increase in the number of mink and raccoons has reduced the value of a marsh nesting area. Remove one habitat from the nesting habitat.

- Wintering habitat is reduced by the conversion of bottomland hardwood forests to cropland. Remove one habitat from the wintering habitat.

- New legislation restricts motorboat traffic on a number of lakes and large marshes, reducing the human disturbance to wildlife. Add one habitat to stopover habitat.

- Several years of sufficient rain and snow has replenished the water supply, thus increasing the food supply. Add one habitat to the nesting habitat.

- A timber company has agreed to preserve a forested wetland in exchange for tax credits. Add one habitat to the stopover habitat.

- Filling and diking reduces the amount of tidal wetlands available to waterfowl. Remove one habitat from the wintering habitat.

## Extensions

1. Research a species of water bird. Conduct this activity again with each student representing a specific kind of water bird.

2. Explore the major factors affecting habitat loss and alteration, or gain and restoration, in your area. Research the causes for long-term habitat loss, as well as any major efforts under way to prevent these increasing losses.

3. Using a map, plot the major migratory routes of North American birds.

4. Visit a national wildlife refuge, state wildlife area, bird observatory, private sanctuary, seashore, or other habitat for migratory water birds.

5. What other animals migrate? Are the problems they face similar to those of migratory birds?

6. There are national laws and international treaties protecting migratory species. Find out about some of these. What is their history? Are they effective? Are there problems enforcing them? What migrating species, if any, are unprotected by such laws?

7. Find out how wetlands have changed or remained the same in your community throughout the past 100 years. Are there wetland regulations or zoning laws in your community?

## Evaluation

1. Name two human activities and two environmental factors that might interfere with water bird migration. For each activity and factor, describe the possible effects on the water birds.

2. Distinguish between effects on individual birds and effects on populations of birds. Indicate if an effect is short term or long term.

3. Why is suitable habitat important for migrating water birds? Include in your response a description of the different kinds of habitat that are needed by migrating water birds.

4. Is habitat loss a greater threat to the survival of migrating populations than for stationary populations of wildlife? Explain your answer.

# Designing a Habitat

## Objective

Students will identify the components of habitat that are essential for most aquatic animals to survive.

## Method

Students design a habitat suitable for aquatic wildlife to survive in a zoo or an aquarium.

## Materials

3″ × 5″ cards, art supplies, writing materials, papier mâché, modeling clay, gallon jars, string, cardboard, cardboard boxes (to use as frames for models)

## Background

Zoos and aquaria are, for the most part, artificial habitats. The basic life-giving conditions of food, shelter, air, water, and space in a suitable arrangement for animals to survive seem obvious. However, in aquaria, water is a uniquely sensitive part of the habitat. The surrounding envelope of water must meet specific requirements for different aquatic life forms. Slight changes in salinity, pH, and dissolved oxygen plus the presence of a wide range of pollutants can spell disaster for certain aquatic organisms.

To successfully house aquatic wildlife in zoos and aquaria, those facilities must pay careful attention to the range of conditions that each life form can tolerate. There are also certain physical requirements in terms of the shape and dynamics of the exhibit that must be compatible with each creature. For example, some fish require moving water or currents. Others prefer almost static conditions. Some prefer deep water and others shallow rocky bottoms. Penguins prefer refrigerated settings. The variations are remarkable when one considers designing habitats for microorganisms in pond water and mammoth habitats for killer whales and walruses.

Concern for the physical requirements of animals must go beyond meeting minimum survival needs. Attention is also given to the animals' comfort, creating conditions as similar to those in their natural habitats as possible.

In the growing practices of aquaculture (human cultivation of freshwater organisms) and mariculture (human cultivation of oceanic organisms), research is conducted regarding habitat requirements. Often natural streams, rivers, lakes, and even the ocean are used in these enterprises. Attention to water quality and disease control is just as important in these settings as it is in the confined habitats of zoos and aquaria.

---

**Grade Level:** 5–8

**Subject Areas:** Science, Language Arts, Expressive Arts, Environmental Education

**Duration:** two or more 45-minute sessions

**Group Size:** groups of two to four students each (can be modified to accommodate different numbers)

**Setting:** indoors

**Conceptual Framework Topic Reference:** HNIB1, HNIIA, HNIIA1

**Key Terms:** habitat, zoo, aquarium

**Appendices:** Field Ethics, Using Local Resources, Aquaria

---

*continued*

The major purpose of this activity is for students to recognize and appreciate the complex life requirements of aquatic wildlife by focusing on the artificial habitat conditions of zoos and aquaria.

## Procedure

1. Prepare 3″ × 5″ cards with the name of one of the following animals written on each card: trout, shark, goldfish, sturgeon, sea otter, large-mouth bass, water strider, beaver, diving beetle, killer whale, penguin, sea turtle, alligator, siamese fighting fish, frog, and oyster (expand the choices as appropriate).

2. Divide the group into teams of two to four. Have each team draw one card from a container.

3. Each team will be responsible for designing an artificial habitat in which its animal could successfully live. Inform the students that each team will be expected to conduct research and consult reference materials or resource people to determine the life requirements of each creature. In addition, students will investigate and establish the characteristics of the natural habitat of the animals.

4. When the research is complete, each team of students is to design and build a model or small replica of a zoo exhibit or aquarium habitat that would be suitable for the team's animal's survival and comfort in captivity. Establish a scale for the exhibits (for example, 1 inch = 5 feet for the large animals; actual size for the insects).

5. Once the models are complete, ask each team to report to the rest of the class. Each report should include a description of the basic biological needs of each animal as well as a description of the characteristics of its natural habitat. The students should point out how their models are designed to meet the needs of the animal.

OPTIONAL: Once all the reports are finished, have the students arrange their models in a plan for a zoo or an aquarium.

6. Ask the students to summarize the components of habitat that seemed to be necessary for the survival of the aquatic animals they studied. (Food, water, shelter, air, and space in a suitable arrangement would be the minimum necessary components.)

## Extensions

1. Visit an aquarium and arrange for a staff person to explain how the aquarium staff addresses the same basic requirements for animals that the students did—that is, the components of habitat.

2. Create a balanced aquarium for the classroom.

3. Discuss the reasons for and against keeping aquatic wildlife in captivity in zoos and aquaria.

## Evaluation

1. List the components of suitable habitat that are necessary for most aquatic animals to survive.

2. Choose an aquatic mammal, fish, amphibian, or other aquatic animal. Describe the biological characteristics of the animal and the kind of habitat requirements it has in order to survive. Compare similarities and differences between this aquatic animal and another aquatic animal. What things, if any, do they both need to survive? What things, if any, must be different in their habitats for each kind of animal to survive?

# Where Does Water Run?

## Objective

Students will describe relationships among precipitation, runoff, and aquatic habitats.

## Method

Students will (1) measure and calculate the area of a study site, (2) calculate the volume and weight of water falling on the study site, (3) determine specific and annual rainfall and runoff, and (4) trace the course of water to aquatic habitats.

## Materials

Writing materials, meter or yardsticks, long piece of twine with marks every yard or meter, rain gauge, local rainfall data; OPTIONAL: calculator, trundle wheel

NOTE: A trundle wheel is a device for measuring linear surfaces. This wheeled device measures yards or meters as it is pushed along a surface. Contact local surveyors or other organizations to check on the availability of trundle wheels in your area.

## Background

Developing an understanding of precipitation and runoff is an important part of understanding the water cycle (see Diagram A). Rainfall is one form of precipitation and is one way water re-enters aquatic habitats. Once rain falls upon a surface, water begins to move both laterally outward and vertically downward. Lateral movement is runoff and finds its way into streams, rivers, and lakes. Vertical movement seeps into the soil and porous rock and recharges groundwater supplies.

Runoff waters are necessary to renew the many aquatic habitats that depend on the inflow of water for continuity. Inflow supports aquatic life by preventing lakes from shrinking because of evaporation and by preventing streams from going below minimum flow levels.

Runoff is the dominant way that water flows from one location to another. It is in runoff that many pollutants find their way into moving waters. These types of pollutants are known as "non-point source." Garden insecticides, automobile oils and transmission fluids, paints and exhaust, and such are washed by runoff into streams, rivers, lakes, and oceans. Eventually, this water becomes part of an aquatic habitat.

Runoff is also responsible for the erosion, transportation, and deposition of sediments scoured from the land's surface. Substandard land practices along with development often leave bare ground ready for the topsoil to be washed away. Paving and compacted soil can reduce an area's

---

**Grade Level:** 5–8

**Subject Areas:** Mathematics, Science, Environmental Education

**Duration:** two 45- to 60-minute sessions; one period, if dimensions of the grounds are provided

**Group Size:** any

**Setting:** outdoors and indoors

**Conceptual Framework Topic Reference:** HNIB1

**Key Terms:** runoff, precipitation, volume, area, weight

**Appendices:** Outdoors, Metric Conversion Chart

---

*continued*

water absorbing ability, thereby increasing runoff. Reduced absorption rates can adversely vegetation and groundwater recharge.

In this activity, the students calculate both the volume and the weight of rainfall and consider relationships between rainfall and runoff, including effects on wildlife and the environment.

## The Water Cycle

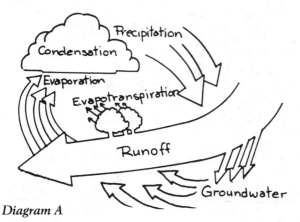

Diagram A

## Procedure

1.  Determine the total area of the study site. For this activity, the outer dimensions of the property will be sufficient. There is no need to subtract the area of the buildings because it is assumed that rain falls on them as well.

    The formula for calculating area is
    Area = Length × Width (or A = LW)

NOTE: See the extensions to this activity for metric approximations.

The length and width of the study site must be measured. The students can use a tape measure or a length of twine (approximately 100 feet [30 meters] in length). Mark the twine every 3 feet (meter). The marking can be done with an ink marker, short pieces of string tied every yard, or a knot each 3 feet (meter). If a trundle wheel is available, it is convenient to use for measuring.

The main difficulty with calculating the area in this activity comes from irregularly shaped study sites. Here are a few examples:

Most accurate

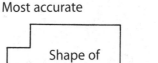

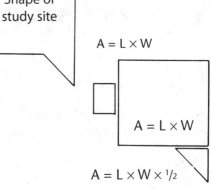

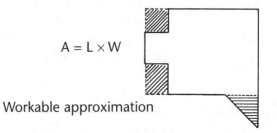

Workable approximation

2.  Once the area of the study site has been established, the next step is to determine the amount of rain that falls in the area. Three options are possible:

    *   Calculate the annual rainfall using information from resource agencies (e.g., weather bureau, soil conservation service, local meteorologists, local newspapers).

    *   Using a rain gauge, measure the amount of rain over a period of time.

    *   Calculate the amount of rain that falls in a given storm.

    When the students have decided on a way to measure the amount of rain that falls during a specified period of time, ask them to calculate the amount. This calculation provides the students with a value for the depth of rainfall on the surface of the land.

3.  The next step is to calculate the volume of rainfall. For example, suppose the area of the study site is 50,000 square feet (4,500 square meters) and the annual rainfall is 6 inches or 0.5 feet (15 centimeters or 0.15 meters).

The volume of rain would be

$50{,}000 \text{ ft}^2 \times 0.5 \text{ ft of rain}$
$(4{,}500 \text{ m}^2 \times 0.15 \text{ m}) =$
$25{,}000 \text{ ft}^3 \ (675 \text{ m}^3) \text{ of rain}$

The volume of rain is 25,000 cubic feet (675 cubic meters) of rain.

4. Knowing the volume, the students can now calculate the weight of the rain. Water weighs 62.5 pounds per cubic foot (1,000 kilograms per cubic meter), thus the weight of rain is:

$25{,}000 \text{ ft}^3 \times 62.5 \text{ lbs/ft}^3 = 1{,}562{,}500 \text{ lbs}$
$(\text{or } 675 \text{ m}^3 \times 1{,}000 \text{ kg/m}^3 = 675{,}000 \text{ kg})$

5. All measurements and calculations in this activity are intended to impress on students that there are remarkable volumes and weights of water moving through the water cycle. Even short periods of rainfall produce amazing amounts of water. All the water that the students measure eventually finds its way to a wildlife habitat. A major issue of concern is how humans affect the quality and quantity of water that eventually reaches aquatic habitats. Consider and discuss the following questions:

- Where does the water from rainfall go when it leaves the study site?

- How much water is absorbed by the different surfaces on the study site?

- What types of potential pollutants does the water come in contact with?

- Where is the location of the nearest wildlife habitat that receives the site's runoff?

- How do people use the water between the time it leaves the site and arrives in the wildlife habitat?

- What are some of the positive and negative effects that the water may have on the environment at various points on its journey?

## Extensions

1. Obtain a map of the study site from your school or organization, and check it against the accuracy of the one made by the students. Make a copy of the study site map; then use the original map and plot runoff routes on it. Check periodically during rainstorms to identify the drainage patterns. Try to find a way to estimate how much water is draining in specific places.

2. Place a rain gauge on the grounds and measure actual amounts of rain. Repeat your calculations.

3. The contamination of groundwater is also an issue. How might water in the groundwater table or aquifer become contaminated and potentially pose a threat to human health? To the health of other animals, including wildlife? Identify as many possible sources of contamination to groundwater and runoff in your community as possible. What can be, or is being done, to reduce or eliminate these sources and their effects?

## Evaluation

1. Describe at least two relationships among aquatic habitats, precipitation, runoff, and surface water.

2. Identify two human activities that have affected the *quality* of runoff.

3. Identify two human activities that have affected the *quantity* of runoff.

4. Identify two ways that runoff can affect humans.

5. Identify and describe two ways that runoff can affect aquatic wildlife.

6. Write a short list of steps to protect the quantity and quality of runoff water.

# Water Canaries

## Objectives

Students will (1) identify several aquatic organisms, and (2) assess the relative environmental quality of a stream or pond using indicators of pH, water temperature, and the presence of a diversity of organisms.

## Method

Students investigate a stream or pond using sampling techniques.

## Materials

Identification books (e.g., *The Golden Guide to Pond Life*), Student Worksheets I and II (page 28); sampling equipment, such as seine nets, sieves, trays, assorted containers, white trays (Styrofoam, plastic, porcelain), magnifying lenses, eye droppers and forceps, water quality test kit (test both pH and dissolved oxygen), thermometer, meter sticks or tape measure; OPTIONAL: stereomicroscope

---

**Grade Level:** 5–8

**Subject Areas:** Science, Environmental Education

**Duration:** one or two 45-minute sessions; may take longer if done as a field study activity

**Group Size:** any

**Setting:** outdoors

**Conceptual Framework Topic Reference:** HNIIB

**Key Terms:** Indicator species, quality, healthy, diversity, temperature, pH

**Appendices:** Outdoors, Field Ethics, Animals in the Classroom

---

## Background

In the early days of coal mining, canaries were brought into mines to be used as indicators of the mine's air quality. Because canaries are more sensitive than humans to the presence of dangerous gases in the air, their discomfort or death indicated that the air was not safe to breathe. Although this practice no longer exists, it stands as an example of how animals have differing sensitivities to environmental factors.

In streams and ponds, the presence or absence of certain organisms, called indicator species, reveals much about water quality. These creatures make up a biotic index (number of living organisms found in an ecosystem). The absence or presence of these organisms is an indicator of water quality.

Water with numerous aquatic species is usually a healthy environment, whereas water with just a few different species usually indicates conditions that are less than healthy. The word *healthy* is used to indicate an environment supportive of life. Pollution generally reduces the quality of the environment and, in turn, the diversity of life forms. In some cases, the actual biomass will increase because of pollution, but the diversity inevitably goes down.

## Procedure

*Before the Activity*

1. Select a small, fairly shallow, slow-moving stream or pond near your school or organization as the sampling site for this activity. Be sensitive to the impact students may have on stream banks and beds, spawning and nesting sites, and vegetation. Have the students establish ethical guidelines for their sampling activities. If the stream is not a public site,

be sure to obtain permission to visit the site. Advise the students in advance to dress for the setting—old shoes and shorts or jeans would be best.

NOTE: If a site visit is not possible, modify the activity to be conducted in the classroom.

2. At the sampling site, brief the students on habitat courtesies, working from the students' own list of ethical guidelines for sampling activities. Instruct them on how to minimize the potential for damaging the habitat, and encourage care in their collecting techniques. Emphasize that all the wildlife is to be returned to its habitat unharmed. Educators may choose whether to take some of the organisms back to school for further study.

3. Begin the activity by observing the water. Identify organisms on the surface and in the depths. Using the sampling equipment (nets, trays, sieves, etc.) have the students collect as many different forms of animal life as possible. Ask them to be alert to differing microhabitats near rocks, in riffles, and in pools. Place the animals to be observed in the white trays for viewing and drawing. The whiteness of the trays allows detail to be seen in the animals collected. Keep an adequate amount of water in the trays, and place them in a cool, shady spot. Change the water as often as needed to keep the animals cool. This is a good time to use the microscopes, if available.

4. On Worksheet I, have the students identify and draw the animals they observed in the aquatic environment and those temporarily removed for observation in the collection containers. Ask them to fill in the number of each kind found and to describe the actual location where the animal was found. Once these observations are completed, carefully return the animals to their natural habitat.

NOTE: If you choose to take some of the animals to the classroom, be sure there is adequate water as cool as that in the natural setting. To have the entire class view the organisms, place the organisms in petri dishes or any shallow transparent dish. Then use an overhead projector, to project the images onto a screen or wall.

5. Encourage the students to discuss their observations. How diverse were the aquatic organisms? Introduce the concept of diversity, or explain that a variety of different kinds of plants and animals is usually an indication of a healthy ecosystem.

6. Now it is time to test the water at the field site for other indicators of quality. Using the water quality test kit, have the students determine the pH and the temperature of the water as well as the air temperature. If you choose to measure the amount of dissolved oxygen as indicated in Extension 1, include those values with water temperature and pH.

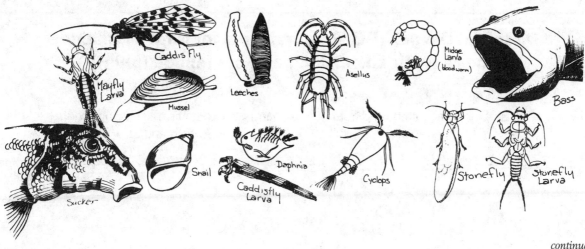

*continued*

# pH Ranges That Support Aquatic Life

**Most Acidic** ———————————————— **Neutral** ———————————————— **Most Basic**

| 1 | 2 | 3 | 4 | 5 | 6 | 7 | 8 | 9 | 10 | 11 | 12 | 13 | 14 |
|---|---|---|---|---|---|---|---|---|----|----|----|----|----|

Bacteria

1.0 ————————————————————————————————————— 13.0

Plants (algae, rooted, etc.)          6.5 ——————————————————— 13.0

Carps, suckers, catfish, some insects    6.0 ————————— 8.5

Bass, crappie                            6.0 ————————— 8.5

Snails, clams, mussels                   6.5 ————————— 9.0

Largest variety of animals               6.0 ————————— 8.5
(trout, mayfly, stonefly, caddisfly)

---

# Temperature Ranges (Approximate) Required for Certain Organisms

**Temperature**

| Greater than 68 °F (20 °C) = Warm water | Much plant life, many fish diseases |
| | Most bass, crappie, bluegill, carp, catfish, caddisfly, dragonfly, mayfly, mussels. |
| 55 – 68 °F (12.8 – 20 °C) = Cool water | Plant life, some fish diseases |
| | Salmon, trout, stonefly, mayfly, caddisfly, water beetles, small-mouth and rock bass, various minnows and darters, mussels |
| Less than 55 °F (12.8 °C) = Cold water | Trout, caddisfly, stonefly, mayfly, various minnows, darters, sculpins |

---

# Dissolved Oxygen (DO) Requirements for Native Fish and Other Aquatic Life (DO in parts per million [ppm])

**(Below 68 °F)**                                    **(Above 68 °F)**

Cold-water organisms including salmon and trout          Warm-water organisms including fish such as bass, crappie, catfish, and carp

6 ppm ——————————————————————————————————— 5 ppm

NOTE: Many educators are not able to have the students measure the dissolved oxygen (DO) because of the difficulty for younger students. If it is convenient, this measure contributes greatly to the overall picture of water quality. These data need to be recorded on Student Worksheet II. Educators may also choose to have the students measure stream velocity, which can be accomplished by timing a floating object (e.g., a ping pong ball) as it travels a known distance (e.g., 10 feet).

7. Assist the students in understanding that the values for pH, water, and air temperature affect the diversity of life forms found in aquatic environments. Ask whether they would expect the same variety of life in other locations. Help them to understand that predictions of animal diversity can be made from measurements of pH and water temperature. Likewise, certain indicator species can also disclose information about pH and water temperature.

NOTE: A simple water quality test kit can be obtained from scientific supply houses dealing with high school biology supplies. Often a hydrion or Hach kit can be borrowed from a high school biology teacher. A local wastewater treatment facility may have kits that you can borrow. Local universities or wildlife agencies may also have aquatic insect kits that you can borrow. (See Extension 8.)

8. Ideally, this activity could be repeated at other sites with different characteristics. Biologists examine hundreds of sites in order to try to understand and predict what is happening in natural systems. If another site is visited, it might be useful to divide the class into two groups with one-half doing Worksheet I and the other half doing Worksheet II. When each group is finished, the students could could come together and mutually predict what the other group had found.

9. Summarize the study with a re-emphasis on the fact that diversity of animals is a useful indicator of habitat quality as well as an overall indicator of environmental quality.

## Extensions

1. Measure and record the dissolved oxygen for the sites visited. Look at the relationships to the values for water temperature and pH.

2. Sample the streams both above and below the local water supply.

3. Find the most diverse and least diverse streams in the area.

4. Contact local wildlife, environmental, and conservation groups to find out what their concerns are regarding water quality. Determine what can be done as an individual and as a community to improve or maintain local water quality.

5. Sample streams above and below your local wastewater treatment plant.

6. What do the conditions in the stream mean for wildlife in and out of the water?

7. Research other examples of biological indicators. Determine how substances such as DDT result in bio-magnification (increased accumulation) in creatures such as birds of prey, fish, shellfish, and such.

8. Contact your local environment department, your state wildlife agency's aquatic education, Project WILD coordinator, or the Izaak Walton League of America (**www.iwla.org** and click on Conservation Programs, then Clean Water Programs, then Save Our Streams) to see if there is an Adopt-a-Stream, river, bay, or lake monitoring project in your area.

## Evaluation

1. Draw a simple illustration of one or more of the following organisms: *Asellus* (water sowbug), water strider, caddisfly larva, crayfish, scud, *Daphnia*, leech, mayfly nymph, midge larva, stonefly nymph, or dragonfly nymph. Identify each organism by writing the correct name beside the picture.

2. You found a trout in a stream with a large variety of other organisms. Predict ranges you would expect to find for pH and water temperature.

*continued*

# Student Worksheet I

| Where Organism Was Found | Sketch of Organism | Number Found |
|---|---|---|
| | | |

# Student Worksheet II

| Observations | Predictions |
|---|---|
| Water Temperature _____ | |
| Air Temperature _____ | |
| pH _____ | |
| Dissolved $O_2$ _____ | |

# Aqua Words

## Objective

Students will describe a variety of ways and reasons that water is important to people and wildlife.

## Method

Students brainstorm water words, make word trees with those words, and write poetic statements about water.

## Materials

Writing materials

## Background

Water is central to all life and life activities. Plants and animals must have water to survive. Almost all plants and animals and all humans need clean water to live healthy lives. To stay healthy, humans need about 1 liter (about 1 quart) of water each day. Water helps blood and its components transport oxygen and nutrients and removes waste through our circulatory systems. Water represents about 75 percent of a

person's body weight. Some animals and plants contain even more water. A jellyfish is 95 percent water and a watermelon is 97 percent water. Most fish and other aquatic animals can live only when they are completely covered with water.

Water covers nearly 75 percent of the Earth's surface. Nearly everything on Earth has a direct or indirect connection with water. Rocks channel water into streams, and streams and rivers carry water across the land. Ponds, lakes, marshes, and swamps often hold water in place. Trees draw water from the soil and transport it into the leaves and out again into the air. Clouds are airborne carriers of water across the sky.

Humans use water for many purposes other than drinking. Water is used for power generation, for industry, and for irrigating crops and lawns. Water is also a source of beauty and recreation. It is the basis of a massive planetary transportation system. Even the driest desert has water—and there are about 320,000,000 cubic miles of water in the oceans. Water grows our food, cools our cars, and is one of the most important substances astronauts take into space.

The major purpose of this activity is for students to increase their appreciation of the importance of water.

## Procedure

1. Have the students bring in magazine photographs that show water habitats. Ask them to look especially for pictures that show how organisms depend on water. Display these photographs, and use them as a basis for discussion.

---

**Grade Level:** K–4

**Subject Areas:** Language Arts, Environmental Education

**Duration:** one or two 20- to 45-minute sessions

**Group Size:** any

**Setting:** indoors

**Conceptual Framework Topic Reference:** IDIA1, IDIIB

**Key Term:** water

**Appendices:** Ecosystem

---

*continued*

2. Ask students to think about some of the ways they have used water today. Any pictures they collect may be used to get them started. Emphasize how all organisms are ultimately connected to water.

3. Using a long strip of paper or an empty chalkboard, ask the students to list at least 100 words that have something to do with water. Ask them to think of words about water, including how it is important to people and wildlife. Keep students stretching into new areas by suggesting examples and categories of ideas if they get bogged down.

NOTE: For younger students, use pictures or a combination of words and pictures.

4. Using the list of words, ask the students to create word trees of water-related words. Begin with a simple word tree like this:

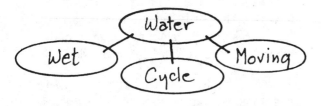

NOTE: You could give students this example for a start if they need it.

Finally, if possible, ask the students to create even more complex word trees like these:

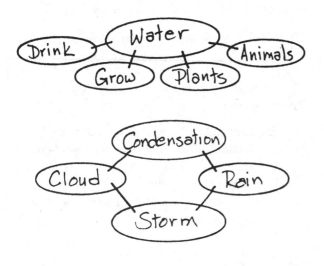

5. When students have finished several word trees, have them look at what they have done and create one or two poetic definitions of water or water-related concepts. These definitions could begin "Water…" or "Water is…" For example, using the word-tree of condensation-cloud-rain-storm, you might get: "Water is gray clouds condensing into a loud summer storm." Students could also simply create sentences or paragraphs about water.

6. When the students have completed their poetic statements, have them write the statements onto various shades of blue, aqua, gray, white, and green construction paper cut to graphically fit the feeling of their ideas. Artistically arrange these cut-outs on a wall or window. OPTIONAL: Examples from students have included arranged words in the shape of a stream, river, pond, lake, or ocean. Others have formed the water cycle from their words and images. Some simply have written each of their words on pieces of paper shaped like water drops.

## Extension

Create a class book with each student's page included. Students write their poetic definitions at the bottom of the page and then illustrate their ideas—for example, with water colors—at the top of the page.

## Evaluation

1. Explain three ways people use water.

2. Explain how plants use water.

3. Explain how animals use water.

4. Explain why water is important.

5. Write and illustrate a short story about the importance of water.

6. Use visual vocabulary techniques (see "Evaluating and Assessing Student Learning" in the Appendices) to demonstrate understanding of concepts and relationships from the activity.

# Water Plant Art

## Objectives

Students will identify aquatic plants as an important component of aquatic habitats and as a necessity for aquatic wildlife.

## Method

Students create artwork showing aquatic habitats using drawings and pressed aquatic plants.

## Materials

Seaweed, grasses, or samples of other aquatic plants; shallow pan filled with fresh water; heavy, porous white watercolor paper; waxed paper; newspapers; several large heavy books or plant press, if available; colored pencils; OPTIONAL: drying rack, 40-watt light bulb apparatus

---

**Grade Level:** K–4

**Subject Areas:** Science, Environmental Education, Expressive Arts

**Duration:** one 20- to 45-minute session for discussion and construction of artwork

**Group Size:** any

**Setting:** indoors and outdoors if students assist in gathering plant material

**Conceptual Framework Topic Reference:** IDIB

**Key Terms:** aquatic, ecosystem

**Appendices:** Using Local Resources, Outdoors, Field Ethics

---

NOTE: Guides to common aquatic plants, pond life, and seashores are helpful resources that tend to be readily available. One excellent resource is *Pond Life* (Golden Guide) by George K. Reid, 1967.

## Background

Aquatic plants grow in a variety of sizes, shapes, and colors. They are essential to the web of life in any aquatic ecosystem. One benefit that aquatic plants provide is that submerged plants release oxygen into the water. The dissolved oxygen can then be used in respiration by aquatic animals.

Another benefit of aquatic plants is their ability to absorb excess nutrients in the water. The aquatic plant parts are also eaten by a variety of animals. Dead plants break down in water to form small particles of organic material called "detritus." This organic material feeds many small aquatic insects, shellfish, and small fish. These animals are then food for larger predators.

Aquatic plants benefit many aquatic animals by providing protected areas for breeding and hiding places for young. Aquatic plants also stabilize shorelines and reduce erosion.

The major purpose of this activity is to heighten students' awareness and appreciation of the importance of aquatic plant life.

*continued*

# Procedure

NOTE: Plants may be collected from outdoors or purchased from pet or aquarium stores, some plant nurseries, and science supply catalogs. When planning to collect plants from the wild, be sure to follow local laws and ordinances for collecting plants. (See "Field Ethics" Appendix on page 230.) Purchased plants that are left over should be disposed of on dry land and not released into local aquatic ecosystems. OPTIONAL: If possible, take the students to a place where they can gather their own samples. They should use the same rules for not damaging animals, plants, or the habitat.

1. Discuss with the students the importance of a variety of plant life in aquatic habitats. Explain that plants are important parts of aquatic ecosystems.

2. Show the students pictures of some different kinds of aquatic plants, animals, and ecosystems. Freshwater habitats (like streams and lakes), and marine habitats (like saltwater bays and ocean environments), can be compared. Ask the students how they think the plants help the animals in each of these environments.

3. Display a small sample of a variety of local aquatic plants to the students. Seaweed from saltwater areas or grasses and algae from freshwater areas work well.

4. Place the seaweed, grasses, or algae in a pan filled with water. Clean the seaweed or other water plants. If necessary, separate the plants into smaller sizes for mounting and designing artwork.

5. Distribute the heavy, white, porous paper to the students. NOTE: Students may work on their own, in small groups, or as a class.

6. Using colored pencils, the students should draw aquatic wildlife on the art paper. Students should not fill the entire page with art because the plants will be placed on top of the art to illustrate plants in the habitat.

7. When the animal drawings are complete, gently lift the plants and place them on paper. Arrange the plant or parts of plants so that they provide a habitat for the wildlife in the students' drawings.

8. Cover the arrangement of plants with waxed paper.

9. Lift the artwork—white paper and wax paper, too—and place it between several sheets of newspaper. (The wax paper protects the plant while the water will seep through the white paper. As the plant dries, it will adhere to the white paper.)

10. Place the stack of newspapers containing the plant on a flat surface. Stack several heavy books on top to serve as a plant press. An actual plant press is ideal, if available.

    (If possible, elevate the stack of newspapers and plants on a rack or a set of bricks. Place a low [40] watt bulb under the stack. Do not let the bulb or socket rest against the stack or any potentially flammable materials. The heat from the lit bulb is just warm enough to dry the stack without damaging the plants.)

11. Drying may take from a few days to several weeks, depending on humidity.

NOTE: These plant prints can serve many purposes, for example, as plant identification keys for classroom use and for bulletin board artistic displays. The wax paper can be retained as protection or can be removed gently, leaving the plant dried flat to the paper. If the plants do not stick to the paper, use a glue stick or spray fabric glue to re-attach loose parts.

12. Display the aquatic art, and ask the students to discuss what they learned. Again talk with the students about the importance of plant life in aquatic habitats. Ask the students to give examples of ways these plants are important.

## Extensions

1. Identify local plants that are found in water. Ask the students to identify the plants used in the activity.

2. Tell how plants that grow in water can provide food and protection for animals that live in water.

3. Give reasons why it is important to have a variety of aquatic plants in aquatic ecosystems.

4. When discussing aquatic life, use a brainstorming technique to discover how plants are similar to animals. Write down common characteristics of plants and animals, or make posters.

5. Find out more about the habitat in which an aquatic plant grows. What is it like? What animals live there? What plant and animal adaptations are evident?

## Evaluation

1. Draw and identify two aquatic plants other than the plants pressed in the activity. What aquatic animals can be added to the pictures to show how these plants help aquatic animals?

# Marsh Munchers

## Objective

Students will (1) identify components of a food web in a salt marsh, and (2) identify their interconnectedness in the food web.

## Method

Students use body movement and pantomime to simulate the feeding motions of marsh animals.

## Materials

Timer; construction paper for tokens in five colors: white, green, yellow, blue, red; predator feeding-behavior cards; detritus-eater cards (master provided on page 38); one envelope per student

NOTE: This activity is written for an estimated 25 students. One-fifth of the class will be designated predators and four-fifths will be other organisms.

---

**Grade Level:** K–4

**Subject Areas:** Science, Environmental Education, Expressive Arts (see Skills Index)

**Duration:** one 20- to 60-minute session

**Group Size:** designed for 25 students (can be adapted for smaller or larger groups)

**Setting:** outdoors or large indoor playing area

**Conceptual Framework Topic Reference:** IDIB, IDIIA, IDIIB, IDIIB1, IDIIB2, IDIIB2b, IDIIC

**Key Terms:** salt marsh, food web, decomposer, detritus; OPTIONAL: predator, prey, producer, consumer

**Appendices:** Ecosystem, Simulations

---

## Background

A salt marsh is an important ecosystem found between a landmass and the ocean. It is a place where fresh water and salt water come together to form a unique habitat for wildlife. Life forms in salt marshes are often more complex and diverse than those in other habitats because of the constantly changing mixture of both fresh and salt water.

Salt marshes are one of the most productive ecosystems on Earth, producing up to two times as much food as the most fertile agricultural lands. The main producer for this important ecosystem is salt marsh grass, which grows and thrives in the nutrient-rich waters of estuaries where salt water from the ocean mixes with fresh water from land drainage. A salt marsh is always producing new grass as old grass dies. Bacteria promote the decay of the marsh grass, which in turn produces detritus. Detritus is dead and decaying plant or animal matter. Fiddler crabs, snails, small shrimp, and fish such as minnows feed on decomposed marsh grasses. Oysters and clams filter detritus and tiny living plants from the water. These organisms become food for crabs, birds, and a variety of fish. Many marine organisms and commercially valuable fish species—including flounder, red drum, and striped bass—depend on marsh ecosystems during their lifetimes.

Countless numbers of birds also depend on salt marshes for food and nesting areas. Ospreys, sandpipers, and members of the heron family can be seen feeding along marsh creeks during the spring and summer, while ducks and northern harriers are common sights in the winter months. Other animals seen wandering

### Table of Materials to Be Prepared and Placed in Envelopes
### (One Envelope per Student Representing One Predator or Other Organism)

|  | Feeding-Behavior Cards | Colored Food Tokens |
|---|---|---|
| **Predators** | | |
| 1 raccoon | 1 each | |
| 1 blue crab | 1 each | |
| 1 red drum fish | 1 each | |
| 1 egret | 1 each | |
| 1 person | 1 each | |
| **Other Organisms (Detritus-Eaters)** | | |
| 4 fiddler crabs | 1 each | 5 red tokens each (20 total) |
| 4 snails | 1 each | 5 blue tokens each (20 total) |
| 4 oysters | 1 each | 5 yellow tokens each (20 total) |
| 4 juvenile fish | 1 each | 5 green tokens each (20 total) |
| 4 shrimp | 1 each | 5 white tokens each (20 total) |

through the marsh in search of food are raccoons and small mammals such as shrews and mice. Deer, grasshoppers, and geese can be seen consuming the grasses at different times of the year.

Salt marshes contribute to flood control and provide water filtration. As water flows through the marsh, much of the sediment load is filtered out to create cleaner and clearer water. Salt marsh grasses and soils also help absorb flood-waters and act as natural buffers between land and ocean. These marshes protect upland organisms as well as billions of dollars worth of human businesses, homes, and cities from storms.

Coastal development and pollution are threatening salt marsh environments. Salt marshes, like other wetlands, are destroyed or damaged when land is converted to agriculture production, filled for coastal development, dredged, or used for other purposes.

The major purpose of this activity is for students to learn about salt marshes and to reinforce their understanding of the concept of a food web.

NOTE: Since this is a simulation, some of the animals' roles are simplified. In actual salt marshes, some animals have several roles. For this activity, one dominant role for each animal has been identified.

## Procedure

1. Cut the appropriate colored construction paper into food tokens, according to the table on this page. Reproduce the feeding-behavior cards (five predator cards, 20 detritus-eater cards). Place feeding-behavior cards and food tokens into the appropriate envelopes.

2. Discuss the characteristics of a salt marsh habitat with the students. Also discuss the importance of salt marshes with emphasis on their high productivity as a place for animals and plants to inhabit. Discuss the role of detritus in the marsh food web. Mention decomposers and their importance. If appropriate, introduce the terms "predator" and "prey", and "producers" and "consumers." Show the students Diagram A, and emphasize the unusual relationship between fresh water and tidal salt water found in this habitat.

3. Give one envelope to each student. Explain that their creatures' identities are a secret. Each envelope contains the identity of one animal that lives in a salt marsh. The only way others will know what they are is by the way they feed. When they receive their envelopes, explain that some students will be detritus-eaters and the others will be predators who prey on the detritus-eaters.

*continued*

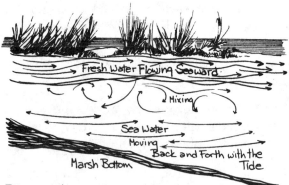

*Diagram A*

4. Instruct the students to open their envelopes and to see what animal they are and what feeding behavior they use. Remind students to keep their identities a secret from the other students. The students will indicate what animals they are by the feeding behavior. OPTIONAL: Model each behavior first, and identify it so the students will know which animal does what. However, it may be more productive to allow the students to improvise.

5. Explain the rules:

   • Each student represents an a *detritus-eater* or a *predator*.

   • Each detritus-eater has five food tokens, representing five individual marsh animals of the same species.

   • The detritus-eater must give a food token to a predator when tagged.

   • Each predator must acquire 10 food tokens to stay alive during a tidal cycle.

   • A tidal cycle is one playing period of the game.

   • Each predator can acquire only one token from each other organism at any one time in a tidal cycle, but needs to acquire as much prey as possible during the tidal cycle.

   • Detritus-eaters keep eating even after predators have eaten them. They represent the remaining animals of that species, until they run out of food tokens. When they run out of food tokens, they sit quietly in place *decomposing* in the salt marsh.

   • Detritus-eater and predators must display their feeding styles during the activity.

   • Detritus-eaters will show their feeding styles from stationary squat positions, while predators will walk as they display their behavior.

6. Establish a play area (inside or outside) and have all detritus-eaters take their envelopes with them as they spread out on the playing field and start pantomiming their feeding behaviors.

7. Tell predators to begin to pantomime their respective feeding behaviors, capture their prey, and secure a food token from the prey, then place it in their envelope.

8. Call time when appropriate (after most predators have acquired 10 food tokens).

9. Tell students to hold on to their food envelopes so that they can participate in the discussions.

10. Discuss the results. Did every predator acquire 10 food tokens during the tidal cycle? If not, why not? (Some animals are more selective in their feeding preferences and, therefore, may have a more difficult time finding food.) Discuss the different ways the animals are connected to each other and to the detritus. Mention that decomposers break down plants and animals to produce the detritus. Be sure the supporting role of the producers—the plants that become the detritus—is not overlooked because of the more intense activity of the consumers.

11. Draw a food web based on the feeding interactions that took place during the game. Include the plants that the decomposers eat to produce detritus.

12. Collect the envelopes, and put the color-coded tokens back into their original envelopes. OPTIONAL: Shuffle the envelopes, and redistribute them to the students. Replay the simulation, and draw a second food web. Compare and contrast the food webs.

13. Summarize by emphasizing the importance of salt marshes. Salt marshes provide habitat for a variety of kinds of animals. Salt marshes are unusually productive habitats, growing large amounts of vegetation that supports a variety of species of wildlife.

## Extensions

1. Draw or paint a food web of a salt marsh as a mural, drawing an accurate portrait of each animal. Place each drawing in the appropriate place in the cycle. With yarn, connect each animal with what it eats.

2. If possible, visit a salt marsh.

3. Modify this activity to simulate a freshwater marsh by substituting the following fresh-water animals for the previously described saltwater animals:

| Detritus-Eaters | Predators |
| --- | --- |
| 4 crayfish | 1 raccoon |
| 4 clams | 1 great blue heron |
| 4 dace (small fish) | 1 bluegill |
| 4 scuds (shrimp-like crustacean) | 1 northern pike |
| 4 mosquito larvae | 1 person |

Follow the rest of the procedures as previously outlined.

## Evaluation

1. Give examples of two predators and two prey species that live in salt marshes.

2. Use some of the organisms listed below, and others of your choice, to construct a food web that might be found in a salt marsh: people, raccoons, marsh grass, bacteria, snails, oysters, detritus, young fish, egrets.

*continued*

# Master for Marsh Muncher

## Predators

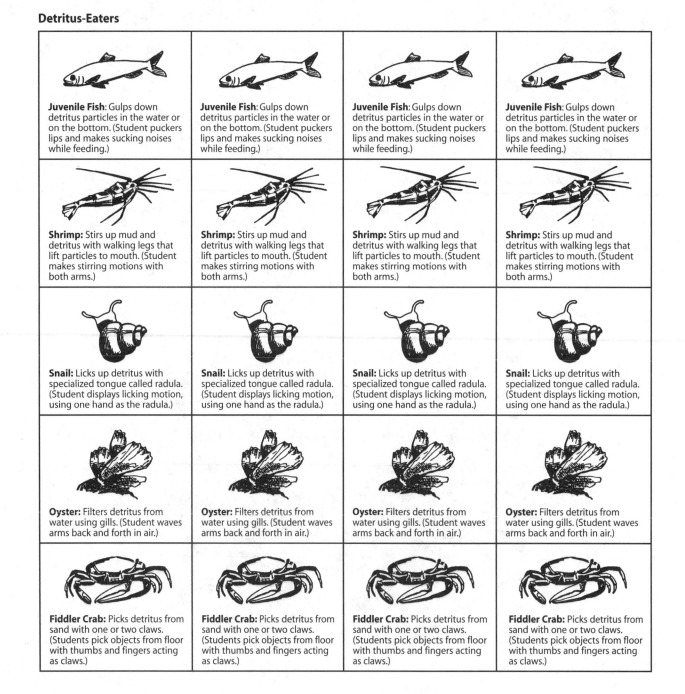

**Person Fishing:** Student walks forward casting line, and tags prey by grasping on the shoulder.

**Blue Crab:** Student walks sideways, waving arms like claws and grasps prey.

**Raccoon:** Student walks forward washing hands and grasps prey.

**Red Drum Fish:** Student walks with hands held forward like a mouth, and grasps prey.

**Egret:** Student struts with hands on hips, so elbows are like wings. Nearing prey, arms become a beak to grasp prey.

## Detritus-Eaters

**Juvenile Fish:** Gulps down detritus particles in the water or on the bottom. (Student puckers lips and makes sucking noises while feeding.)

**Juvenile Fish:** Gulps down detritus particles in the water or on the bottom. (Student puckers lips and makes sucking noises while feeding.)

**Juvenile Fish:** Gulps down detritus particles in the water or on the bottom. (Student puckers lips and makes sucking noises while feeding.)

**Juvenile Fish:** Gulps down detritus particles in the water or on the bottom. (Student puckers lips and makes sucking noises while feeding.)

**Shrimp:** Stirs up mud and detritus with walking legs that lift particles to mouth. (Student makes stirring motions with both arms.)

**Shrimp:** Stirs up mud and detritus with walking legs that lift particles to mouth. (Student makes stirring motions with both arms.)

**Shrimp:** Stirs up mud and detritus with walking legs that lift particles to mouth. (Student makes stirring motions with both arms.)

**Shrimp:** Stirs up mud and detritus with walking legs that lift particles to mouth. (Student makes stirring motions with both arms.)

**Snail:** Licks up detritus with specialized tongue called radula. (Student displays licking motion, using one hand as the radula.)

**Snail:** Licks up detritus with specialized tongue called radula. (Student displays licking motion, using one hand as the radula.)

**Snail:** Licks up detritus with specialized tongue called radula. (Student displays licking motion, using one hand as the radula.)

**Snail:** Licks up detritus with specialized tongue called radula. (Student displays licking motion, using one hand as the radula.)

**Oyster:** Filters detritus from water using gills. (Student waves arms back and forth in air.)

**Oyster:** Filters detritus from water using gills. (Student waves arms back and forth in air.)

**Oyster:** Filters detritus from water using gills. (Student waves arms back and forth in air.)

**Oyster:** Filters detritus from water using gills. (Student waves arms back and forth in air.)

**Fiddler Crab:** Picks detritus from sand with one or two claws. (Students pick objects from floor with thumbs and fingers acting as claws.)

**Fiddler Crab:** Picks detritus from sand with one or two claws. (Students pick objects from floor with thumbs and fingers acting as claws.)

**Fiddler Crab:** Picks detritus from sand with one or two claws. (Students pick objects from floor with thumbs and fingers acting as claws.)

**Fiddler Crab:** Picks detritus from sand with one or two claws. (Students pick objects from floor with thumbs and fingers acting as claws.)

# Wetland Metaphors

## Objectives

Students will (1) describe the characteristics of wetlands, and (2) evaluate the importance of wetlands to wildlife and humans.

## Method

Students are presented with a selection of objects to investigate as metaphors for the natural functions of wetlands.

## Materials

A large pillowcase, bag, or box; sponge; small pillow; soap; eggbeater or mixer; small doll cradle; sieve or strainer; paper coffee filter; antacid tablets; small box of cereal or rice; 3″ × 5″ cards with pictures that could be used to show other wetland metaphors (a zoo could represent the idea of wildlife diversity in a wetland; a lush vegetable garden could represent the

idea of a productive wetland in which food is abundant; a vacation resort could represent the idea of a resting or wintering place for migrating waterfowl)

NOTE: A metaphoric approach such as this allows a variety of objects to suggest appropriate linkages to the basic characteristics of wetlands.

## Background

Wetlands are many different things to many different people. Some people have never heard of or thought about wetlands. Others are working actively to protect wetlands because of their importance.

Wetlands include areas such as freshwater and saltwater marshes, wet meadows, swamps, lagoons, bogs, and prairie potholes. All wetlands, whether coastal or inland, provide special habitats that serve areas far beyond their boundaries. Wetlands are especially important to plants, animals, humans, and the total environment.

Because of the abundance of food, vegetative cover (shelter), and water found there, most wetlands are rich with diverse wildlife species.

Coastal and inland marshes, for example, provide breeding, resting, and wintering habitats for thousands of migratory birds—including ducks, geese, swans, cranes, and shore birds. Many species of fish that are important for commercial and personal use by humans reproduce and spend part, or all, of their life cycles in fertile wetlands adjacent to larger, more open bodies of water. These fish species include bass, salmon, walleye, perch, and pickerel. A wide variety of reptiles, amphibians, insects, and crustaceans also

---

**Grade Level:** 5–8

**Subject Areas:** Environmental Education, Language Arts

**Duration:** one or two 30- to 60-minute sessions

**Group Size:** any

**Setting:** indoors or outdoors

**Conceptual Framework Topic Reference:** IDIA2b

**Key Terms:** wetlands, metaphor

**Appendices:** Outdoors, Simulations

---

*continued*

breed and live in wetlands. Frogs and toads, turtles of all kinds, salamanders, snakes, dragonflies, water striders, clams, and crayfish flourish in wetland habitats. Many mammals—from muskrats and beaver to white-tail deer and moose—also depend on wetland areas.

Wetlands are often referred to as "nurseries" because they provide critical breeding and rearing habitats for countless numbers and kinds of wildlife.

Wetlands also have the unique ability to purify the environment. They act as natural filtering systems and have been shown to be extremely effective. For example, they can trap and neutralize sewage waste, allow silt to settle, and promote the decomposition of many toxic substances.

The importance of vegetation associated with wetlands cannot be overlooked. Plants absorb nutrients and help cycle them through food webs. Plants also help keep nutrient concentrations from reaching toxic levels. Plants slow down water flow, causing silt to settle out. Through photosynthesis, plants add oxygen to the system and provide food to other life forms. Of great importance to humans are the flood-control characteristics of wetlands. When runoff from rains and spring thaws is high, wetland areas absorb excess water until it gradually drains away down streams and rivers and through the soil. Acting as buffers, healthy wetlands prevent flooding and erosion. In dryer periods, wetlands hold precious moisture after open bodies of water have disappeared.

The many activities that take place in wetlands make them among the most productive ecosystems in the world.

As remarkable and resilient as wetlands are, these unique areas have limits. Their destruction or abuse can have devastating effects on wildlife, humans, and overall environmental quality.

Many of the major attributes of wetlands can be explored through the use of metaphors. To use a metaphor is to apply a word or phrase to an object or concept that the word or phrase does not literally denote in order to suggest a comparison between the two. A metaphor represents a concept or idea through another concept or idea. "A tree is a home" and "Books are windows of thought" are two examples. In this activity, a variety of everyday objects can be used to represent the natural functions of wetlands. For example,

| Object | Metaphoric Function |
|---|---|
| *sponge* | absorbs excess water caused by runoff; retains moisture for a time even if standing water dries up (e.g., sponge placed in a small puddle of water absorbs water until saturated, then stays wet after standing water has evaporated) |
| *pillow or bed* | is a resting place for migratory birds |
| *mixer or eggbeater* | mixes nutrients and oxygen into the water |
| *cradle* | provides a nursery that shelters, protects, and feeds young wildlife |
| *sieve or strainer* | strains silt, debris, and such, from water |
| *filter* | filters smaller impurities from water |
| *antacid* | neutralizes toxic substances |
| *cereal or rice* | provides nutrient-rich foods (rice is grown in wetland areas) |
| *soap* | helps cleanse the environment (as wetlands do) |

Wetland habitats are being converted to other uses (agriculture, roadways, housing developments) or otherwise being altered (drained for pest control or polluted) at the rate of about a half million acres per year. And although many wetlands are protected by federal and state laws, there still appears to be a significant need to create a greater understanding of the importance of wetlands as ecosystems and as wildlife habitat.

The major purpose of this activity is for students to develop an appreciation and understanding of wetlands through the power of metaphor, linking the characteristics and natural functions of wetlands to the familiar realm of everyday life.

## Procedure

1. Prepare a "Mystery Metaphor Container" (pillowcase, bag, or box). It should be possible for students to put their hands into the container and pull out an object without being able to see inside the container. Educators may want to collect as many as one metaphoric object per student, but at least have enough for one per group of four students. Put the container aside to use later.

2. Discuss the variety of wetlands found in your local area, state, country, and elsewhere. Then invite the students to sit quietly and close their eyes. Ask them to picture a wetland. Have them examine what it looks like and look carefully at the plants and animals, including insects and small creatures. What does the air feel like? How does it smell?

3. Invite the students to tell what they imagined. Compile a list of their offerings. Encourage discussion and mutual sharing.

4. With their lists as a point of reference, help the students identify which plants and animals are most likely to be found in a wetland. If possible, have them classify the plants and animals according to the kind of wetland in which they would be found. State or federal wildlife officials and representatives of private conservation or nature-related organizations can be helpful.

5. Next provide the students with background information to serve as an overview of the basic ecological activities that characterize the wetland habitat. For example, educators might include the following:

   - **sponge effect:** absorbs runoff
   - **filter effect:** takes out silt, toxins, wastes, and such
   - **nutrient control:** absorbs nutrients from fertilizers and other sources that may cause contamination downstream
   - **natural nursery:** provides protection and nourishment for newborn wildlife

   Suggest that these activities and many more that they could probably think of are taking place in wetlands all the time.

6. Now bring out the "Mystery Metaphor Container." Tell the students that everything in the container has something to do with a wetland. Have the students divide into groups of four. Announce that when it is their team's turn, a representative from the group will draw an object from the container. Then, as a group, they must figure out how the object could represent what a wetland is or does.

7. Have the designated student reach into the container and withdraw one object. When each group has an object, ask them to work as a team to identify and describe the relationships between their metaphoric object and wetlands. Encourage the students to build on each other's ideas. You can also assist by strengthening their connections.

NOTE: Allow the students time to discuss their ideas within their groups before doing so in front of the entire class.

8. Ask each group to report its ideas to the class.

*continued*

9. Following discussion and review of the functions represented by each metaphor, ask the students to summarize the major roles that wetlands perform in contributing to habitat for wildlife. List the ways in which wetlands are important to humans. Why do humans convert wetlands to other uses? Ask the students if their own attitudes about wetlands are different now. If yes, how? If not, why not?

10. For the final part of this activity, encourage the students' understanding of how the wetlands' condition depends on each of us. Many kinds of wildlife depend on wetlands. Our own well-being requires wetland ecosystems. Strengthen the students' understanding of how humans are connected to wetlands. Recreation, aesthetics, utilitarian uses, environmental quality, and nature study are but a few of the connections we each have with wetlands.

## Extensions

1. Visit a wetland to verify the appropriateness of the metaphors explored in the classroom. Identify and discuss any limitations to the appropriateness of those metaphors. Identify what seem to be the most compelling attributes of the metaphors in helping you understand the characteristics and nature of the wetland. Expand on your understanding of those metaphors. Identify new and appropriate metaphors.

2. Investigate local, county, state, and federal regulations and laws that govern uses of wetlands.

## Evaluation

1. Explain why wetlands are among the world's most productive ecosystems.

2. Wetlands are important to a range of organisms in the animal kingdom, from zooplankton to humans. Select five species of animals, and describe how wetlands are important to each.

## Additional Resources

wetlandsfws.er.usgs.gov/NWI/index.html

www.epa.gov/owow/wetlands/

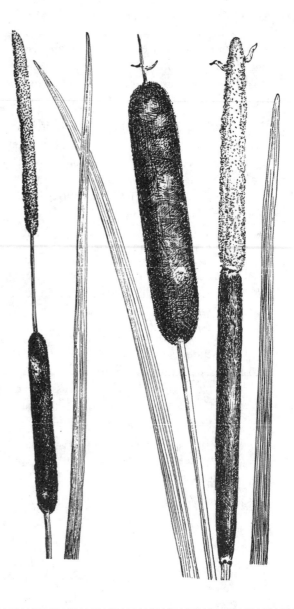

# Hooks and Ladders

## Objectives

Students will (1) describe how some fish migrate as part of their life cycles, (2) identify the stages of the life cycle of one kind of fish, (3) describe limiting factors affecting Pacific salmon as they complete their life cycles, and (4) generalize that limiting factors affect all populations of animals.

## Method

Students simulate the Pacific salmon and the hazards faced by salmon in an activity portraying the life cycle of these aquatic creatures.

## Materials

Large playing area (100 feet × 50 feet), about 500 feet of rope or string or six traffic cones for marking boundaries (masking tape may be used if area is indoors), two cardboard boxes, 100 tokens (3″ × 5″ cards, poker chips, macaroni, etc.), jump rope

> **Grade Level:** 5–8
>
> **Subject Areas:** Social Studies, Science, Environmental Education, Expressive Arts
>
> **Duration:** one 30- to 60-minute session
>
> **Group Size:** 20 to 30 students or more
>
> **Setting:** outdoors or large indoor area
>
> **Conceptual Framework Topic Reference:** IDIIB
>
> **Key Terms:** life cycle, limiting factors, population, migration
>
> **Appendices:** Simulations, Ecosystems

## Background

Many fish migrate from one habitat to another during their lives. Both the Atlantic and Pacific salmon are examples of fish that endure a spectacular migration.

The life cycle for Pacific salmon begins when the female deposits 1,000 to 5,000 eggs in her freshwater spawn. The eggs are deposited in a shallow gravel depression that she digs by flapping her tail from side to side. Once the eggs are deposited, the male fertilizes them; then both fish nudge the gravel back over the eggs to offer as much protection as possible. The eggs are susceptible to factors such as predation or oxygen deprivation. Within a few days, both the male and female salmon have completed their reproduction cycle and soon die.

Newly hatched salmon, called "alevins," live in the gravel and survive by absorbing proteins from their yolk sacs. After a few weeks, the yolk sacs are gone and the small fish, known as "fry," move into deeper water to find food on their own. Salmon remain in freshwater streams feeding and growing for many months or even years before migrating downstream to the ocean. These small ocean-bound salmon are now called "smolts." These salmon will feed in estuaries where fresh and salt water mix. After a few weeks of adjusting to the brackish water, the young salmon swim into the ocean.

In the ocean, the salmon grow rapidly by feeding on a rich food supply that includes other fish, shrimp, and crustaceans. Young salmon may encounter many limiting factors, including sharks, killer whales, other marine mammals, and humans who are fishing for salmon for commercial and personal uses.

*continued*

**Life Cycle of the Pacific Salmon**

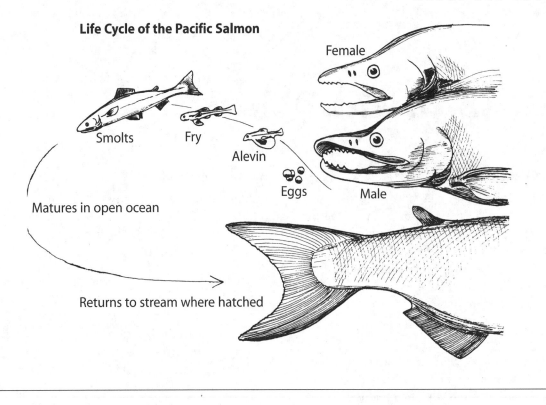

After 2 to 5 years in the ocean, the Pacific salmon begin the journey that guides them to their own hatching sites. Pacific salmon spawn only once in their lives. Salmon have an inherent ability to return to their original streams. Juvenile salmon imprint or memorize the unique odors of their home streams. As returning adults, they use their senses of smell to detect those odors and guide them upstream to where they were hatched. Once there, the salmon spawn and then die.

Salmon face a variety of limiting factors in the completion of their life cycle. A limiting factor is a reason or cause that reduces the population of an organism. Some limiting factors are natural, and some result from human intervention into natural systems.

Natural limiting factors include drought, floods, predators, and inadequate food supply. Throughout their lives, salmon depend on a habitat that provides plants to shade streams and deep pools of water for spawning and resting. Incorrect logging practices, grazing, mining, road building,

and development often destroy streamside vegetation, erode land, and fill streams with silt that covers gravel beds.

Dams are another limiting factor that block or slow migration to and from the ocean. Salmon become disoriented by the reservoirs formed by dams and become exposed to unhealthy conditions like high water temperatures and predators. Fish ladders can be installed to help salmon through the dams. Fish ladders can be water-filled staircases that allow migrating fish to swim around the dam.

Another threat to salmon is overfishing. Overfishing, combined with habitat destruction, is viewed by biologists as a cause for the decline of salmon populations.

NOTE: All possible conditions are not covered by the design of this activity. However, the activity does serve to illustrate three important concepts: life cycle, migration, and limiting factors.

## Procedure

1. Ask the students what they know about the life cycles of fish that live in their area. Do any local fish migrate to spawn? If yes, which ones? (Mullet, shad, lake trout, striped bass, suckers, carp, and salmon are examples of fish that migrate to spawn.)

2. Set up a playing field as shown in Diagram A, including spawning grounds, reservoir, downstream, upstream, and ocean. The area must be at least 100 feet by 50 feet. Assign roles to each of the students. Some will be salmon; others will be potential limiting factors to the salmon. Assign the students roles as follows:

   • Choose two students to be the turbine team. They will operate the jump rope, which represents the turbines in hydroelectric dams. Later in the simulation, when all the salmon have passed the turbine going downstream, those students move to the upstream side to become the waterfall-broad jump monitors. (See diagram.)

   • Choose two students to be predatory wildlife. At the start of the simulation, the predators will be stationed in the reservoir above the turbines to catch the salmon fry as they try to find their way out of the reservoir and move downstream. Then they will move to below the turbines where they catch salmon headed downstream. Later in the activity, when all the salmon are in the sea, these same two predators will patrol the area above the "broad jump" waterfalls. There they will feed on salmon just before they enter the spawning ground. (See diagram.)

   • Choose two students to be humans in fishing boats catching salmon in the open ocean. The students in the fishing boats must keep one foot in a cardboard box to reduce their speed and maneuverability.

   • All remaining students are salmon.

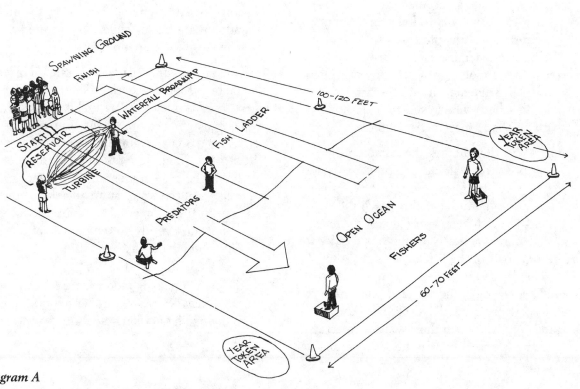

*Diagram A*

*continued*

NOTE: These figures are based on a class size of 25 to 30. If the group is larger or smaller, adjust the number of people who are fishing and predatory wildlife accordingly.

3. Begin the activity with all the salmon in the spawning ground. The salmon first move into the reservoir above the dam. They must stay in the reservoir while they count to 30. This pause simulates the disorientation that salmon face because of a lack of current in the lake to direct them on their journey. During this time the predators may catch the salmon and escort them one at a time, to become part of the fish ladder. The salmon then start their journey downstream. The first major limiting factor that the salmon encounter is the turbines at the dam. At most dams, escape weirs guide migrating salmon past the turbines. The student salmon cannot go around the jump-rope swingers, but they can slip under the swingers' arms if they do not get touched while doing so. A salmon dies if the turbine (jump rope) hits it. The turbine operators may change the speed at which they swing the jump rope. Any salmon that "dies" at any time in this activity must immediately become part of the fish ladder. The student is no longer a fish, but becomes part of the physical structure of the human-made fish ladders now used by migrating salmon to get past barriers such as dams. The students who are the fish ladder kneel on the ground as shown on page 47, with one body space between them.

4. Once past the turbines, the salmon must pass some predatory wildlife. The predators, who have moved from the reservoir area to the area below the turbine, must catch the salmon with both hands—tagging isn't enough. Dead salmon are escorted by the predator to become part of the fish ladder. Later, the salmon that survive life in the open ocean will pass through the fish ladder to return to the spawning ground. NOTE: Both the predatory wildlife in the downstream area and the people fishing in the open ocean must take dead salmon to the fish ladder site. This action moves the predators and fishing boats off the field regularly, helping to provide a more realistic survival ratio.

5. Once in the open ocean, the salmon can be caught by fishing boats. The salmon must move back and forth across the ocean area in order to gather four tokens. Each token represents 1 year of growth. Once each fish has four tokens (4 years' growth), that fish can begin migration upstream. The year tokens can be picked up only one at a time on each crossing. Remember, the salmon must cross the entire open ocean area to get a token. The "4 years" that these trips take make the salmon more vulnerable; thus they are more readily caught by the fishing boats. For this simulation, the impact of this limiting factor creates a more realistic survival ratio on the population before the salmon begin the return migration upstream.

6. When four of the year tokens have been gathered, the salmon can start upstream. The salmon must walk through the entire pattern of the fish ladder. This enforced trip through the fish ladder gives the students a hint of how restricting and tedious the upstream journey can be. In the fish ladder, predators may not harm the salmon.

7. Once through the ladder, the salmon face the broad-jump waterfall. The waterfall represents one of the natural barriers salmon face going upstream. Be sure the jumping distance is challenging but realistic. The two former turbine students will monitor the jump. The salmon must jump the entire breadth of the waterfall to be able to continue. If the salmon fails to make the jump, then it must return to the bottom of the fish ladder and come through again.

NOTE: When playing indoors, the broad-jump waterfall may be changed into a stepping-stone jump defined by masking tape squares on hard floors.

8. Above the falls, the two predators who started the simulation as the predators below the turbines have now become the last set of limiting factors faced by the salmon. They represent bears—one example of predatory wildlife. Again, remember that the predators must catch the salmon with both hands. If they catch a salmon, they must then take the student they caught to become part of the structure of the fish ladder.

9. The activity ends when all the salmon are gone before the spawning ground is reached—or when all surviving salmon reach the spawning ground.

10. Next engage the students in a discussion. Explore topics such as

- the apparent survival or mortality ratio of salmon,

- the role of the barriers,

- the role of the predatory wildlife and the people fishing,

- where the losses were greatest,

- where the losses were least,

- what the consequences would be if all the eggs deposited made the journey successfully, and

- what seemed realistic about this simulation and what did not.

11. Ask the students to summarize what they have learned about the life cycle of salmon, the salmon's migration, and limiting factors that affect salmon. Make sure the students have a clear working definition of limiting factors. Encourage the students to make the generalization that all animals—not just the Pacific salmon—are affected by limiting factors. Ask the students to give examples of limiting factors. They might mention the availability of suitable food, water, shelter, and space; disease; weather; predation; and changes in land use and other human activities.

## Variation: Atlantic Salmon

This activity can easily be adapted to feature Atlantic salmon. The most significant difference between Pacific and Atlantic salmon is that the Atlantic salmon can spawn more than once. Many Atlantic salmon make their complete migratory journey and spawn two or more times. All Pacific salmon die after spawning only once. To adapt this activity for Atlantic salmon, students are to make as many complete migratory trips as possible. After the activity is finished, ask students to report how many times they successfully completed the migratory cycle. Graph the data. Have the students explain how age influences mortality rates and susceptibility to limiting factors.

## Variation: Striped Bass

This activity can also be adapted to feature striped bass rather than salmon. The striped bass is more widely distributed along the United States' coastlines than either the Atlantic or Pacific salmon. Like the salmon, striped bass reproduce in fresh water and migrate to and mature in salt water. They also must face the same limiting factors described in this activity.

*continued*

## Extensions

1. Write a report on the life history of one of the species of salmon (e.g., chinook or king, chum or dog, pink or humpback, coho or silver, sockeye or red, Atlantic). Create a mural showing the life cycle of this salmon.

2. Research and illustrate the life cycle of any local fish. If possible, look for one that migrates.

3. Compare how the life cycle of a Pacific salmon is similar to and different from the life cycle of one or more local fish.

4. Investigate similarities and differences in the migration and life cycles of an Atlantic and a Pacific salmon. Investigate the life cycle of salmon in the Great Lakes region of the United States.

5. Visit fish hatcheries that work with migratory species and investigate how they function.

6. Explore ways that dams can be modified to let fish safely pass downstream and upstream. Design the "perfect" fish ladder.

7. Investigate and discuss commercial fishing for salmon. Investigate and discuss personal, including recreational, fishing for salmon.

8. Find out about laws protecting migratory species, including fish.

9. Consider this approach, and try the activity again:

   In the past 100 years, salmon have experienced many new, human-caused limiting factors. Dams, commercial fishing, timber harvest, and road construction have had a tremendous impact on salmon populations. In 1991, the Snake River sockeye salmon was placed on the federal endangered species list. In the past, tens of thousands of sockeyes would make the 900-mile return trip from the sea to Idaho's mountain streams

and lakes. There they spawned and died. Their offspring hatched and began their early development in fresh water. The actual migration to the Pacific Ocean could be completed in as few as 9 days. Today that trip takes more than 60 days. In 1991, only four Snake River sockeye salmon returned to their spawning grounds.

   To simulate these increases in salmon limiting factors, play several rounds of "Hooks and Ladders." Allow each round to represent the passage of 25 years. Start in 1850. In that year, do not include dams or commercial fishing operations in the scenario. As time passes, add the human commercial fishing operations. Build dams (jump ropes) as the scenario progresses into the 21st century.

   Describe some of the possible effects on salmon from increased limiting factors as a result of human activities and interventions. Discuss possible positive and negative effects on both people and salmon from these increases in limiting factors affecting salmon. When the activity reaches "the present," predict what might happen to salmon in the future. Recognizing the complexity of the dilemma, discuss possible actions, if any, that might be taken to benefit both people and salmon.

10. Find out if salmon exist in your state. If so, are they native or were they introduced?

## Evaluation

1. List, describe, and illustrate the major stages in a Pacific salmon's life cycle.

2. Identify and describe some of the limiting factors that affect salmon as they complete their life cycles.

3. Identify and describe some limiting factors that might affect other animal populations.

# Micro Odyssey

## Objectives

Students will (1) identify forms of microscopic life that live in water, and (2) describe how various aquatic organisms are interrelated.

## Method

Students will examine, draw, paint, and identify microorganisms in pond water.

## Materials

Pond water; hand lens; magnifiers; nets (of fine mesh); microscopes, slides, cover slips, eyedroppers; writing materials; art supplies (paints, poster paper, mural paper, tape)

## Background

When Anton Van Leeuwenhoek and Robert Hooke, the inventors of the first microscope, looked into the micro-world of stream and pond water, they were surprised to find life forms. As time went by and more researchers gazed into this world, it became clear that there were thousands of tiny organisms that made their homes in water. Research has shown that without these microscopic life forms the entire aquatic eco-system could not function. Micro-organisms are vital in the food supplies of fish, aquatic birds, reptiles, amphibians, and mammals—including humans.

The major purpose of this activity is to provide students with ways of becoming familiar with various microscopic life forms and their roles in larger-scale habitats and ecosystems.

## Procedure

1. Collect samples of pond water that contain abundant microorganisms. One or two gallons should be adequate.

NOTE: Some educators may want to start a small aquarium. This phase can be done by the educator or as a field trip. Obtain enough pond water to stock a small aquarium and collect pond bottom materials with soil and detritus. Aquatic plants can be transplanted into the aquarium. Certain aquatic insects, like diving beetles and water striders, may be placed in the aquarium. See page 243 of the Appendices for additional information about preparing classroom aquaria.

2. Invite the students to remove about a tablespoon of the pond water from the container. Remember to tell them to get the water from within the container and not just at the surface. Have them examine the water with hand lenses and microscopes. Tell them to make sketches of the living things they find. They should note how the organisms move and how they interact. Do some seem to be predators? Which of the other life forms do the predators prey upon?

---

**Grade Level:** 5–8

**Subject Areas:** Science, Environmental Education

**Duration:** three 45-minute sessions, additional time if field trip to pond is included

**Group Size:** any for individual study of pond organisms, group for development of mural

**Setting:** outdoors and indoors

**Conceptual Framework Topic Reference:** IDIB, IDIIB2, IDIIC

**Key Terms:** microorganism, pond, habitat, predator, prey, food web

**Appendices:** Field Ethics, Aquaria

---

*continued*

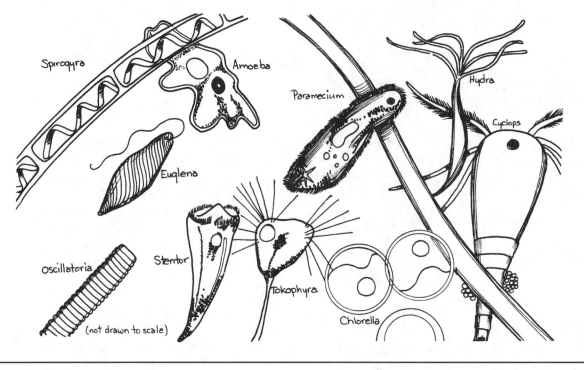

*Diagram A*

3. After they have sketched several organisms, encourage the students to choose life forms to portray in a painting. The students should strive for detail and accuracy in portraying the organisms. Next have the students identify the organisms they painted. Ask them to write a short paragraph about the habits and habitat of the organisms. Some common pond microorganisms are shown in Diagram A. "Pond Life: Golden Guide" (Reid, George K. 1967, Golden Press, NY) can assist with identifying common microscopic organisms. Because there may be microorganisms that are difficult to identify, you may have the students give those organisms temporary names. Locate additional reference materials to identify the species.

4. Create a class mural of a pond and its aquatic environment. The paintings done in Step 3 could be added to the mural at appropriate locations. The written reports could be displayed near the mural. Which animals should be shown preying on others? Which are decomposers? Which are producers? Which are consumers? Where should the plants be placed? Each student could do additional research to discover more about their organism, its role in the aquatic system, and other things of interest about it. If possible, return the water to the pond when it is no longer needed in the classroom for instruction.

Ecological Knowledge
.............................................................................................................

Micro Odyssey

## Extensions

1. What natural or unnatural events in the pond or stream could be major disasters to all the inhabitants?

2. Divide the class into crews, and have each crew create a log of an imaginary journey through their micro-world. They are to act as if they were micro-size. The logs should be filled with written descriptions and illustrations. Students might make maps, plotting their journeys and noting the places where they had adventures. The crews should then exchange logs with other crews. Using the logs, maps and drawings, the crew members should decide how to prepare themselves and their craft for a future micro-journey.

3. Find examples of maps, drawings, and writings made in the past by some of the famous explorers. Old World maps drawn at the time of Columbus, accounts written by explorers, and drawings of animals made by these explorers can be interesting introductions to this activity.

4. Read examples of great mythical voyages, such as those of Ulysses. Find old bestiaries (fables about mythical creatures popular in the Middle Ages) and read about mermaids, unicorns, and sea monsters. With these fables for inspiration, along with your writings and paintings of pond life, create a 20th-century bestiary.

## Evaluation

1. Draw a simple illustration of one or more of the following pond organisms: *Daphnia*, *Euglena*, *Hydra*, *Spirogyra*, rotifer, water mite. Label your drawing and add information about the characteristics of the organisms and its habitat.

2. Identify each of the organisms in the list above, plus sulfur bacteria, as a producer (P), consumer (C), or decomposer (D).

3. Use at least three of the organisms listed above, plus others, to construct an aquatic food web that might be found in a pond.

# Blue-Ribbon Niche

## Objectives

Students will (1) identify different organisms that live in riparian areas, (2) describe the ecological role of some organisms in riparian zones, (3) describe some basic characteristics of riparian zones, and (4) evaluate potential positive and negative effects from changes in riparian zones.

## Method

Students create a variety of representations of wildlife that can be found in riparian zones.

## Materials

A variety of art materials (e.g., paints, clay, glue, wire, string, brushes), papier mâché, construction paper; OPTIONAL: Nature magazines for photos, books of references about riparian habitats and wildlife

---

**Grade Level:** 5–8

**Subject Areas:** Science, Language Arts, Environmental Education

**Duration:** two or three 30- to 45-minute sessions, may be longer if field trip is involved

**Group Size:** any, designed for classroom-sized group

**Setting:** outdoors and indoors, outdoors is optional, but recommended

**Conceptual Framework Topic Reference:** IDIIB

**Key Terms:** niche, predator, prey, producer, consumer, decomposer, riparian, ecosystem, habitat

**Appendices:** Outdoors, Field Ethics

---

## Background

The role of an animal in its community—including its preferences for food, shelter, and space—is known as a niche. Different species cannot live in the same niche, because they would compete for resources and living space until one is forced out of the niche. As a metaphor, if niche is an animal's "occupation," then habitat is its "address." This activity is designed to focus on riparian niches and habitats.

Riparian zones are found wherever streams or rivers at least occasionally cause flooding beyond their channels. These zones are an important and valuable habitat that supports a variety of plant and animal life. Each plant and animal has an important niche in the riparian zone. Some are predators, some are prey. Some are producers, some consumers, and some decomposers. Some are herbivores, some carnivores, and some omnivores. The plants and animals in the riparian zone are interdependent, with each species contributing to the well-being of the overall system.

Many animals living in riparian zones cannot survive without the special conditions the zones provide. Riparian zones often provide a wide variety and great abundance of vegetation, along with a higher percentage of shade, high humidity, and high diversity in animals and plants. Riparian zones can be as broad as alluvial valleys several tens of miles wide or a narrow strip of a stream bank. The width of a riparian zone depends on factors such as the amount of available water, soil types, minerals, water table, and geologic structures.

Riparian zones are both aquatic and terrestrial and are characterized by a diversity of life forms. For example, frogs are commonly found in areas of calm waters in riparian zones. Frogs are predators, after they mature beyond their algae-eating tadpole stages. They need moisture, sunlight, and grasses or other vegetative shelter. Their eggs must be deposited in water that is permanent enough to allow a lengthy gestation period, growth into gilled tadpoles, and finally transformation into predatory, and air-breathing frogs. Both tadpoles and frogs affect other animals' niches. Fish and wading birds prey on both. Raccoons, foxes, and other animals eat both tadpoles and frogs as well as fish. What is important is how the "occupations" and "addresses" are interrelated and contribute to the uniqueness and beauty of riparian zones.

Riparian zones are easily affected by natural and nonnatural changes. For example, spring flooding and flash floods dramatically affect vegetation and wildlife. Excessive use of riparian zones by humans, livestock, and wildlife can greatly modify riparian vegetation and destabilize the stream or riverbanks, thus causing increased rates of erosion. Development and recreational pressures also jeopardize those unique habitats. Riparian zones have aesthetic, ecological, scientific, social, economic, recreational, and intrinsic value.

## Procedure

NOTE: This activity is designed to involve a visit to an actual stream site. If that is not possible, see the Variation section for an alternative approach.

1. Using local maps, select a body of water to use as a study site for this activity. Discuss with the students the dozens of different animals and plants that live in, around, above, and below this area. Ask the students to generate a list of the animals that they think inhabit the water and the nearby environment. Consider the water and the adjacent land of the riparian zone.

2. Assist the students in verifying which animals actually live in the region and might live in this riparian zone. The list may be obvious, making it possible for educators and students to quickly decide. However, some animals may be in question, and educators may want the students to consult reference materials. Also, without additional research, many animals that live in the area may not be identified.

3. Once the list is verified, have the students choose an organism. Ask each student to express the animal through art. Students can use drawing, painting, collage, sculpture, magazine images, or any other art form of their choice. Be sure to ask the students to make their work durable enough to be displayed outside. Each art piece needs to include a hook, string, or other support to allow it to be hung on branches, placed in the soil, or put on a solid surface.

4. The students need to research how the organisms they have chosen depend on other animals and which organisms depend on their animal. Discuss the concepts of niche and habitat with the students at this point for emphasis. Again, habitat is the animal's "address." Niche is the animal's "occupation" at that address. OPTIONAL: Add terms such as predator, prey, consumer, producer, decomposer, herbivore, carnivore, omnivore, and food web.

5. Visit the local stream or body of water that was selected in the first step of this activity. Emphasize personal safety and regard for the habitat. Select a central gathering place to which everyone can return for discussion. Choose this central place so that all the animal art is visible from this spot.

6. Ask the students to place their animal art appropriately within the habitat. Afterward, have the students return to the central gathering place.

*continued*

7. Ask each student to present a 3-minute report on the characteristics, habitat, and niche of their animal. Make sure all of the students can hear and see one another clearly during this process.

8. When the presentations are complete, gather the students in the central gathering place, and discuss the concepts of niches and habitats, plus how the organisms are interrelated in any ecosystem. Describe the effects that water has on the surrounding area. Emphasize the word "riparian" in the discussion. Have the students identify and discuss the characteristics of riparian zones.

9. Now ask the students to consider things that might change this riparian zone and could affect the habitat for the animals. Here are examples of potential changes that could take place in some areas:

   • draining to expand acres under cultivation on nearby farms;

   • removing shade-producing trees or shrubs along the bank of a flowing stream;

   • introducing an exotic plant;

   • harvesting a slope of trees above a stream, thus producing more silt from increased runoff;

   • straightening or channelization of a stream, thereby increasing the speed of water flow;

   • moving livestock or people who are wading or hiking in streams, thereby disturbing fish spawning beds;

   • planting vegetative cover on a previously bare slope above a riparian zone; and

   • using the area in ways that compact soil and create erosion problems.

   Identify and describe changes that would have negative consequences for one or more kinds of animals. Identify and describe changes that would have positive consequences for one or more kinds of animals.

Diagram A

10. Have one or two students demonstrate and evaluate the consequences of a change that would damage the habitat for one or more of the animals found in the riparian zone. To illustrate, the students could remove the animal art form that would be immediately affected by the change. For example, severe pollution would affect the aquatic dwellers—fish, frogs, mosquitoes, and such. Ask the students to discuss the possible effects on the remaining animals in the area when animals are removed. Repeat with a different change, such as fire, development, damming, or stream diversion. OPTIONAL: Invite the students to work in small teams to investigate the area for evidence and observation of actual animal life in this riparian zone. List and quantify any species they observe. Ask the students to compare similarities and differences between the diversity of animals they actually find evidence for and the diversity they represented in their drawings of animals.

11. Ask the students to summarize what they have learned about niche, habitat, and riparian environments. Ask the students to gather their animal art and return to class.

## Variation

There is no substitute for the quality of experience gained from an actual site visit. If, however, a site visit is impossible, these alternatives are suggested:

1.  Create a simulated riparian zone in an outdoor setting using chalk, paper cutouts, and other materials. (An example is shown in Diagram A.)

2.  Limit the scale of a simulated riparian zone to the size of a room or even a tabletop.

## Extensions

1.  Identify some basic niches found in all environments, such as those of producers, consumers, and decomposers. Divide the consumer category into predator and prey groupings. Identify examples of predator and prey animals in local riparian and other aquatic habitats.

2.  Investigate the kind of repairs that can be done to riparian zones after extensive damage has occurred. If it seems useful and appropriate, explore the possibility of a riparian restoration team working in your community to reinstate the health of any riparian zones that have been degraded. Consult wildlife and conservation groups for advice.

## Evaluation

1.  Identify and describe the habitat and niche of each of these organisms: raccoon, frog, fish, heron, and mosquito.

2.  Identify three other animals that are common in riparian ecosystems in your area. What is the niche of each?

3.  Describe two things that could have a positive effect on a riparian habitat.

4.  A large stand of trees in a riparian zone is being evaluated for its economic potential. What other values would you ask the owners to consider before making a decision whether or not to harvest the trees? Explain.

# Fashion a Fish

## Objectives

*Grades K–2*

Students will classify fish according to body shape and coloration.

*Grades 3–4*

Students will (1) describe adaptations of fish to their environments, (2) describe how adaptations can help fish survive in their habitats, and (3) interpret the importance of adaptation in animals.

## Method

Students design a fish adapted for various aquatic habitats.

## Materials

*Grades K–2*

Body shape and coloration are the only cards needed for younger students. The first three steps in this activity are optional for younger

students. Steps four through seven can include the adaptation cards for body shape and coloration; reproduction and mouth cards are optional

*Grades 3–4*

Five cards are needed for each adaptation from the masters provided on pages 59 and 60: mouth, body shape, coloration, reproduction; art materials; paper

## Background

Aquatic animals are the products of countless adaptations over long periods of time. Those adaptations, for the most part, are features that increase the animals' likelihood of surviving in their habitat.

When a habitat changes, either slowly or catastrophically, the species of animals with adaptations (that allow them many options) are the ones most likely to survive. Some species have adapted to such a narrow range of habitat conditions that they are extremely vulnerable to change. These species are usually more susceptible than other animals to death or extinction.

In this activity, the students design a fish. Students choose the adaptation that their fish will have; each choice would actually take countless years to develop. As those adaptations become part of the fish's design, the fish becomes better suited to the habitat in which it lives. Because of the variety of conditions within each habitat, many different fish can live together and flourish. Some adaptations of fish are shown on page 59 and 60.

---

**Grade Level:** K–4

**Subject Areas:** Science, Expressive Arts, Environmental Education

**Duration:** one or two 20-minute sessions for younger students, two 30- to 45-minute sessions for older students

**Group Size:** any; groups of four students each

**Setting:** indoors or outdoors

**Conceptual Framework Topic Reference:** CAIIA1b, CAIIA1c, CAIIB

**Key Terms:** adaptation, coloration, camouflage, habitat

**Appendices:** Using Local Resources

---

## Procedure

1. Assign students to find a picture or make a drawing of a species of animal that has a special adaptation. For example, giraffes have long necks for reaching vegetation in tall trees, while owls have large eyes that gather light and aids with night vision.

2. Conduct a class discussion on the value of different kinds of adaptations to animals. As a part of the discussion, ask the students to identify different kinds of adaptations in humans.

3. Collect the students' pictures or drawings of adaptations. Categorize them into the following groups:

   • protective coloration and camouflage,

   • body shape or form,

   • mouth type or feeding behavior,

   • reproduction or behavior, and

   • other (one or more categories the students establish, in addition to the four above that will be needed for the rest of the activity).

4. Divide the adaptation cards into five groups of four cards each: one for coloration, mouth type, body shape, and reproduction.

5. Pass one complete set of cards to each group of students. There might be five groups with four to six students in each group. If the class size is larger than about 30 students, make additional sets of adaptation cards.

| Adaptation | Advantage | Examples |
|---|---|---|
| **Mouth** | | |
| Sucker-shaped mouth | Feeds on very small plants and animals | Sucker, carp |
| Elongated upper jaw | Feeds on prey it looks down on | Spoonbill, sturgeon |
| Elongated lower jaw | Feeds on prey it sees above | Barracuda, snook |
| Duckbill jaws | Grasps prey | Muskellunge, pike |
| Extremely large jaws | Surrounds prey | Bass, grouper |
| **Body Shape** | | |
| Torpedo shape | Fast moving | Trout, salmon, tuna |
| Flat bellied | Bottom feeder | Catfish, sucker |
| Vertical disk | Feeds above or below | Butterfish, bluegill |
| Horizontal disk | Bottom dweller | Flounder, halibut |
| Hump backed | Stable in fast-moving water | Sockeye salmon, chub, razorback |
| **Coloration** | | |
| Light-colored belly | Predators have difficulty seeing it from below | Most minnows, perch, tuna, mackerel |
| Dark upper side | Predators have difficulty seeing it from above | Bluegill, crappie, barracuda, flounder |
| Vertical stripes | Can hide in vegetation | Muskellunge, pickerel, bluegill |
| Horizontal stripes | Can hide in vegetation | Yellow and white bass, snook |
| Mottled coloration | Can hide in rocks and on bottom | Trout, grouper, rockbass, hogsucker |
| **Reproduction** | | |
| Eggs deposited in bottom | Hidden from predators | Trout, salmon, most minnows |
| Eggs deposited in nests | Protected by adults | Bass, stickleback |
| Floating eggs | Dispersed in high numbers | Striped bass |
| Eggs attached to vegetation | Stable until hatching | Perch, northern pike, carp |
| Live bearers | High survival rate | Guppies |

*continued*

6. Ask the students to "fashion a fish" from the characteristics of the cards in the set they receive. Each group could

   • create an art form that represents their fish,

   • name the fish, and

   • describe and draw the habitat for their fish.

7. Ask each group to report on the attributes of the fish they have designed, including identifying and describing its adaptations. Ask the students to describe how this kind of fish is adapted for survival.

*Grades 3–4*

Ask the students to make inferences about the importance of adaptations in fish and other animals.

## Extensions

1. Take an adaptation card from any category, and find a real fish with that adaptation.

NOTE: A collection of books about fish is useful. Do not be as concerned about reading level as much as the accuracy of the illustrations.

2. Look at examples of actual fish. Describe the fish, and speculate on its habitat by examining its coloration, body shape, and mouth.

## Evaluation

*Grades K–2*

Circle the fish with vertical stripes. Circle the fish with the horizontal, flat shape. Circle the fish that would be difficult to see from above. (Use the masters provided on pages 59 and 60 for drawings of fish.)

*Grades 3–4*

1. Name two fish adaptations in each of the following categories: mouth and feeding, shape, coloration, and reproduction. Then describe the advantages of each of these adaptations to the survival of the fish in their habitats.

2. Invent an animal that would be adapted to live in your community. Consider mouth, shape, coloration, reproduction, food, shelter, and other characteristics. Draw and describe your animal.

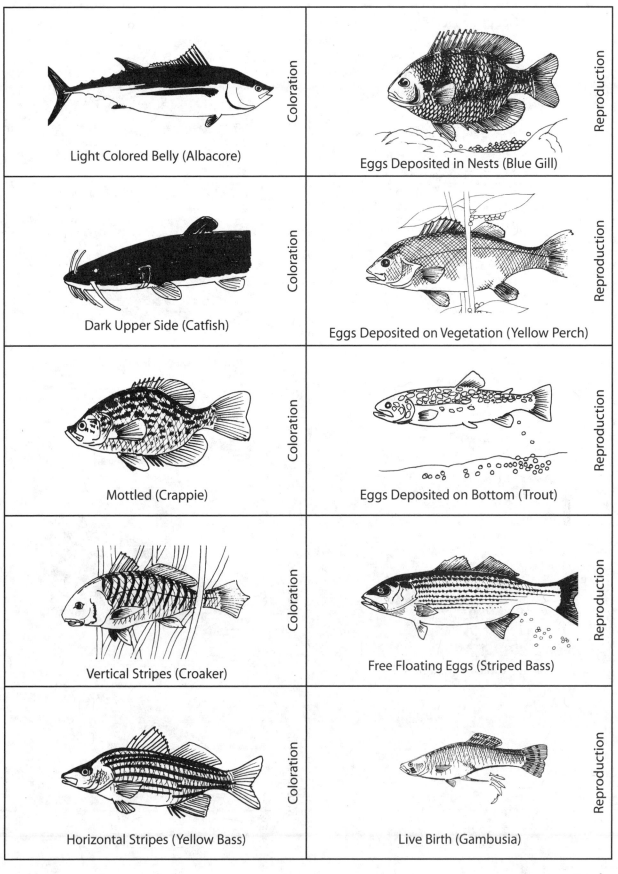

Light Colored Belly (Albacore) — Coloration

Eggs Deposited in Nests (Blue Gill) — Reproduction

Dark Upper Side (Catfish) — Coloration

Eggs Deposited on Vegetation (Yellow Perch) — Reproduction

Mottled (Crappie) — Coloration

Eggs Deposited on Bottom (Trout) — Reproduction

Vertical Stripes (Croaker) — Coloration

Free Floating Eggs (Striped Bass) — Reproduction

Horizontal Stripes (Yellow Bass) — Coloration

Live Birth (Gambusia) — Reproduction

continued

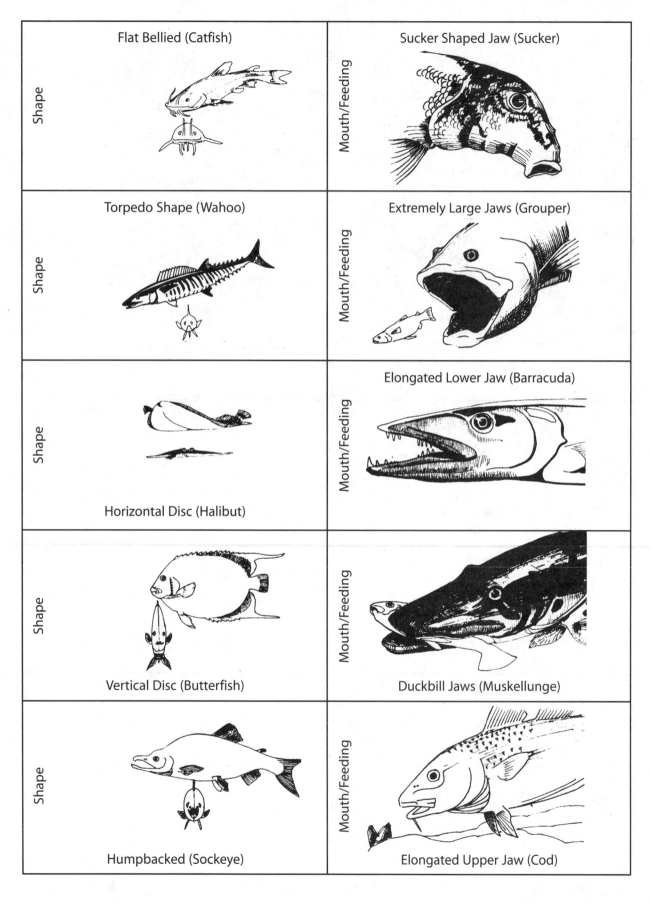

| Shape | Flat Bellied (Catfish) | Mouth/Feeding | Sucker Shaped Jaw (Sucker) |
| Shape | Torpedo Shape (Wahoo) | Mouth/Feeding | Extremely Large Jaws (Grouper) |
| Shape | Horizontal Disc (Halibut) | Mouth/Feeding | Elongated Lower Jaw (Barracuda) |
| Shape | Vertical Disc (Butterfish) | Mouth/Feeding | Duckbill Jaws (Muskellunge) |
| Shape | Humpbacked (Sockeye) | Mouth/Feeding | Elongated Upper Jaw (Cod) |

# Sockeye Scents

## Objectives

Students will (1) trace and label the migratory route that sockeye salmon take from the ocean to an upstream lake, (2) describe one theory about how a salmon can find its birth stream, and 3) explain how adaptations enable some species to survive and maintain their populations.

## Method

Students participate in map and simulation exercises that help them understand the migration of the sockeye salmon.

## Materials

A map of a the Columbia River system in Oregon (or local maps); pencils, crayons, and markers; 40 paper cups; paper towels; 40 rubber bands; 25 (if indoors) to 75 (if outdoors) yards of blue ribbon or chalk; four sample scents such as garlic, mint, chocolate, and anise; cotton balls

**Grade Level:** 3–4

**Subject Areas:** Social Studies, Science, Expressive Arts, Language Arts, Environmental Education

**Duration:** 2 hours

**Group Size:** small groups of four students

**Setting:** indoors or outdoors

**Conceptual Framework Topic Reference:** CAIIA, CAIIA1, CAIIA1c

**Key Terms:** migration, spawning, scent

**Appendices:** none

## Background

Salmon begin life as eggs in the gravel of a stream or (in the case of some sockeye) lakeshore. They migrate down rivers and spend several years in the ocean. Then at a certain time, the salmon swim back to their "home" rivers and migrate upstream to their exact birthplaces to spawn.

Scientists think salmon migrate back to their home streams by sensing their orientation to the Earth's magnetic field and receiving clues from the sun's position in the sky. They also think scent plays a major part in the ability of a salmon to find home. This adaptation is important for the salmon to reproduce and survive. Students might give some thought to how well they would find their own homes if they had to rely only on smell.

The purpose of this activity is to demonstrate that organisms exhibit adaptations to the environment in which they live and that these adaptations maximize the survival of the species. This activity is specific to the salmon of the Columbia River, Oregon; however, it can easily be adapted to any anadromous or catadromous animal found in coastal systems. Anadromous species, such as salmon, shad, bass, and others, migrate from the ocean to a stream to spawn. Catadromous species, such as eels, begin life in the ocean, migrate upstream where they spend much of their life, and then return to the ocean to reproduce.

NOTE: For more information on salmon, see the activity "Hooks and Ladders" on page 43 or "Where Have All the Salmon Gone?" on page 166. Also contact the Idaho Department of Fish and Game at (208) 334-2633. Check with your state's fish and wildlife agency for examples of life histories of other migrating aquatic organisms.

*continued*

# Historic Salmon Range in the Columbia River Basin

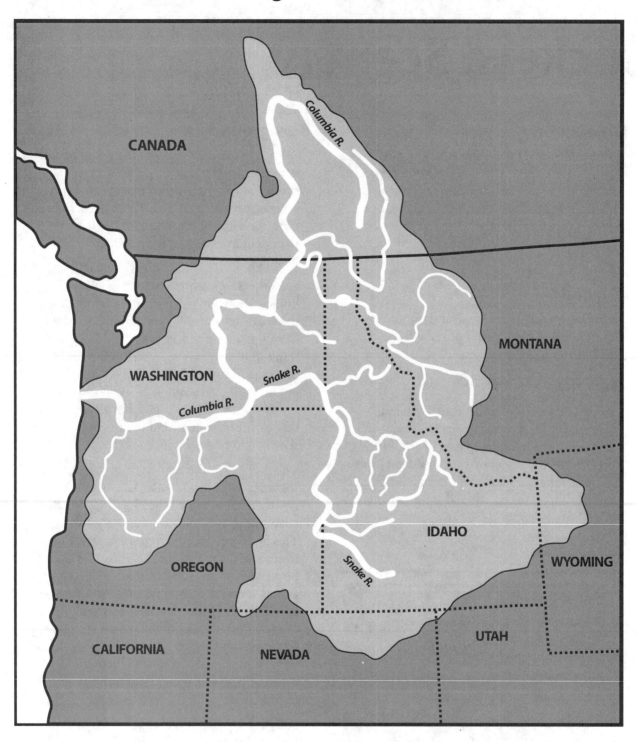

Adapted from "Wild About Salmon, An Educators Guide", Idaho Department of Fish and Game, 1999.

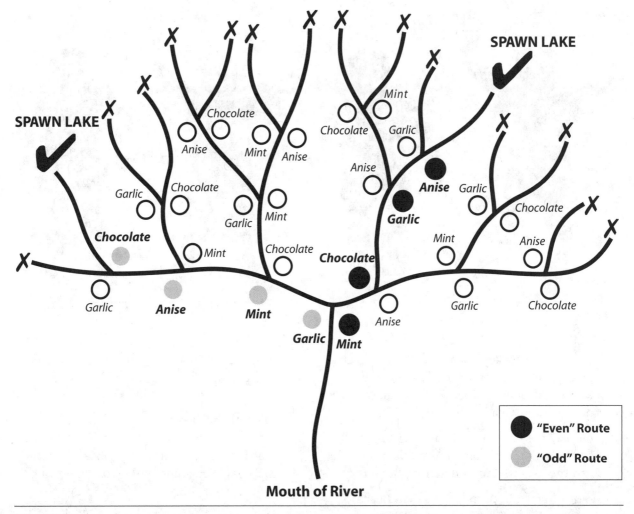

*Diagram A*

## Procedure

*Before the Activity:*

Prepare the scent samples. Choose four scents such as garlic, mint, chocolate, and anise. Place two drops of each scent on two cotton balls, and put each cotton ball in its own cup (eight cups will be used). Cover each cup with a paper towel held in place by a rubber band. Number the cups one through eight, and make a note of which scent is in which numbered cup. Prepare 30 additional cups to be placed on the "river" system shown in Diagram A on this page.

Lay out the river system as shown in Diagram A. Either ribbon or chalk may be used. Establish two correct "spawning routes" by placing scents in the correct order at each fork in the migration path. (One route follows the odd-numbered order of scents; one route follows the even-numbered order of scents.) Be sure to note the two correct routes.

Mix up the scents for the remaining routes.

1. Ensure that students are familiar with the life cycle of the sockeye salmon, especially the spawning migration. (If time is limited, educators can convey the information through a discussion, guest speaker, or individual reading assignment. If time is available, educators may allow students to construct their own diagram of the life cycle.)

2. Divide the students into groups of four. Give each group a map of the Columbia River drainage system, and ask them to trace the

*continued*

*Diagram B*

route of the sockeye salmon from the ocean to a specific spawning lake. They need to locate and label the following: ocean, states, dams, rivers, streams, lakes, and reservoirs.

3. Display the maps and discuss each group's findings. Come to consensus on the route and the major features described in Step 2.

4. Enlist four "migration helpers." Give each helper two different scents in paper cups. (See Diagram B.) Line up the four helpers near the exit door for the classroom, facing the students.

5. Ask the remaining students to line up and count off in twos. The "twos" will sniff the even-numbered cup being held by each helper; the "ones" will sniff the odd-numbered cup. Make sure all the students understand that they are to move in a line from left to right (as shown in Diagram B), stopping in front of each helper and sniffing from **just one** of the cups each helper holds. As soon as each student completes sniffing the four cups, he or she can move to the river system.

6. When all the "salmon" have completed their scent imprinting, gather them at the "mouth" of the river system. Explain that they will

"migrate" in single file. They must find their way to their spawning site by following the scents they smelled in the same order.

7. Allow the students to proceed. Make sure they do not discuss their decisions with each other and that all students make their decisions based on scent and not just following another student.

8. Once all the salmon have reached what they think are their spawning grounds, reveal the two correct spawning routes. The students who chose the correct migration routes are the successful salmon for this year's spawning run. They will be able to lay eggs to produce young salmon.

9. After students complete the spawning migration, discuss what the students (sockeye salmon) experienced, and brainstorm and discuss the many other obstacles (dams, pollution, fishing pressure, bears, etc.) that salmon encounter along the route to the spawning grounds. Discuss what might happen to the salmon that make mistakes in their return journey. Do they spawn? Would they try to retrace their route? How did the salmon's special abilities (adaptations) help it survive?

## Extensions

1. To increase the challenge and learning opportunity of this activity, educators may wish to have the students choose their method of learning about the life cycle of sockeye. For example, one group could decide to interview a fisheries biologist or to look for information on the Internet. Allow a specific time for this phase, and then set aside a period for the groups to share their information with each other. Have the entire class contribute to a large drawing that shows the life cycle.

2. Ask students to create either visual images or a piece of creative writing that describes the life of the sockeye.

3. Ask each group to choose another species of salmon and investigate its life cycle and migration.

4. Ask each group to choose another animal that migrates (bald eagle, yellow-rumped warbler, monarch butterfly, elk, etc.) and to develop a class presentation (verbal or visual) describing that migration.

## Evaluation

1. Participation in the closing discussion can serve as an evaluation.

2. Have the groups collectively create a spawning migration map for sockeye salmon that shows obstacles they might encounter.

3. Invite another class to participate in the migration maze; have students lead the discussions and the migration.

# Pond Succession

## Objectives

Students will (1) recognize that natural environments are involved in a process of continual change (2) discuss the concept of succession, (3) describe succession as an example of the process of change in natural environments, and (4) apply understanding of the concept of succession by drawing a series of pictures showing stages in pond succession.

## Method

Students create murals showing three major stages of pond succession.

## Materials

Long pieces of drawing paper for murals, tape for securing paper to walls, drawing materials

**Grade Level:** 5–8

**Subject Areas:** Science, Social Studies, Environmental Education, Expressive Arts

**Duration:** one or two 30-minute sessions or longer

**Group Size:** any

**Setting:** indoors (outdoors optional)

**Conceptual Framework Topic Reference:** CAIA, CAIB, CAIB1

**Key Terms:** succession, sediment, change, pond

**Appendices:** Ecosystem

## Background

Succession is a term used to describe the ever-changing environment and the gradual process by which one habitat is replaced by another. Many habitats that appear to be stable are changing before us, perhaps at a slow rate in human eyes, but are evolving rather quickly according to the Earth's clock.

For example, a shallow pond may be transformed into a marshy, then a forested, area in only a thousand years or so. Windblown or waterborne spores of algae are the first inhabitants. Eggs of flying insects are deposited. Small fish and amphibians arrive through the inlet. Surrounding sediments begin to fill the pond, some borne on wash-out from rainfall, some entering through the pond's inlet. Marshy plants growing along the shoreline spread inward as sediments fill the pond. Land plants also spread inward and replace the marsh plants as the ground is consolidated. As more plants and animals enter the system, more opportunities for habitat become available to others. Changes from ponds to forest are only one example of succession.

Succession is generally thought of as an orderly process in which plant communities change over time in an environment. Theoretically, succession begins with bare ground and is completed when a climax forest, grassland, or other environment becomes established. Seral or early successional plants are generally short-lived, thrive in sunlight, colonize rapidly, and spread their seeds far and wide. Roadsides, recent burns, clear-cuts, and other areas of recent disturbance are good places to find examples of early succession.

The first plants change the environment by adding nutrients to the soil from fallen leaves and other plant parts, and by providing shade to the soil. These changes allow other plants to grow. The presence of the newer plants changes the environment to allow even later stage successional plants to develop. Climax or late successional plants usually thrive in shade, live a long time, and reproduce more slowly. Old growth forests are good examples of a climax stage of succession.

Succession influences what kinds of animals live in an area. As the plants in an area change, the habitat available to animals changes character. Therefore, the kinds of animals that live in the area are associated with the area's stage of succession.

## Procedure

1. Review with students the idea of succession, a process that is generally an orderly, gradual, and continual replacement of one community of organisms in an environment with another.

2. Start the activity by talking about a pond. How many people have seen a pond? What did it look like? After a description of ponds, ask the students to imagine what a pond would look like from a side view if you could see under the water and show the nearby environment. For example,

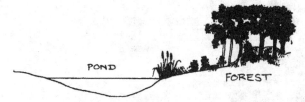

3. Explain to the students that they will be drawing a series of three views of a pond over a period of about 800 years. The first (left-hand) section will show the pond as it is today, the middle section will show how it might look 500 years later after natural changes, and the third (right-hand) will show how the pond could look in 800 years. (These time periods are approximate and can vary greatly.)

4. Discuss with students the possibilities of plant and animal life in the first section. What kinds of plants and animals live

   • in the water,

   • along the shoreline, and

   • in the surrounding area?

5. Then give each group a piece of paper that members will divide into three equal sections (by folding or drawing). Instruct students to fill in the first section with their drawing of the pond and the surrounding area. Set a specific time frame for the students to draw (about 10 minutes).

6. Bring the class together again for a discussion of the second section, which will be labeled "500 Years Later." Consider the following items:

   • What changes have taken place in the environment?

   • How will the pond look now?

   • What lives and grows in the water now that it is much shallower and smaller?

   • What lives and grows around the shoreline, which is now more marsh-like? (Marsh animals and plants, perhaps some willow bushes.)

   • What lives and grows in the surrounding area? (Larger trees, same types of animals.) Have each group complete the second section of their mural, labeling it "500 Years Later."

7. Repeat the process for the third section, labeling it "800 Years Later" and discussing the following topics:

   • By this time, the pond is almost totally filled with sediment, leaving only a small marshy area with perhaps a stream running through. What changes have taken place?

   • What lives and grows in the environment?

   • What lives and grows where the shoreline used to be? (Bushes, small trees.)

*continued*

• What effects does the pond succession have on the surrounding area? (Different animals, trees requiring less water.)

8. After the murals are completed, students should sign them. Then they may be displayed in the classroom so all students can see and discuss differences and similarities among the various murals. Ask the students to summarize what they have learned, including how succession is one example of the ongoing process of change in natural environments.

*Variation:* Use a stream table filled with standard soil to illustrate three-dimensionally the processes of succession. Fill the table with soil; make an indentation in the center to represent the pond; run water into the table to represent rainfall, streams feeding the pond, and so forth; and watch the pond fill as sedimentation takes place. This table can show the geologic life cycle of the pond. Add replicas of plants and animals during successional stages for even more interest.

## Extension

What might happen to your model of succession if an intense forest fire burned the trees surrounding the pond? Would the pond silt in faster? Would there be a source for tree seeds to colonize the pond site? Would there be differences if the fire were not as hot? How might fires affect the species that live there? Describe some possible differences in environments where fire affects succession and where it does not.

## Evaluation

1. Draw a picture, with explanations, to show stages in pond succession.

2. Select a field, vacant lot, park, or other area in your community. Make a sketch and write a paragraph to describe the area as it appears today. Make a sketch and write a paragraph to describe what the area might look like in 100 or 500 years from now if a gradual process of succession took place.

# Eat and Glow

## Objectives

Students will (1) observe, demonstrate, and describe how life forms are affected by changes in their habitats; (2) observe, demonstrate, and describe how different species differ in their ability to adjust to changes in their habitat; and (3) observe, demonstrate, and describe how isolated ecosystems are more vulnerable to environmental changes.

## Method

Students conduct an experiment using *Daphnia* and brine shrimp to demonstrate adaptations to environmental change by organisms.

## Materials

For 28 students, 210 *Daphnia*, 210 *Artemia* (brine shrimp),* 1 gram sugar-dye compound;** 3 milliliters of vinegar; water from a natural source (lakes, streams, or ponds), ultraviolet light

---

**Grade Level:** 7–10

**Subject Areas:** Science, Mathematics, Environmental Education

**Duration:** one 45-minute session each for activity #1 and #2, and two 45-minute sessions with preparation time in between for activity #3.

**Group Size:** about 28 students

**Setting:** Indoors

**Conceptual Framework Topic Reference:** CAIA, CAIC, CAIIA, CAIIA1, CAIIA2, CAIIC

**Key Terms:** pH, tolerance, toxic, variable, control, treatment, isolated ecosystem

**Appendices:** none

---

(UV) light source (a black light works best); viewing box for black light; 42 30-ml beakers or baby food jars; seven droppers or pipettes with wide openings; graduated cylinders (100 ml, 50 ml, and 5 ml); one 1-liter bottle; Styrofoam trays or other soft carving material such as balsa wood; 60 copies of the Student Worksheet (30 for *Daphnia*, 30 for brine shrimp) on page 74

If the students prepare their own dilution series, educators will need 21 graduated cylinders— seven of each size. Educators will need one of each size of the graduated cylinders if they prepare the dilution series themselves.

*The *Daphnia* and the brine shrimp can be purchased from major biological supply catalogs.

**The sugar-dye compound, 4-methylumbelliferyl-beta-d-galactose, may be ordered from major suppliers such as Flinn Scientific, Inc., (800) 452-1261; or Sigma-Aldrich Corporation, (800) 325-3010, catalog # M1633. It is recommended that educators purchase 250 mg for this experiment.

## Background

NOTE: See the Project WILD Aquatic activity "Water Canaries."

Variations and changes occur in terrestrial and aquatic ecosystems. Those changes can either be natural to the system, such as changes in pH and temperature caused by weather or forest fires, or human-related, such as changes caused by pollution or acidic deposition.

Wildlife species differ in their ability to adapt to such changes. Some animals can withstand substantial changes in temperature, pH, or oxygen levels. Others are very sensitive and will die with only the slightest difference. Aquatic organisms tend to be more fragile than terrestrial organisms because aquatic environments tend to be more constant than most terrestrial environ-

*continued*

ments. For instance, the slightest temperature change of a trout stream caused by the removal of shading vegetation may severely limit the life span of young trout. If a stream continues to stay too warm to support the trout, then another species of fish, more adapted to variations in temperature, may increase its abundance and may move into the habitat.

Terrestrial animals, conversely, are adapted to handle the greater changes found in the environment. However, changes in soil acidity or temperature often result in changes in the microbiotic community and the associated plants living there. Those changes can be due to natural occurrences, such as forest fires, or to human-induced events, such as agricultural production, lawn care practices, or leaching from cement foundations and sidewalks. Microorganisms are crucial to the health of the soil, which affects the health of the plants and ultimately the health of animals.

Effects of chemical changes are often subtle. A chemical may not kill an organism directly, but may affect its ability to capture food or escape a predator. The chemical may also interfere with an organism's ability to reproduce. Chemicals that are potentially harmful to a living organism are said to be toxic. Toxicity is a relative property that depends on the concentration of the chemical, the duration of exposure, and the tolerance range of the organism. Toxicity tests are used to evaluate the adverse effects of a chemical on a living organism. In a toxicity test, organisms are typically exposed to various levels of the chemical while all other factors are held constant.

In this experiment, students will be looking for nonlethal effects resulting from pH variation, particularly the loss of the desire or ability to eat. The chemical introduced will be vinegar. Vinegar is an acid and will change the pH level enough to cause changes in the behavior of the organisms being used. However, the level of vinegar used in the activity will not kill the

*Daphnia* or the brine shrimp. Please see "Guidelines for Responsible Use of Animals in the Classroom" on page 233 in the Appendices.

In these activities, *Daphnia* and brine shrimp will be used to determine the effects of small changes in habitat. *Daphnia*, commonly called water fleas, are tiny crustaceans. They reside near the bottom of the food chain, eating small plants and being eaten by larger organisms. *Daphnia* are found in most freshwater aquatic environments. Because they are sensitive to changes in the ecosystem, they are excellent indicators of the health of the ecosystem. Brine shrimp, otherwise known as sea monkeys, are also at the bottom of the food chain, but live in a highly saline environment and are more tolerant to changes than *Daphnia*.

To see how the change in pH (acidity) affects the *Daphnia* and the brine shrimp differently, students will introduce a "sugar-dye" into the system. Students will then record which organisms are eating and which are not. In this compound, the sugar and the dye act in such a way that the dye is not seen until it is eaten, allowing the dye to be seen through the transparent bodies of the *Daphnia* and shrimp with an ultraviolet light.

Isolated systems tend to be more vulnerable to environmental changes. For instance, a pond that has no incoming or outgoing water to help balance chemical levels or temperature changes will be a harsh environment for living organisms. In the third activity of the lesson, students will create a nonisolated environment for the *Daphnia* and will determine if the ability of the flea to move out of the contaminated habitat increases its ability to survive.

The purpose of this activity is (1) to show that organisms exhibit adaptations to their environment that allow them to survive and that (2) species differ in their ability to adjust to changes in their habitat.

## Procedure

*Before the Activity*

- Order the sugar-dye compound from a chemical supply house, and order *Daphnia* and brine shrimp from a biological supply house.

- Establish a safe black-light viewing station. **SAFETY NOTE:** UV light is harmful to eyes. To view UV light safely, use a commercial viewer or construct one. Limit the light in the room and prevent students from looking directly at the UV bulb. One method is to cut a window in a cardboard box and to place the UV bulb below the window in such a way that the sample will be illuminated but the students cannot view the bulb.

- Prepare the sugar-dye solution. The sugar-dye compound will come in a crystalline form. Mix 500 ml water to 1 gram of compound in a plastic 1-liter bottle. Use water from a natural system such as a lake, stream, or pond. Do not use tap water or even bottled spring water because these will kill the organisms. Shake well, label, and store in a refrigerator. Shake well before each use.

- Prepare and label a series of solutions using the following table. Educators may choose to have the students mix their own solutions.

  Vinegar solution: 3 ml of vinegar with enough lake water to make 600 ml of solution.

  Jar #C, control jar, 30 ml of lake water.

  Jar #5, add 30 ml of vinegar solution.

  Jar #4, add 16 ml of vinegar solution and fill to 30 ml with lake water.

  Jar #3, add 8 ml of vinegar solution and fill to 30 ml with lake water.

  Jar #2, add 4 ml of vinegar solution and fill to 30 ml with lake water.

  Jar #1, add 2 ml of vinegar solution and fill to 30 ml with lake water.

### Activity #1: Daphnia and Acidity

1. Using the background information provided with this activity, introduce the idea of a toxicity test. Ask the students if they can list ways that a chemical can harm a living organism.

2. Ask the students how increased levels of acid might affect the *Daphnia*. What will happen as the acid level increases? (The small amount of vinegar is not expected to kill the *Daphnia*, but it may upset them enough that they lose their desire to eat for a time. This response is what the students will be observing—movement and food consumption. The *Daphnia* are expected to recover.)

3. Next, using the background information, discuss with the students how the sugar-dye will be used in this activity.

4. Divide the class into teams of four. Each team should fill and label the six baby food jars with the six treatment solutions (Jars 1–5 and Jar C). Explain that the "treatments" represent the various levels of a variable. A variable is added to an experiment to see what effect it will have on the subject. The subject in this activity is the organism, the variable is acidity (the amount of vinegar added to the water), and the different acid concentrations are the different levels of the variable. Ask the students why Jar C has no acid added. Why do they think this treatment is called the "control"? The students will change the acidity in this experiment. Ask the students what factors did not change for the *Daphnia*. List those factors on the board. (All *Daphnia* had the same temperature, light, water type, etc.) Let the students know that the factors that did not change are known as "constants."

5. Have the students add five *Daphnia* to each of the jars, including the control jar. Demonstrate how to add *Daphnia* to a solution as follows: take the *Daphnia* from

*continued*

a beaker in a pipette. Put the end of the pipette below the surface of the solution it is being added to, and gently squeeze the *Daphnia* out of the pipette. If a *Daphnia* is exposed to air, air will be trapped underneath its outer covering, and it will float on the surface. If a *Daphnia* floats or does not move, it has been injured during the transfer and should be replaced by another.

NOTE: Remove some of the water that the *Daphnia* were shipped in and put it in a clean container to serve as a recovery tank. To avoid contamination, do not put the experimental *Daphnia* back in the original water with the *Daphnia* that were not used. Educators may want to set up a recovery tank for each class that will participate in this experiment.

6. Allow the *Daphnia* to swim in the treatments and control jars for 30 minutes. Observe. Then add approximately 10 ml of sugar-dye solution to each of the six jars, and let the *Daphnia* feed for 15 minutes.

7. Observe the *Daphnia* under the UV light using a viewer, making sure the students cannot look directly at the light. Count the numbers of glowing *Daphnia* (which is evidence that they are eating) in each jar. Note their activity and complete a *Daphnia* Student Worksheet. After viewing and recording, remove the *Daphnia* from their treatments, and place them together in the recovery tank.

8. Have the students graph their data.

9. Discuss with the students the results of the experiment. At what treatment level did the change in the *Daphnia's* environment affect the organisms' need to eat, and eventually their ability to survive? In the real world, what would cause this kind of pH (acidic) change? If the *Daphnia* were to die because the change in pH levels, how would that affect the rest of the ecosystem? If the *Daphnia* live in a habitat that is isolated, meaning they cannot leave, what would their chance of survival be? If the pH changes, why might animals living in a non-isolated ecosystem, such as a river or lake, have a better chance of survival than organisms found in an isolated environment?

NOTE: With limited mobility, *Daphnia* can move to less-contaminated parts of their environment, but they are not likely to to leave altogether.

### Activity #2: Brine Shrimp, Acidity, and Tolerance Differences

1. Discuss with students that changes in pH or acidity affect some organisms different from others because some are more tolerant. Follow the same procedures for the brine shrimp as with the *Daphnia*, and observe the differences in tolerance. Discuss the results with the class.

2. To clean up, pour the solutions down the drain. *Daphnia* and shrimp may be retained as pets in a small aquarium. NOTE: Many elementary classrooms would appreciate those donations.

3. Discuss the differences in the results with the *Daphnia*. Which organism was more tolerant of low pH levels? What is the advantage for this organism to have a wider tolerance for pH? What is the advantage to the other organism for not having such a wide tolerance range? (It requires energy output that is usually not necessary.) In what type of environment is each animal normally found? How are these two organisms adapted for their environments? How does the response of each animal to such an environmental stress, such as an increase in pH, affect its chances for survival?

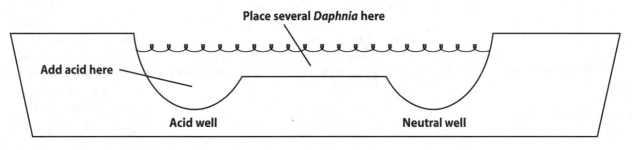

*Diagram A*

### Activity #3: Changing the Isolation Factor

1. Discuss the difference between isolated and non-isolated ecosystems and the varying tolerance for changes as found in the background section.

2. Have students work in teams to create a non-isolated environment that will allow the *Daphnia* to move between a high acidity area and a more neutral (lake water) area. It should be set up so that the *Daphnia* are allowed to choose between the two. For example, using Styrofoam trays or a piece of balsa wood, carve deep wells for the acidic and neutral areas plus a shallow channel for the *Daphnia* to move between the two areas. (See Diagram A.) Because the vinegar will soon diffuse throughout the system, have the students add three to five *Daphnia* to the channel and then add the vinegar to the acidic well *simultaneously*. (Use approximately one drop of the prepared vinegar solution per milliliter volume of the acidic well.)

3. Have the students design a chart to collect data that will show how many *Daphnia* chose the neutral environment.

4. Repeat the experiment, but add the *Daphnia* to the acidic well instead. Repeat again but add the *Daphnia* to the neutral well instead. Add a new set of *Daphnia* each time, and add the same number of *Daphnia* as were added in Step 2. Were the results the same in all three cases (i.e., adding *Daphnia* to the channel, to the acidic well, and to the neutral well)? Is the experiment truly a non-isolated ecosystem?

## Extensions

1. Suggest that students volunteer with the state department of fish and game, natural resources office, or county conservation district to test for pH levels in local water. They may also want to collect invertebrates to determine the health of the ecosystem.

2. Set up an experiment to see if *Daphnia* will adjust to a higher level acidic environment over time. Or from the classroom experiments, have the students determine if some of the *Daphnia* are more tolerant to higher acid levels than other *Daphnia*. Isolate those that are more tolerant, and conduct further experiments.

3. Follow the same procedures as above, but focus on temperature changes, oxygen levels or turbidity.

4. Brine shrimp are commercially harvested from the Great Salt Lake in Utah. Research this industry and its impact on this organism. Explore how changes in the salinity of the Great Salt Lake affect brine shrimp survival.

## Evaluation

Use Activity #3 as a performance-based evaluation tool.

Adapted from "A Healthy Glow," EPA/600/K-96/00, June 1997, World of Fresh Waters.

*continued*

# Student Worksheet

| | Room Light | | UV Light | |
|---|---|---|---|---|
| | **Moving** | **Not Moving** | **Glowing** | **Not Glowing** (or glowing more faintly than controls) |
| **Control Jar** | | | | |
| **Treatment 1 (mildest)** | | | | |
| **Treatment 2** | | | | |
| **Treatment 3** | | | | |
| **Treatment 4** | | | | |
| **Treatment 5 (strongest)** | | | | |

# Edge of Home

## Objective

Students will identify the characteristics of ecotones, or transitional zones, between two wildlife habitats.

## Method

Students explore the concept of ecotones by visiting places where habitats overlap.

## Materials

Pencils, paper, long rope or string for marking intervals in 1-foot segments, clipboards

## Background

Ecology is the study of the interactions between living things and their environments. Ecology comes from the Greek word *oikos*, which means *home*. The word "ecosystem" refers to the system of interactions between living and nonliving things.

An ecotone is a special environment created by the overlap of two or more surrounding habitats. This area of overlap between two ecosystems creates a habitat *edge* where parts of each surrounding habitat are present. Those places where the edges of ecosystems come together and overlap are the places where the action occurs and change takes place. (See Diagram A.)

In local communities there are abundant edges and overlaps of edges that may be accessible to the students. Playgrounds, school grounds, parking lots, stream banks, lake shores, and marsh edges can be found within walking distance for many students.

In ecotones, overlapping ecosystems are more complex than any ecosystem by itself. For example, in an overlap of forest and marsh it is common to find forest plants growing within the marsh. Often the growth of the forest plants is stunted due to the water in the marsh.

The overlapping ecosystems also offer a wider diversity of wildlife because animals common to both ecosystems are brought together. Even though they may not be seen, there is indirect evidence of the animal populations—for example, footprints, droppings, and feathers are all common.

**Grade Level:** 5–8

**Subject Areas:** Science, Environmental Education

**Duration:** one or two 45-minute sessions

**Group Size:** any

**Setting:** outdoors and indoors

**Conceptual Framework Topic Reference:** BDIB4

**Key Terms:** ecosystem, ecotone, edge effect

**Appendices:** Ecosystem, Outdoors, Field Ethics, Observations and Inferences

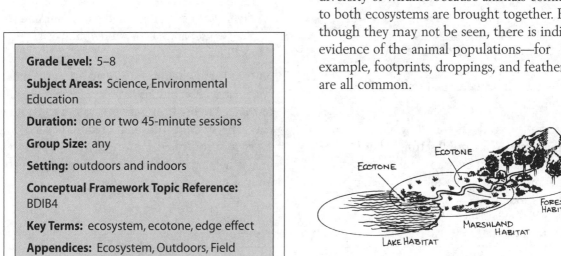

*Diagram A*

*continued*

Although ecotones play an important role in the overall landscape, it is also important to keep these areas from becoming too fragmented. This fragmentation can adversely affect wildlife that depends entirely on one ecosystem. The concept of maintaining ecotones and all of their components in a dynamic natural balance is defined as preserving the biodiversity of that area. The absence of diversity in ecotones is often a clue that problems may exist in the ecosystems that overlap.

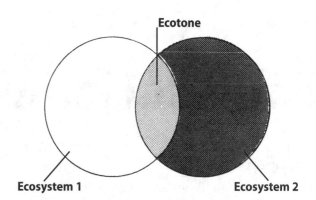

## Procedure

*Before the Activity*

Locate an outside study site for this activity. Choose a place where plants are invading a parking lot or playing field, or the edge of a forest where it meets a meadow.

1. On the chalkboard, draw two large overlapping circles. Put a large number of small squares and triangles in one circle. Avoid the area of overlap. In the second circle draw many tiny circles and stars. Again, avoid the overlap area. Ask the students to predict what kinds of things they would expect to find in the overlapping circles. Draw circles, squares, triangles, and stars in the area of overlap. Ask the students where the greatest diversity exists. Label the whole area of the overlap the ecotone (this is the area of greatest diversity). Label the original two circles as Ecosystem 1 and Ecosystem 2. Ask the students to point out the "edges" of the overlap. These are the places where the two ecosystems come together and interact. The process and results of this interaction are called the "edge effect."

2. Inform the students that they are going to investigate a natural setting where there are habitats that overlap similar to the illustration. Ask them to take paper, pencils, and clipboards on which to record their observations.

3. Take the students to the selected site. Ask them to work in teams of two or three to list the things found on either side of the edge. Each team should examine two different ecosystems, not examining the interactions and area where the two ecosystems meet and overlap. Have the students list the different species of plants and animals they observe, and then tally what they find. Include direct and indirect evidence of life. Ask them to discuss the similarities and differences, and to keep notes.

4. Next, ask the students to carefully examine the edge. Determine how wide the ecotone or zone of shared characteristics is. Point out that this is a miniature ecotone. The students might try to estimate the size of the ecotone as well as the diversity of species within the ecotone. Compare the diversity of plants and animals found within the ecotone with the diversity of the plants and animals found in the two separate ecosystems they originally examined.

NOTE: It may help the students organize more systematic observations if they stretch a length of rope or string from one ecosystem to another. Have the students make and record observations every foot (or other unit of measure) along the line. It helps to mark the string or rope at these intervals.

5. After the trip, compare and interpret the students' findings. Ask them for evidence they found to support the idea that populations of plants and animals tend to be more diverse within ecotones than in separate ecosystems.

OPTIONAL: Take the class to a site in the community that has aquatic edges. Educators may be able to find a beach, the highway edges, the edge of town, a place where a stream enters or exits a lake, or others that might be available in the community. Once there, ask the students to use the same investigating techniques, working again in teams of two or three. They should identify at least two ecosystems; list and describe the characteristic organisms in each; identify the ecotone; and list, observe, and describe the organisms in the ecotone.

## Extensions

1. Create an ecosystem map or model of your community. Indicate the location of the principal ecotones.

2. Take a simple piece of paper and measure the edges. Cut the paper into four equal pieces, and then measure the edges again. Repeat this twice again, measuring the edges each time. Support the idea that each new rectangle is a suitable habitat for some aquatic organism, and discuss how diversity is related to "edges."

3. Assess the overall health of any ecotones that seem particularly important to the quality of life for aquatic species in your community. What could be done to protect the area from being damaged, degraded, or lost?

## Evaluation

1. Write a paragraph about the characteristics of ecotones. Write two additional paragraphs to describe two ecosystems and an associated ecotone.

2. Choose a species of wildlife, and write a story about its life as it roams through several different ecosystems and ecotones. Explain how the animal's experiences are different at each of the various locations.

# Section Two

Social and
Political Knowledge

# Mermaids and Manatees

## Objectives

Students will (1) describe how imaginary creatures may be inspired by actual animals, (2) distinguish between mythical and actual aquatic wildlife, and (3) give examples of how wildlife can inspire myth and art.

## Method

Students describe aquatic animals using a narrative style of writing that, in turn, is the basis for a drawing or painting done by other students.

## Materials

Library or Internet resources, art materials, a variety of photographs of real aquatic animals (insects, amphibians, fish, mammals, etc.)

## Background

For years, wondrous and terrifying accounts of water-dwelling creatures were brought back by sailors and early explorers. These tales gave birth to belief in mermaids, sea serpents, and monsters "too terrible to mention." The Loch Ness monster, Champy in Lake Champlain, N.Y., and the strange happenings of the Bermuda Triangle are a few contemporary examples of the lure of the sea's mysteries. But were there ever such real creatures? Early sailors claimed to have seen beautiful mermaids with long, flowing hair and undulating fish-finned tails. Later accounts shifted the mythic images to the wondrous and real manatee. This aquatic mammal (sometimes called the "sea cow") inhabits rivers, estuaries, and the open sea. Manatees bear no resemblance to the legendary mermaid. An active imagination plus, perhaps, a long isolated sea voyage seem necessary to convert the manatee into the more conventionally captivating image of the mermaid.

Bizarre perceptions are possible if one chooses to describe ordinary organisms with detailed imagination, such as aquatic insects or other organisms found in pond water. Investigating such life forms in this way can provide an increased awareness of the characteristics of local habitats and species.

## Procedure

1. Ask the students to sit quietly with their eyes closed and to try to picture a mythical creature that lives in a water environment. A mythical creature means an animal that you create in your mind and one that probably never lived outside your mind. Ask each student to picture a creature and prepare to describe it to the class.

2. Ask a few of the students to volunteer to describe the creature that they pictured. Many of their images will likely be the result of film or television experiences.

---

**Grade Level:** 5–8

**Subject Areas:** Language Arts, Environmental Education, Social Studies, Expressive Arts

**Duration:** two 45-minute sessions

**Group Size:** an even number of groups with three to five persons each

**Setting:** indoors or outdoors

**Conceptual Framework Topic Reference:** CPIB1, CPIIA, CPIIC

**Key Terms:** myth, mythical, imaginary, real

**Appendices:** none

---

3. Offer the students an opportunity for discussion about classic marine myths regarding mermaids, sea serpents, and lake monsters. Explore their beliefs about whether they think such creatures were and are real or imaginary.

4. Tell the students that they are going to go off on a mythic voyage where they will meet a wondrous aquatic creature. Their responsibility will be to have each crew of three to five sailors write as accurate a description of the creature as they can. The crew is to work together to produce a single written description.

5. Divide the students into an even number of crews with three to five students in each crew. Provide each crew with an image of an actual aquatic animal. Use the collection of photographs. Be sure to select aquatic insects as well as larger animals. Some of the images in the Project WILD Aquatic activity "Are You Me?" could be helpful. Tell each crew to keep its animal a secret so that the students on other crews do not see the creature.

6. Have the members of the different crews find out as much as they can about their animal's actual appearance, behavior, and habitat. Allow them to use any references or resources that are available.

7. Once the research is finished, ask each crew to begin to develop the written descriptions that will be presented to the other crews. Each student should contribute at least two or three lines to the group description. Each student could describe a different characteristic. For example,

- This creature eats fish and other things in the ocean. It has a parrot-like beak in the middle of long tubes. It swims by forcing water out of its body. It has gigantic, glistening eyes (an octopus).

- This is a hump-backed creature with stout, powerful wings. Its offspring live in capsules under water, where they hang on to stationary objects in flowing streams. When they grow up, the females often feed from the blood of humans. The

humans that are attacked by those creatures develop huge sucker-like welts that ooze fluid from their centers. Discomfort to the humans lasts for days (a blackfly).

8. Once the descriptions are complete, each crew should prepare to read that group's description to another crew. Copy the descriptions so they can be exchanged in writing, as well as prepared to be read aloud.

9. Have the crews pair up, and ask one crew to read aloud its description to the other crew. Provide the written descriptions at this point. The crew that receives the description then must create an image of the creature that was described. Reverse and repeat the process so that both of the paired crews have written descriptions to work with. The members of each crew must now draw or paint images of what they understood the other crew to have described. Individual drawings or paintings can be done by each student or a composite can be created by the entire crew. Limit the number of questions the crews can ask of each other.

10. Once both crews have completed their images, compare the written or oral descriptions with the resulting artwork. The crews can now reveal their original source photos or specimens, looking for similarities and differences.

11. Display the original source images, written descriptions, and interpretive art works in clusters on the bulletin board or other display area.

12. Ask the students to summarize and review the steps they took, analyzing where they seemed most accurate and inaccurate. Emphasize how readily descriptions can be distorted so as to provide exaggerations of what is described. Review the actual physical characteristics, habitats, and behaviors of all the real-life source animals as a way to emphasize the fascinating variety of real-life wildlife. Ask the students to give examples of any artwork or myths they think may be based on actual wildlife.

*continued*

## Extensions

1. Write a mythical story about a real aquatic creature. Show how the myth might have a basis in fact.

2. Research historical mythical creatures, and propose animals that may have provided the source for the myth.

3. Many times people see only part of an aquatic animal while the rest of the creature's body may remain unseen in dark or murky water. To simulate that experience, cover up most of a photograph of an aquatic animal. The animal's identity should not be obvious. Draw pictures of what you think the entire animal might look like. Compare your drawings with the photographs. Discuss how human perceptions form when people have only partial information.

## Evaluation

Identify three mythical creatures that may have been inspired by a real animal; then identify the real animal in each case.

Describe what the mythical creature is supposed to be able to do that the real animal cannot.

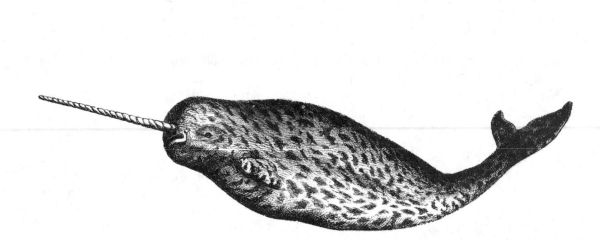

# Water We Eating?

## Objectives

Students will (1) identify foods derived from aquatic sources and their geographic origins, and (2) describe the importance of aquatic environments as food sources.

## Method

Students visit a local supermarket and compile a list of products that originate in aquatic habitats.

## Materials

Writing materials, a world map, magazines or newspapers (if field trip is not possible); OPTIONAL: clipboard

## Background

Aquatic ecosystems (oceans, estuaries, marshes, lakes, rivers, etc.) provide humans with a variety of products, including fish, shellfish, and wild and domestic rice. Other products, such as fertilizer, soup stock, watercress, water chestnuts, and

**Grade Level:** K–4

**Subject Areas:** Social Studies, Science, Environmental Education

**Duration:** one or two 20- to 60-minute sessions; additional time if field trip is included

**Group Size:** any

**Setting:** indoors

**Conceptual Framework Topic Reference:** ECIB1, ECIB3

**Key Terms:** food, aquaculture, mariculture

**Appendices:** Using Local Resources

ingredients for vitamins, are not as well known. Seaweed is a source of algin, carrageenin, and agar, which are used as stabilizers, thickeners, and emulsifiers in hundreds of food products. Those seaweed derivatives are used to smooth the texture of things like ice cream and to make them creamy. They help to keep ingredients like the chocolate in suspension in chocolate milk. Certain types of seaweed, which are actually forms of algae, are consumed directly by humans. For example, nori is used in sushi, and irish moss, lauer, and dulce (dulse) are used in other dishes. In another example, the meat in oysters is eaten directly by humans, while the shells are ground up for use as calcium supplements for humans and poultry.

Aquaculture is another source of aquatic food products. Aquaculture is an ancient form of cultivating aquatic plants, fish, and shellfish for food. In the United States, aquaculture produces perhaps as much as 99 percent of the rainbow trout consumed in the United States. Catfish, lobster, shrimp, oysters, and salmon are all examples of aquatic animals being raised commercially through aquaculture programs. The hatching and raising of aquatic animals or release in streams, lakes, and oceans are also considered forms of aquaculture.

NOTE: This activity does not specifically address potential ethical questions that may be raised concerning human aquaculture and mariculture practices. The activity is designed to focus on students' recognition of the role of water in the production of foods, including those from aquatic environments.

*continued*

## Procedure

*Before the Activity*

Obtain permission from the manager of a local supermarket to bring your class or group to the store to find out how many products are derived from aquatic environments. If a field trip is not possible, educators might use the following as sources to identifying aquatic products:

- Supermarket advertisements or photos from a variety of magazines,

- Products in students' cupboards and pantries in the students' homes, and

- A variety of products that represent the diversity of foods and other goods people use from aquatic environments.

1. Before the field trip, ask the students to make a list of all the things that they would expect to find in a supermarket that come directly from an aquatic environment. Be inclusive—everything from ocean to pond and from swamp to river—is appropriate. Also, design a form to record students' observations while at the supermarket. This form could be as simple as a place to record the products, to a more detailed form that includes where the product is manufactured, its exact ingredients, and so forth.

2. Visit the supermarket and complete the observation forms.

3. After the field trip, compile a master list of aquatically derived products. Answer the following questions (some research may be needed): Where do the products come from? How are they obtained? Where and how are these products processed? How are they used?

4. On a world map, locate the country of origin of as many products as possible on the list above.

5. Ask the students to draw a picture of the aquatic food products they most like to eat, or to make a collage of such products from magazine pictures.

6. Summarize the lesson by asking the students: How do our lives depend on aquatic environments? What do aquatic environments provide us with? What do aquatic environments provide for wildlife?

## Extensions

1. Compare aquatic products found in conventional markets in the United States with products found in markets specializing in foods from Asia (Japan, China, Philippines, Vietnam, Thailand, etc.).

2. Classify the aquatic food products found in the supermarket according to the type of aquatic habitats they inhabit: salt water (ocean, estuary, marsh, etc.) and fresh water (lake, pond, stream, river, etc.).

*For Older Students*

3. Research aquacultural practices. Compare the food produced by each to the food produced through commercial fishing. What kinds of products are being produced by each? What effects, if any, are there on populations of fish and shellfish as a result of each approach?

4. Does agriculture, and particularly irrigation, affect natural aquatic habitats?

## Evaluation

1. Identify five specific foods derived directly from aquatic sources. List their country or region of origin.

2. Identify an aquatic plant or aquatic animal that you can find in a local store and that is also found growing or living in your state.

3. Identify an aquatic product that is used in food production but is not necessarily eaten directly. How is it used?

4. Describe three ways that aquatic habitats are important to humans as sources of food.

# Net Gain, Net Effect

## Objectives

Students will (1) describe the evolution of fishing techniques, and (2) interpret the changes in technology on fish populations.

## Method

Students conduct a simulation to explore the evolution of fishing and the effects of changing technology on fish populations.

## Materials

Nets of differing mesh size (see table on page 89): onion bags, potato bags, fruit bags, netting from hardware store, or plain cloth fabric for nets; 1 pound each of lima beans, pinto beans, black beans, lentils, and rice; writing materials; four containers that are large and deep enough to hold one-fourth of the beans and grains

## Background

Throughout history, people have caught fish for food, to sell to others, for fun, and for sport. One type of fishing is subsistence fishing, where the number of fish caught is no more than a family could consume. Commercial fishing is another type of fishing and differs from subsistence fishing because the fish are caught and then sold to others. Sport fishing differs from commercial fishing because the catch is not sold for profit. (Source: American Sportfishing Association)

Humans have been engaged in fish gathering since prehistoric times. Research suggests that methods of catching fish started with humans wading into drying wetlands at the edges of large shallow lakes, and using bare hands and clubs. These are the first known uses of fish as a human food source. As time passed, new techniques were invented. Native people built rock weirs or dams on streams and rivers to trap and spear the fish in holding ponds. Eventually, baskets were formed that allowed fish to swim downstream into intricately woven baffles that prevented their escape. (Source: American Sportfishing Association)

Fishing equipment has evolved over the years. Stone Age anglers used some sort of line, such as vines, and tied gorges to the end of the line. Gorges were a type of primitive hook that was made of bone, flint, and thorns or turtle shells. The earliest hook was made from copper about 7,000 years ago. Today, fishhooks are made from steel.

Fishing poles and lines written about in Chinese literature 4,000 years ago were described as wooden fishing poles with lines made from silk. Fishing lines were also made from plant fibers, human hair, cotton, and linen. Today, nylon is the most preferred material used for fishing line. Fishing rods have been made from many materials such as bamboo and steel, but today are typically made from fiberglass.

*continued*

---

**Grade Level:** 5–8

**Subjects Areas:** Mathematics, Social Studies, Environmental Education, Science

**Duration:** one 30- to 60-minute session

**Group Size:** any

**Setting:** indoors or outdoors

**Conceptual Framework Topic Reference:** ECIB, ECIIA

**Key Terms:** technology, fishing

**Appendices:** Simulations

---

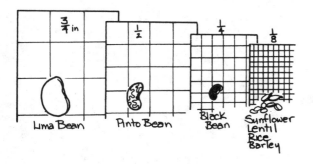

The use of boats and rafts for fishing purposes evolved during the Stone Age. The first evolution in boat design came about when fishing boats shifted from a dugout—a narrow boat, made from hollowed trees and propelled by paddles—to sailing vessels. The development of sails allowed fishing vessels to extend their range and catch. The creation of steam and diesel-driven fishing fleets provided a method for the vessels to rapidly maneuver to any spot in the ocean.

The invention of the net enabled fishing to move from sustaining a family or tribe to an economic venture. Over time, the net evolved in size, design, and effectiveness. Many nets are now available for catching different fish species in a variety of situations. Gill nets, purse seines, trammel nets, and drift nets have all improved the fishers' catch rate. Yet these advancements have also introduced new problems, such as the impact on other marine life, size discrimination, over-fishing, and loss of marine habitats.

Nets, combined with the range and maneuverability of steam and diesel boats, made it possible to catch larger amounts of smaller fish. For commercial fishing companies, a problem is created when mixed species are caught in the same net. Because most fishers have a specific fish species to catch, the other species that are caught inadvertently must be discarded. Over 20 million tons of fish and other marine animals, about one-fourth of the global catch, are killed and discarded by commercial fishers. (Source: National Coalition For Marine Conservation) Those discarded fishes are known as "bycatch."

Along with the developments in boats and nets, changes have taken place with fishing equipment. Commercial fishers now routinely use complex sonar fish finders, radio communications, spotter aircraft, computerized navigational equipment, at-sea catch processing, and other similar sophisticated tools.

With the remarkable advances in technology and the growth in investment of fishing trawlers and factory processing ships, fisheries became overfished and exploited. The amount of fish caught in the world's oceans grew from 19 million tons in 1950 to 88 million tons in 1988. With the oceanic fisheries being fished at or beyond capacity, scientists saw a substantial change in the oceanic fish catch in 1989. According to the U.S. Department of Agriculture's National Marine Fisheries Service, 90 fish species found off the shores of the United States have been depleted.

In the United States, the fishing industry is a $3.5 billion business. The largest fishing nations of the world are Japan, Russia, and China. Fish supply the main source of protein for nearly half of the more than 5 billion people on the planet. Nearly 14 million tons of sardines, herring, and anchovies are netted commercially each year, while approximately 32 million tons of other kinds of fish are caught annually.

The high demand for seafood and the modern, technologically advanced fishing fleets have led to a modification in the world's fish species. Widespread depletion of certain ocean predators such as sharks and tunas can upset the predator-prey relationship of the oceans. Overfishing not only disrupts food chains but also can threaten marine ecosystems.

One example of a fish species on its way to recovery is the swordfish. Swordfish roam most of the world's tropical and temperate oceans. They have a large dorsal fin and a rigid, sword-like beak. Swordfish can weigh up to 1,200 pounds but average 250 pounds.

Commercial fishers use long fishing lines stretched dozens of miles and baited with hundreds of hooks to catch and kill swordfish. Since the introduction of this fishing method, there has been a decline in the weight and age of the swordfish catch. Today, the average catch size of the swordfish is 90 pounds compared to a 250-pound average in the 1960s. At 90 pounds, females have not reached a reproductive age and weight, and thus the population size declines. Restoring populations to a healthy level could take up to 10 years or more. Plans are in effect to reduce the international quota for North Atlantic swordfish and the "Give Swordfish a Break" campaign is being supported by chefs, grocers, and consumers throughout the nation. This campaign is aimed at convincing consumers not to buy—and chefs not to serve— swordfish until the government develops and implements a plan for replenishing the depleted swordfish stocks and returning populations to a sustainable level. (Sources: SeaWeb and the Natural Resources Defense Council)

One species of fish that was once considered endangered and now has reached a balance between catch and reproduction rates is the striped bass. The striped bass, also called rock-fish, lives in estuarine waters along the Atlantic coast as a juvenile, then moves to coastal waters to feed. In spring, the mature striped bass re-turns to brackish and fresh water to spawn. The striped bass is a major food and sport fish on the East Coast from Maine to North Carolina. In the late 1970s, the striped bass population began to decline. In 1984, the Atlantic Striped Bass Conservation Act was passed to help re-cover this species. Effective state and federal programs to protect the striped bass allowed the recovery of stocks, and the species was officially recovered in 1995. (Sources: National Oceanic and Atmospheric Administration and Sea Grant: University of Delaware)

NOTE: This activity does not address ethical questions related to the appropriateness of catching fish for human uses. This dimension may be added at the professional discretion of the educator conducting the activity.

## Procedure

1. Prepare the "ocean" by mixing all the beans and grains listed under "Materials," and dividing the mixture equally into the four containers. These will be the four "fishing grounds."

2. For this activity, ask the students to decide what species each bean will represent. Fish species can be hypothetical or can represent local fish species.

   Make a chart matching the beans or grains with the fish they represent. Post the chart.

3. Divide the students into four groups, and ask each group to go to the fishing grounds (the containers of beans and grains).

4. Discuss how fish are caught. Have students seen people catch fish? How were they catching the fish? Could large numbers of fish be caught if all fish were caught with rods or poles? What are some ways to catch large groups of fish at one time? What are some of the ways people traditionally caught fish? After a general discussion on the methods people use to fish, inform the students that they will now simulate the catching of fish using nets.

5. Next, distribute the netting materials. The net materials must be cut into 4" × 6" squares. The number of nets needed will depend on how many students share a net. Provide one net for every three students.

6. With the coarsest netting in hand, ask the students to "fish." Using only one hand, students are to hold the nets between their thumb and first finger (see Diagram A). This distance is known as the catching area. Ask the students to make one pass with their nets through the fishing grounds.

*For Younger Students*

Educators may want to demonstrate how to use each net. When it is the students' turn, allow the students to make only one pass through the "ocean." Give each student a sheet of paper rep-resenting a boat. Instruct the students to deposit

*continued*

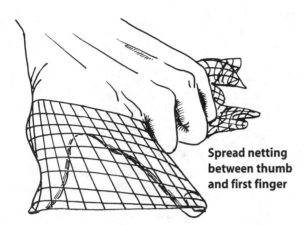

**Spread netting between thumb and first finger**

*Diagram A*

their "fish" on the boat. Count the number of each species of fish caught, and record the numbers on a data sheet.

7. Next allow the students to use both hands (see Diagram B). Make one pass through the "ocean." Count the number of each species of fish caught, and record the numbers on a data sheet. Repeat this process several times.

8. Discuss the results between the one-hand and two-hand techniques. Relate those results as an improvement in technology. For example, using both hands may represent the shift from hand-powered boats with cast nets to trawlers.

9. Analyze the species the students have netted. The smaller lentils and the rice will often slip through the netting and escape capture. The larger species—the limas and the pintos—are the most likely to have been caught. Ask students what they could do to catch more fish. Discuss possible options with them.

10. Ask the students to return all the fish to the ocean containers so that they can try fishing with a smaller-mesh net. Distribute a net with fine mesh (less than one-fourth inch). Again, the net needs to measure about 4″ × 6″.

11. Tabulate and discuss the results. OPTIONAL: Repeat with the nets of other size mesh. Discuss.

12. Return all the fish to the ocean.

*For Younger Students*

The activity may conclude with a discussion at this point. What happens when the different kinds of nets are used? Is it good to let the smaller fish through the net? Why or why not? What might happen if people fished from just one part of the ocean? OPTIONAL: Construct a bar graph to show the numbers of fish caught using the different nets and different techniques of netting.

13. Inform the students that all the fish, beans through rice, are all the same species and that no fish smaller than the black bean species size can be caught. A fine of one point will be added to the score for each of the smaller fish caught during this round. A regulatory agency responsible for monitoring fishing practices gives each team 10 seconds to put the undersized fish back in the ocean after each netting. Appoint two members of each fishing team to play the regulatory agency role.

*Diagram B*

14. Instruct the commercial fishers to use the fine mesh net (less than one-fourth inch mesh). Empty the net onto the table, and return the undersized fish to the ocean. At the end of 10 seconds, the team must stop. The representatives of the regulatory agency will count the undersized fish that are still left on the table and fine them one point for each one.

15. Discuss the economics involved. Can the people fishing afford to return all the undersized fish to the sea? What are their options? Should we release undersized fish? If yes, why? If no, why not?

16. Repeat this round with one of the larger–mesh nets. Is there an advantage to letting the smaller fish get through the net over returning them by hand? What aquatic animals might be caught in these larger nets?

17. Ask the students to summarize what they have learned. Review the general history of fishing, including how each change may have affected fish populations. Consider possible impacts on fish habitats as well. Identify some of the potential positive and negative issues related to the advancement of commercial fishing.

The Netting worksheet provided below may be helpful.

## Extensions

1. Create an illustrated history of the fishing net.

2. Use nets of different sizes to try to catch aquatic organisms in a local pond or stream. Observe and record any differences in what the nets catch. Be extremely careful to return any animals to their habitats unharmed.

NOTE: Check regulations with your state's wildlife agency regarding net use; in some areas it is against the law to use nets in local waters.

3. Who "owns" the fish in the sea? In streams? In lakes? In ponds? In other aquatic habitats? Who is responsible for conserving and protecting fish species?

4. Research the regulations on personal, non-commercial fishing in fresh water and in marine environments.

5. Research the regulations on commercial fishing in fresh water and in marine environments.

6. Discuss the role of aquaculture (fresh water) and mariculture (marine) aquatic farming. How will this emerging field affect commercial fishing? What possible positive effects, if any, on fish populations and habitat might there be from a change to aquaculture?

## Netting

| Species | Coarse Net | | | Fine Net | | Comments |
|---|---|---|---|---|---|---|
| **Number of Hands Used** | 1 | 2 | | 1 | 2 | |
| Lima lunker | | | | | | |
| Pinto porgies | | | | | | |
| Black bass | | | | | | |
| Lentil moonbeans | | | | | | |
| Rice wrasses | | | | | | |

*continued*

Mariculture? What possible negative effects, if any?

7. Research the fishing industry in your state. What methods are most commonly used to catch fish in your state? What regulations apply to commercial fishing in your state? Are they different from, or similar to, the regulations for personal and recreational fishing?

8. Research the international treaties and organizations dedicated to conserving and protecting oceanic habitats.

## Evaluation

*For Younger Students*

1. Draw three pictures showing different ways that fish are caught. Mark the picture that shows the way most fish are caught.

*For Older Students*

2. Describe how fishing has changed from prehistoric times to the present. How have these changes affected fish populations?

# Watered-Down History

## Objectives

Students will (1) describe human, plant, and animal life associated with a waterway over a period of time; (2) predict the future of the waterway; and (3) analyze cause-and-effect relationships between events affecting the waterway.

## Method

Students investigate the history of a chosen waterway through research methods, a taped personal interview, and public records, and then display their findings on a mural

## Materials

County, city, state, regional maps or a combination; names of agencies responsible for historical records; art materials. OPTIONAL: names of citizens who might be interviewed, a tape recorder

**Grade Level:** 5–8

**Subject Areas:** Social Studies, Environmental Education

**Duration:** several class sessions, minimum of three 45-minute sessions

**Group Size:** any, several small groups are recommended

**Setting:** indoors; a visit to an outdoor site is recommended, but optional

**Conceptual Framework Topic Reference:** HGIA, HGIB, HGIIB

**Key Terms:** waterway, events, consequences, change, wildlife, habitat, vegetation, geology, archaeology, culture, history, geography

**Appendices:** Outdoors, Using Local Resources, Interview

## Background

Historically, waterways have provided an available path for exploration, transportation, and amenities for human settlement. Most waterways also provide a rich habitat for wildlife. Ancient fossils offer evidence that those areas were once homes for marine life, dinosaurs, and ancient mammals.

When early settlers began to immigrate into the United States, waterways provided a needed source of water, so towns and homes were built along the shores. Waterways were used to transport logs, furs, fish, and agricultural products from one town to another. As the country has grown, waterways now provide transportation, power, and irrigation to communities. Waterways such as rivers, canals, dams, and channels are used for navigation, hydropower, flood control, coastal protection, and municipal and industrial water supply. Navigable channels provide an efficient and economic corridor for moving commerce. Thousands of cities, towns, and industries rely on the water supply from the lakes and reservoirs. Waterways also provide recreation for people to enjoy swimming, kayaking, whitewater rafting, and fishing.

Over time, the United States' waterways have been modified. Wetlands are filled in for development, lakes and reservoirs are created by dams, and beach areas are developed for recreation. Changes in waterways have an impact on wildlife as well as on humans. Some effects may be beneficial, while others may be damaging.

*continued*

# Procedure

1. After introducing this activity, ask the students to refer to a county, city, state, or regional map and to select one waterway that will be the focus of their research. It might be a stream, river, lake, or pond.

NOTE: If possible, the students could visit the waterway as a pre-research field trip. This trip would provide an awareness of the present conditions so that historical perspectives and future recommendations would have a base in experience.

2. Once the choice has been made, divide the class into small working groups. Ask the students in each of the groups to choose a major topic area (e.g., geology, plants, animals, ancient people, or recent history) to establish historical perspective. More specific topics that the students might explore include floods, dams, agriculture, recreation, fishing, irrigation, and so on.

3. Ask the students to identify resources for their research. If possible, try to include living reference sources such as older citizens, members of local historical societies, and governmental professionals (geologists, water quality experts, etc.). History, science, and social studies teachers from high schools or colleges may be viable sources. Old newspapers and historical archives may be available at local libraries and resource centers. Questions such as the following might provide guidance:

   - What forms of ancient life populated these regions?

   - What was life like for ancient peoples who lived here?

   - How did explorers find this location?

   - What were the explorers looking for?

   - What kinds of wildlife did the explorers and early settlers find?

   - What kinds of vegetation did the explorers and early settlers find?

   - Are these same life forms still here?

   - How has the waterway changed?

4. After the research is complete, have the students create a large base map of the waterway. Each team could create artwork to illustrate the major findings of its research. The artwork could be attached temporarily to the map and removed or replaced as needed.

5. After the map is complete, have the teams report in an historical sequence, starting with the team with the earliest history and finishing with the team with the most recent history. By establishing a sequence for presenting each report, each geological, archaeological, and biological topic can be addressed during its major time period. This process also creates a layering of history represented as an historical collage on the map of the waterway.

6. After the reporting is complete, ask the students to collectively analyze major changes involving the waterway and its associated life. Ask them to attempt to identify cause-and-effect relationships between events and consequences of events affecting the waterway. Create a time-line, noting major events in the waterway's history.

7. Finally, have the students collectively create a vision of the future for the waterway. For example, students could go back in history and undo events that they feel modified the waterway in some fashion. First, they could illustrate an event by replacing artwork they may have removed. Second, they could create an image of the future that they feel

represents an effective ecological balance among people, wildlife, and the environment in association with this waterway. Add the future possibilities to the time-line created in Step 7. Consider the option of the students compiling a biography of their waterway to summarize the activity.

## Extensions

1. Implement a project that demonstrates ecological balance between humans and wildlife in association with an aquatic environment.

2. Write a play with traditional or original music to portray the course of your waterway through time. End with possible futures being depicted—emphasizing human responsibilities for the consequences of our choices. Present the play to other groups or to the community.

## Evaluation

1. Write at least two paragraphs describing how a waterway might have changed over a 100-year period of time—for example, from 1865 to 1965. Write another paragraph predicting what might happen between now and the year 2100.

2. Role-play the following scenario: Each student is an elected official. Mr. or Ms. Smith represents a group in favor of building a dam on a river to produce irrigation water and recreation opportunities in your area. Ms. or Mr. Jones represents another group that thinks the dam will have a damaging effect on the animals and plants in and along the river. Pick one position to support and debate the topic.

# When a Whale Is Right

## Objectives

Students will (1) describe general characteristics and status of whales, (2) recognize that international alliances affect wildlife, and (3) evaluate the possible impact of wildlife issues on alliances and other relationships between and among nations.

## Method

Students hold a hypothetical meeting of the International Whaling Commission.

## Materials

Writing materials, research materials

## Background

Whales are the largest animals on Earth. There are approximately 80 known species of whales, which range in size from approximately 4 to almost 100 feet in length, and from 160 pounds to 220 tons in weight. Whales are mammals, bearing live young. Some research suggests that

> **Grade Level:** 9–12
>
> **Subjects Areas:** Social Studies, Environmental Education
>
> **Duration:** two or three 45-minute sessions
>
> **Group Size:** any, excellent for large group
>
> **Setting:** indoors
>
> **Conceptual Framework Topic Reference:** PLIIA
>
> **Key Terms:** whale, Cetacea, alliance, regulation, commission, harvest, subsistence, sanctuary, species
>
> **Appendices:** Agencies and Organizations

whales and other Cetacea, including the dolphins, are creatures of such intelligence that—among other things—they have unusual capacities for communication.

Out of concern for maintaining viable populations of whales, the International Whaling Commission (IWC) was established under the International Convention for the Regulation of Whaling. This treaty was signed in December 1946. The main duty of the IWC is to keep under review and revise as necessary the measures laid down in the Schedule to the Convention, which governs the conduct of whaling throughout the world. Those measures provide for the complete protection of certain whale species, designate specified areas as whale sanctuaries, set limits on the numbers and size of whales that may be taken, prescribe open and closed seasons and areas for whaling, and prohibit the capture of suckling calves and female whales accompanied by calves. The compilation of catch reports and other statistical and biological records is also required.

In addition, the commission encourages, coordinates, and funds whale research; publishes the results of scientific research; and promotes studies into related matters. Membership in the IWC is open to any country in the world that formally adheres to the 1946 Convention.

There are many stocks or populations of the twelve species of "great whales." Many of those have been depleted by overexploitation, some seriously, both in recent times and in earlier centuries. Fortunately, several species are showing signs of increase since their protection. Whales, like any other animal population, have a natural capacity to increase and a natural rate of mortality. A stock remains more or less in equilibrium at its initial level because those two factors balance one another. If the number of whales in a stock is reduced, the population will begin to rebound—possibly as a result of greater food availability—by higher pregnancy rates, earlier maturation, increased survival rates, or a combination of these factors.

In 1975, a new management policy for whales was adopted by the IWC using those character-istics. This policy was designed to bring all stocks to the levels that provide the greatest long-term harvests, as it sets catch limits for individual stocks below their sustainable yields. However, because of uncertainties in the scientific analysis and, therefore, the precise status of the various whale stocks, the IWC decided at its meeting in 1982 that there should be a pause in commer-cial whaling on all whale stocks from 1985 to 1986. A Revised Management Procedure has been developed subsequently, which the com-mission accepted and endorsed in 1994, but it has yet to be implemented. This plan balances the somewhat conflicting requirements to ensure that the risk to individual stocks is not seriously increased, while allowing the highest continuing yield. It is an important step in the development of wildlife resource management in that it takes into account the inevitable scien-tific uncertainty and requires relatively simple data to obtain information (knowledge of popu-lation size, past and present catches, and stock identity).

The pause in commercial whaling does not affect aboriginal subsistence whaling, which is permitted from Denmark (Greenland, fin and minke whales), the Russian Federation (Siberia, gray whales), St. Vincent and the Grenadines (humpback whales), and the United States (Alaska, bowhead, and occasionally gray whales).

As part of their response to the decision for a pause in commercial whaling, some member governments have implemented major research programs that may include the sampling of whales caught under special permits that the convention allows them to grant.

The commission also sponsors and promotes international research. A major undertaking has been a series of ship surveys of the Antarctic minke whale stocks. This series has now been expanded into a new Southern Hemisphere research program called SOWER. Other funded research includes work on developing and improving new techniques such as photo-identification studies, acoustic and satellite/radio tracking of whales, and genetic analysis of populations.

The Scientific Committee has been concen-trating on a "Comprehensive Assessment" of whale stocks, defined as an in-depth evaluation of the status of the stocks in the light of man-agement objectives. This latter emphasis led to the development of the Revised Management Procedure. The committee is also working to assess the effects on cetaceans of environmental change, such as global warming and pollution, and of whale watching activities.

The commission has no enforcement powers. Beyond economic sanctions and national laws by members, the commission relies on voluntary adherence to its rules. World public opinion is an important force on the commission and its member nations to make and enforce respon-sible conservation decisions.

## Procedure

1. Divide the students into four groups. One group will research the International Whaling Commission, one will research nonwhaling nation members of the IWC, one will research whaling nation members of the IWC, and one will research whales.

2. Ask each group to conduct library and Internet research. Possible questions for each group might include the following:

### International Whaling Commission

What is the International Whaling Commission? When, why, and how was it established? Who are its members? What members are whaling nations? Are there any active whaling nations that are not members of the IWC? If so, what

*continued*

are their current practices affecting whales? What are the major reasons for and against continued whaling? Include economic, political, cultural, scientific, and ethical considerations.

What positions do member nations tend to take on issues? For what reasons? What are the accomplishments of the IWC? What problems does the IWC face? What is the role of world opinion in affecting the activities of the IWC and its member and nonmember nations? What recent recommendations and regulations has the IWC passed? How effective does the IWC seem to be in meeting its objectives? What other international agreements affect whales? Which countries participate in these agreements?

### Nonwhaling Nation Members of the IWC

Have these nations ever actively engaged in whaling? If yes, what are historic reasons for whaling among people of their nation? For what reasons are these nations now nonwhaling nations? How did they vote on the moratorium decision of 1982? What, if any, national laws do they have involving whales?

### Whaling Nation Members of the IWC

What are historic and contemporary reasons for whaling among people of their nation? What practices have they used and do they use in killing whales? What regulations, if any, do they support that affects the killing of whales? How did they vote on the moratorium decision of 1982? What, if any, national laws do they have involving whales?

### Whale Researchers

How many different kinds of whales exist today in the world? Have any whales become extinct? If yes, which? What are the characteristics of the different whale species? What is the status of each of these species? What is the reproductive rate and success of these species? What population increase is possible? What food and other

habitat needs do they have? What problems do they face? What species are most hunted and for what purposes, historically and in the present? Which species are most scarce and which are most abundant? How intelligent might they be? What does the future hold for whales?

3. After students have completed their research, set up the classroom to resemble a meeting hall. Hold a meeting of the IWC attended by scientific advisors and any guests, including other interest groups. Organize discussion and debate among the students, representing different interests (e.g., commercial interests, subsistence hunters, preservationists, animal welfare interests, conservation organizations).

4. The next task is to come up with a set of recommendations and regulations that the IWC, including its member whaling and nonwhaling nations, can agree upon. This task may be done through discussion by the whole class or by a subcommittee approach. If done by subcommittee, ask for volunteers to represent the IWC, with representatives of both whaling and nonwhaling nations. They should come up with a set of recommendations and regulations to present in written form to the rest of the class for review. Include other interest groups as well. Note whether this approach is actually how the IWC makes decisions.

5. Discuss any final recommendations. Evaluate the possible impact of wildlife issues on relationships between and among nations.

## Extension

Identify any other international bodies that have an influence on aquatic species of wildlife. Research these groups and what issues are of concern to their organizations.

## Evaluation

1. List four basic characteristics of two different species of whales.

2. Identify 10 countries that are members of the International Whaling Commission. Indicate the countries that are whaling countries, and list which species of whales they harvest. Explain how each country uses its harvested whales.

3. What is the purpose of the International Whaling Commission? Describe one action the Commission has taken to achieve its purpose. How are actions of the IWC enforced? What is your assessment of the IWC's importance and effectiveness?

4. Summarize your impressions of the impact of this issue—and other wildlife issues, if possible—on alliances and other relationships between and among nations.

NOTE: The name of this activity is not intended to imply that human use of whales is, or is not, a right. Students may want to investigate how the right whale was named, and discuss various interpretations of the meaning of "right" in this context.

# Sea Turtles International

## Objectives

Students will (1) analyze the policies and philosophies that countries have relating to wildlife ownership and protection and to habitat management, (2) explain the importance of international agreements and organizations that manage species that cross national boundaries, and (3) define the difference between ownership of land and ownership of wildlife.

## Method

Students portray the political interactions of citizens from different countries who have a variety of perspectives on the conservation of wildlife and habitat.

## Materials

Copies of the Scenario Cards (one card per student) and the Haves Cards

---

**Grade Level:** 9–12

**Subject Areas:** Social Studies, Environmental Education

**Duration:** two 45-minute sessions

**Group Size:** at least 18 students

**Setting:** indoors

**Learning Framework Concepts:** PLIB, PLIC, PLIIA, PLIIB

**Key Terms:** political process, international agencies, wants, needs, entrepreneur, compliance

**Appendices:** none

---

## Background

The boundaries that exist between countries are more often political in nature than actual barriers and allow for the free movement of people and wildlife. Nations and their governments throughout the world vary on how they perceive the protection of wildlife and their habitats. The policies are based on the country's economics and culture. For instance, a developed country may be secure enough economically to be able to afford banning the sale of wildlife products or restricting the sale of property that would harm wildlife habitat. Developing countries often do not have this luxury. Those countries need to use all of the natural resources within their boundaries to sustain themselves economically. Even if a country has entered international agreements to protect wildlife and habitat, it may not have the funds to enforce those agreements, and its citizens may feel that the financial gain is worth the risk of breaking the law. Additionally, in some countries, land ownership includes the wildlife found on the land. Therefore, even if laws exist to protect wildlife and the habitat, private landowners are exempt.

With respect to culture, the people of some countries have used wildlife products for centuries as part of their lifestyle and customs. Cultures may use ground shells to treat arthritis, gall bladders to treat disease, or ground horns to improve fertility. People from such countries may have been eating rare animal parts as delicacies for generations. Wildlife products are often an integral part of cultural celebrations and ceremonies. As a result, countries may be reluctant to join international agreements banning the possession of animal products. Where usage is restricted, citizens may resort to obtaining the product illegally.

The sale of wildlife products has caused a decline in many populations of animals throughout the world. In the 1970s, four conventions were held among nations to protect certain migratory species: (1) the Convention on Migratory Species of Wild Animals, (2) the World Heritage Convention, (3) the Convention on Wetlands of International Importance Especially as Waterfowl Habitat, and (4) the Convention on International Trade in Endangered Species of Wild Flora and Fauna (CITES). CITES was adopted on July 1, 1975, and currently has 146 member countries. Those countries have agreed to ban commercial, international trade of listed endangered species and require a license for trading threatened species as a way of monitoring those that may become endangered. While most countries have joined CITES and have ratified those agreements found within, not all comply stringently, as enforcement is decided by the individual country.

All species of sea turtles are either listed as endangered or threatened and are covered by CITES. Although sea turtle populations have declined, they are still being captured for their value and ties to cultural traditions. Sea turtles are found in oceans throughout the world. Some species migrate as many as 3,000 miles in a year often crossing one or more international boundaries. Besides being harvested in many countries, sea turtle populations are threatened by pollution and habitat loss. The turtles' nesting grounds, found on ocean beaches, are also declining because of development. Another threat to the sea turtle populations is the lights from homes and businesses along beach areas. After they hatch, baby sea turtles instinctively go toward light, which is usually moonlight over water. When sea turtle eggs hatch near developed areas, the lights from homes and businesses sometimes confuse the baby sea turtles and cause them to head inland instead of out to the ocean. Anglers catch sea turtles in their nets or cages. Turtle hunters around the world harvest sea turtles either legally or illegally to sell their shells, meat, or body parts to international traders. In some countries, sea turtle eggs are a delicacy and can be found in the open market.

Students will represent citizens of three different countries either trying to make a living, make a profit, gain wealth, enforce laws, or enforce international agreements. Each student will receive a description of their character, a list of their *"wants,"* and a list of *"haves"* (items to be exchanged to obtain their *"wants"*). It is the understanding of this exchange of *"wants"* and *"haves"* that drives the political process and allows the citizens to achieve their goals. In this activity, the characters are all connected by chains of need, and certain players are key to moving the solutions forward: the CITES representative who supports the judge, the judge who then issues a judicial order allowing the government bureaucrat to permit critical business developments, and the sea turtle advocate who supplies needed funding.

The purpose of this activity is to show that governments and societies develop different programs and policies relating to wildlife ownership and protection and to wildlife management. The movement of wildlife species across national boundries often necessitates the adoption of international agreements and the formation of international organizations to ensure the protection and management of these species.

## Procedure

1. Review the background information with the students.

2. Hand out a Scenario Card to each student. If more than 18 students are in the class, ask the students to team up. Direct the students to group themselves into the three countries according to the information assigned to their character in their Scenario.

3. Describe each country using the background information on page 101. Briefly describe the various characters from each of the countries. Discuss probable economic and cultural issues found within each country that would affect the safety of sea turtles. Also, review any vocabulary that may be unfamiliar to the students, such as "entrepreneur" and "compliance."

*continued*

4. Give students time to review their own characters. Tell them that the objective of the activity is to collect ONE *Haves Card* for each *Want* listed in their scenario. They will get these *Haves Cards* from the other students during the activity.

5. Pass out the *Haves Cards*. Tell the students they will be keeping their scenario information, but they will distribute the *Haves Cards*. During the activity, they will (1) give away their initial *Haves Cards* to classmates who request them and (2) obtain the new cards they want. To find their cards, each student must first determine who the other characters are and who has the cards they want. Cards are obtained simply by asking for them. No direct trading is required. However, sometimes the initial holder of the card may not be permitted to give the card away until certain conditions specified on the card are met. Students should pay attention to and follow these conditions.

6. Begin the activity by letting the students move around the room to meet the other characters and fulfill their goals. Allow students time to work through their Scenarios. Tell the students to write on the cards the name of the character from whom they received the card. This information will help the class track the interactions during discussion later.

7. When all characters have fulfilled their needs by obtaining the necessary *Haves Cards*, tell the students to return to the three countries. Have the students describe their characters, what they wanted, and where they got the item they needed.

8. Discuss as a class the reactions and interactions that came about from the Scenario. Did all characters fulfill their *Wants*? Which characters had their *Wants* fulfilled by a character outside of their country? What difficulties did they find in getting their *Wants* met? How did the international organizations and agreements facilitate the protection of the sea turtles in this activity? What might have happened without their contributions? What more might be done?

9. Ask the students to differentiate between ownership of land and ownership of wildlife. In the United States, who owns wildlife? Ask the students if they can articulate the different policies and philosophies that these three countries had relating to wildlife ownership and protection and to habitat management. Did the students think the landowner wanted the poachers arrested in order to protect the turtles or to eliminate competitors? Students should support their responses.

## Extensions

1. Investigate the Sea Turtle Survival League, and track a turtle's health and movement around the world. Go to the Sea Turtle Migration-Tracking Education Program at **www.cccturtle.org/tracking.htm**.

2. Research all of the products that have been made from migrating animals and that can be found in the United States. Determine their worth and their economic impact on both the buyer and the seller.

3. Research the endangered or threatened species that migrate between the United States and Canada or Mexico. Determine if there are any economic, cultural, or political circumstances that may create a desire to protect or poach these animals.

## Evaluation

Have students choose a current conflict in the world dealing with the protection of wildlife species and international borders. Have students research the topography; natural features; economic, cultural, and political structures of the countries involved; and what, if anything, is being done internationally or locally to help the migrating wildlife. Students should specifically address how culture, economics, and politics of the selected countries determine the fate of wildlife species that cross international borders.

## COUNTRY BACKGROUND INFORMATION

### Pargimo

- Developing country.

- Some coastal land development.

- Coastal village income is based on fishing.

- Borders the Republic of United Peoples (RUP).

- Sea turtle and sea turtle eggs are a common food.

- Sea turtles, sea turtles eggs, and products made from sea turtles have been traded internationally for centuries and were an important part of the country's and individuals' incomes.

- Sea turtles migrate from the RUP coast to the Pargimo coast to spend their nonbreeding season.

- Some of the turtles migrate from the south of Pargimo to the north where they lay their eggs on the furthest northeast shores.

- A member of CITES, but lacking financial resources for enforcement.

- Ocean pollution by industrial sources is a concern.

### The Republic of United Peoples (RUP)

- Developed country.

- A very active member of CITES with active enforcement.

- Borders Pargimo.

- Sea turtles migrate from the coast of Pargimo to the coast of RUP to lay eggs.

- Coastal lobster and shrimp fishery is a large source of income for many coastal communities.

- Extensive coastal land development.

### Chumas

- Developed country.

- Landlocked, therefore, no sea turtles.

- Nonenforcing member of CITES.

- Culture encourages the use of sea turtles and sea turtle products as a food source, as a health aid, and for ceremonial uses.

- Black market for sea turtle products that goes unchecked by the government.

*continued*

# Scenario Cards

Country: Chumas

**Sea turtle jewelry dealer**
Because you know how valuable sea turtle jewelry is all over the world, you buy as much as you can, even though it is prohibited.

*Wants:*
Turtles
Money

---

Country: Chumas

**Restaurant owner**
The people of your community have been eating sea turtle eggs and sea turtles for thousands of years as a delicacy. You buy as many eggs and turtles as you can.

*Wants:*
Turtles
Turtle eggs
Money

---

Country: Chumas

**Turtle trader**
Middle class. You buy sea turtles from collectors in Pargimo to sell to companies in Chumas that make medicine, ceremonial products, and traditional food. Although your work has been respected and needed, it has now become illegal.

*Wants:*
Job

---

Country: Chumas

**Ceremonial sea turtle buyer**
You buy products made from sea turtles to sell for ceremonial uses. People in your community have been using sea turtle products for generations. Without them, the ceremonies would fail and harm would fall on the village.

*Wants:*
Turtles

---

Country: Chumas

**Turtle egg trader**
Middle class. You buy sea turtle eggs from collectors in Pargimo to sell to companies in Chumas that make medicine and traditional food. Although your work has been respected and needed, it has now become illegal.

*Wants:*
Job

---

Country: Pargimo

**Government bureaucrat**
You are interested in the agency operating efficiently. You have received a request for a special land development permit, but because of the new CITES regulations, must wait for judicial orders before you can fulfill this request.

*Wants:*
Judicial order (requiring beach habitat to be set aside) for coastal building permits

Country: Pargimo

**Landowner**
You have extensive coastal land holdings but are cash poor and need money to rejuvenate other businesses. You believe wild animals are property of landowner. You want poachers arrested.

*Wants:*
Capital investment funds

Country: Pargimo

**Judge**
You are frustrated by a lack of professional recognition for community efforts. You would like to further CITES by requiring developers to set aside beach natural areas for turtle habitat when applying for building permits. You hope that ecotourism will develop. You believe wildlife belongs to the public for protection.

*Wants:*
Professional recognition

Country: Pargimo

**Collector of turtles** (poacher)
You poach turtles from beach and ocean to sell to traders in Chumas in order to support large family. You believe wildlife should be available for public taking, but would prefer a legal job.

*Wants:*
Job

Country: Pargimo

**Collector of turtle eggs** (poacher)
You poach turtle eggs from beach to sell to traders in Chumas in order to support large family. You believe wildlife should be available for public taking, but would prefer a legal job.

*Wants:*
Job

Country: Pargimo

**Wildlife biologist and manager**
You are frustrated by poaching of turtles and by news of potential beach development. You would like to see the beaches protected and have a way to replenish the population of baby turtles. You believe wildlife belongs to the public.

*Wants:*
Beach in natural condition
Compliance by poacher
Turtle eggs

Country: Pargimo

**Law officer**
You are required to arrest poachers and traders of turtles or turtle products. Your position is difficult because you personally know the families that are trying to subsist through this illegal activity. You believe wildlife should be available for public taking, and you wish you did not have to arrest poachers.

*Wants:*
Compliance by poacher
Compliance by trader
Compliance by ceremonial sea turtle buyer

*continued*

Country: The Republic of United Peoples

**CITES organization head stationed in Pargimo**
You are trying to ensure that the agreements of CITES are being enforced. You are well connected to government and environmental organizations in your country, and are willing to help anyone achieve recognition who facilitates compliance with CITES regulations.

*Wants:*
Compliance by poacher
Compliance by trader
Compliance by ceremonial sea turtle buyer

---

Country: The Republic of United Peoples

**Sea turtle advocate**
You are an advocate for the protection of endangered and threatened species. You would like to see the coastal areas left in a natural state and the citizens respecting the new laws to protect the turtles. You are well financed.

*Wants:*
Beach in natural condition
Compliance by poacher
Compliance by trader
Compliance by ceremonial sea turtle buyer

---

Country: The Republic of United Peoples

**Wealthy developer**
Because of increased demands for isolated vacation sites, your company plans to buy land on the southeast coast of Pargimo—natural areas that are prime sea turtle egg laying habitat. You plan to develop the area by building an elegant but rustic-looking hotel/lodge and to make a profit for the company and its investors.

*Wants:*
Money
Land
Land development permit

---

Country: The Republic of United Peoples

**Entrepreneur**
You would like to make a fresh start and move to Pargimo. The business you would like to develop is a turtle farm. Most of the turtles raised on the farm will be sold to local companies, although a set number of turtles can be donated to natural resource agencies each year if needed to maintain populations. You need a loan to begin the business.

*Wants:*
Start-up funds
Business operating license
Hotel

---

Country: The Republic of United Peoples

**Tourist**
You are looking for rare items (food and jewelry) to buy. You also need some experimental medicines not found in the RUP. On future trips, you would like to find a safe, comfortable hotel for your family to "get away from it all." You would also like to find out about local natural features for this next trip.

*Wants:*
Food          Jewelry
Medicine          Safety
Information on natural features

---

Country: The Republic of United Peoples

**Owner of pharmaceutical company**
Your company makes medicines, but the high cost of labor in the RUP is forcing you to move to Pargimo, where salaries are lower. It would also be closer to a source of turtle eggs, which contain chemicals that are ingredients in some medicines.

*Wants:*
Money
Turtle eggs
Business operating license

# Haves Cards

Initially hand these cards out to the students representing the character typed in bold on the card. Most characters will get several cards. These cards will be traded to other characters during the activity. (Note trading conditions in *italics*.)

| | |
|---|---|
| Country: Chumas<br>**Sea turtle jewelry dealer**<br>Jewelry<br>*May not be sold until receives turtles.* | Country: Chumas<br>**Restaurant owner**<br>Food<br>*May not be sold until receives turtles.* |
| Country: Chumas<br>**Turtle trader**<br>Compliance to laws<br>*May not be given until receives a job.* | Country: Chumas<br>**Ceremonial sea turtle buyer**<br>Compliance to laws<br>*May not be given until receives a job.* |
| Country: Chumas<br>**Turtle trader**<br>Compliance to laws<br>*May not be given until receives a job.* | Country: Chumas<br>**Ceremonial sea turtle buyer**<br>Compliance to laws<br>*May not be given until receives a job.* |
| Country: Chumas<br>**Turtle trader**<br>Compliance to laws<br>*May not be given until receives a job.* | Country: Chumas<br>**Ceremonial sea turtle buyer**<br>Compliance to laws<br>*May not be given until receives a job.* |
| Country: Chumas<br>**Turtle egg trader**<br>Compliance to laws<br>*May not be given until receives a job.* | Country: Chumas<br>**Turtle egg trader**<br>Compliance to laws<br>*May not be given until receives a job.* |
| Country: Chumas<br>**Turtle egg trader**<br>Compliance to laws<br>*May not be given until receives a job.* | Country: Pargimo<br>**Landowner**<br>Beach in natural condition<br>*Card may not be given away until judicial order is issued setting aside this land.* |
| Country: Pargimo<br>**Landowner**<br>Land<br>*May not sell until notified that developer has received a land development permit.* | Country: Pargimo<br>**Landowner**<br>Beach in natural condition<br>*Card may not be given away until judicial order is issued setting aside this land.* |
| Country: Pargimo<br>**Collector of turtles** (poacher)<br>Compliance to Laws<br>*May not be given until receives a job.* | Country: Pargimo<br>**Judge**<br>Judicial order (to set aside habitat)<br>*Will not be issued until receives professional recognition from CITES.* |

*continued*

| | |
|---|---|
| Country: Pargimo<br>**Collector of turtles** (poacher)<br>Compliance to laws<br>*May not be given until receives a job.* | Country: Pargimo<br>**Collector of turtle eggs** (poacher)<br>Compliance to laws<br>*May not be given until receives a job.* |
| Country: Pargimo<br>**Collector of turtles** (poacher)<br>Compliance to laws<br>*May not be given until receives a job.* | Country: Pargimo<br>**Collector of turtle eggs** (poacher)<br>Compliance to laws<br>*May not be given until receives a job.* |
| Country: Pargimo<br>**Collector of turtles** (poacher)<br>Compliance to laws<br>*May not be given until receives a job.* | Country: Pargimo<br>**Collector of turtle eggs** (poacher)<br>Compliance to laws<br>*May not be given until receives a job.* |
| Country: Pargimo<br>**Wildlife biologist and manager**<br>Information<br>*May be given at any time.* | Country: Pargimo<br>**Collector of turtle eggs** (poacher)<br>Compliance to laws<br>*May not be given until receives a job.* |
| Country: Pargimo<br>**Government bureaucrat**<br>Land Development Permit<br>*Cannot be given until a judicial order is received.* | Country: Pargimo<br>**Law enforcement officer**<br>Safety<br>*May be given at any time.* |
| Country: Pargimo<br>**Government bureaucrat**<br>Business operating license<br>*May be given at any time.* | Country: Pargimo<br>**Government bureaucrat**<br>Business operating license<br>*May be given at any time.* |
| The Republic of United Peoples<br>**CITES organization head stationed in Pargimo**<br>Professional recognition<br>*May be given at any time.* | The Republic of United Peoples<br>**Sea turtle advocate**<br>Start-up funds<br>*May be given at any time.* |
| The Republic of United Peoples<br>**Wealthy developer**<br>Capital investment funds<br>*May be given at any time.* | The Republic of United Peoples<br>**Entrepreneur**<br>Job<br>*May not be given until start-up funds and business operating license are received.* |
| The Republic of United Peoples<br>**Wealthy developer**<br>Hotel<br>*May not be given until a land development permit is received.* | The Republic of United Peoples<br>**Entrepreneur**<br>Job<br>*May not be given until start-up funds and business operating license are received.* |

| | |
|---|---|
| The Republic of United Peoples<br>**Entrepreneur**<br>Turtles<br>*May not be given until start-up funds and business operating license are received.* | The Republic of United Peoples<br>**Entrepreneur**<br>Turtles<br>*May not be given until start-up funds and business operating license are received.* |
| The Republic of United Peoples<br>**Entrepreneur**<br>Turtles<br>*May not be given until start-up funds and business operating license are received.* | The Republic of United Peoples<br>**Entrepreneur**<br>Turtle Eggs<br>*May not be given until start-up funds and business operating license are received.* |
| The Republic of United Peoples<br>**Entrepreneur**<br>Turtle eggs<br>*May not be given until start-up funds and business operating license are received.* | The Republic of United Peoples<br>**Entrepreneur**<br>Turtle eggs<br>*May not be given until start-up funds and business operating license are received.* |
| The Republic of United Peoples<br>**Tourist**<br>Money<br>*To be exchanged directly for item on "Wants" list only.* | The Republic of United Peoples<br>**Tourist**<br>Money<br>*To be exchanged directly for item on "Wants" list only.* |
| The Republic of United Peoples<br>**Tourist**<br>Money<br>*To be exchanged directly for item on "Wants" list only.* | The Republic of United Peoples<br>**Tourist**<br>Money<br>*To be exchanged directly for item on "Wants" list only.* |
| The Republic of United Peoples<br>**Owner of pharmaceutical company**<br>Job<br>*May not be filled until business operating license and turtle eggs are received.* | The Republic of United Peoples<br>**Owner of pharmaceutical company**<br>Job<br>*May not be filled until a business operating license and turtle eggs are received.* |
| The Republic of United Peoples<br>**Owner of pharmaceutical company**<br>Medicine<br>*May not be filled until business operating license and turtle eggs are received.* | |

*Notes*

# Section Three

## Sustaining Fish and Wildlife Resources

# Water Wings

## Objectives

Students will (1) illustrate the water cycle; (2) describe the interrelatedness of the world's waters; and (3) state the importance of water to people, plants, and animals.

## Method

Students will visualize a simulated field trip and then create artwork and poetry.

## Materials

Tape recorded music, water sounds, or "ecosystem" recordings of an aquatic habitat; art materials (water-based paints such as acrylics, water color, or poster paints; brushes, paper, containers for water); writing materials

---

**Grade Level:** 5–8

**Subject Areas:** Environmental Education, Expressive Arts, Language Arts

**Duration:** one or two 30- to 60-minute sessions

**Group Size:** any

**Setting:** outdoors and indoors, outdoors for first part of activity if appropriate site is available

**Conceptual Framework Topic Reference:** AAIA

**Key Terms:** water cycle, planet, ocean, precipitation, condensation, evaporation, transpiration, ground water, watershed

**Appendices:** Ecosystem, Simulated Field Trips

---

## Background

There is, in a sense, only one body of water on Earth. Its rivers reach out in sinuous paths from the hearts of every continent. All water, everywhere, is somehow connected. Almost everyone can easily see and sometimes physically touch this universal body of water in some form—perhaps by turning on a water faucet or by looking at clouds moving high in the sky. Lakes, ponds, and inland seas are webbed together by waters flowing across the surface of the land or in the seeping flow of ground water. Through evaporation, condensation, and precipitation the atmosphere transports water from place to place.

Plants are an especially active part of the water cycle in many ways—including transpiration. Transpiration is a process by which plants lose moisture through their leaves by evaporation. People seldom think of the waters of the world as being connected into one body. Maps emphasize the continents and political boundaries on land. Geographers have named dozens of seas, which in reality cannot be delineated from each other—similar to the way that territorial boundaries on land tend to be more political than geographical.

Human beings are linked to the planet's watery world. Our bodies are approximately 75 percent water. Each molecule within us has been part of the oceanic realm in times past. Molecules of our bodies' water may have flowed in streams, lofted in air, or been locked in glacial ice. Other animals and plants are also tied to the planet's waters—directly and indirectly. Living things are partly made of water; all life depends on water in some way.

The continuous dynamic of the movement of water is called the water cycle. The concept of the water cycle is a way to view the moving connectedness of water in its many forms. Here is one illustration of the concept of the water cycle:

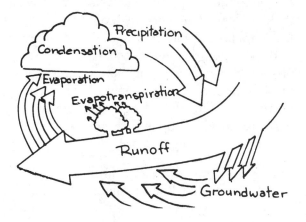

## Procedure

1. If at all possible, the students should visit a real stream, pond, lake, river, or beach. Try to choose one where human-made sounds are at a minimum. If possible and not dangerous, allow the students to touch the water during the simulated field trip portion of this activity. Consider the possibility of taking battery-operated tape recorders on the field trip to tape some of the natural sounds the students experience so you can later play it back in the classroom.

   If the outdoor field trip is not possible, then try to use a tape player with recordings of natural ecosystems. The sounds of oceans, rivers, streams, swamps, or brooks are often available on tape from bookstores, music stores, and shops that specialize in nature. A number of selections of contemporary music are excellent. You can also make your own tape recordings.

2. Ask the students to sit or rest quietly in a comfortable position. Begin the simulated field trip. If water is available, invite the students to relax and listen carefully to the water, or to musical sounds. These sounds are simply background for the ideas you are going to ask them to visualize in their minds.

NOTE: Educators may want to modify the water images in the text for local regions.

"You are to try to imagine the things you will hear me describing. Sit comfortably and close your eyes…. Relax, and do your best to picture what I am describing…. You are sitting on the edge of a stream (lake, ocean, etc.)…. Your bare feet are swinging in clean, clear water…. The water feels good, but it is cool…. You feel a current washing over your feet, pulling at them…. Think about the water flowing past your feet until it reaches a larger stream…. The water connects you with the larger stream…. Feel its more powerful flow…. See the green ribbon of trees and plant life on the banks…. The larger stream carries the water past flat farmlands, cities, factories, and forests until it eventually reaches the sea…. Through your feet and the continuous currents of water you can sense the sea…. Now stretch your mind and realize that you interconnect with all the world's oceans…. You are now touching one single body of water that stretches all around the world…. Your own body contains water that is part of this system…. Your touch laps against the shores of the Pacific Ocean; it flows under the Golden Gate bridge in San Francisco Bay; it leaps and plunges around oil drilling platforms in the North Atlantic…. It pours from the sky as a storm rages, dark and gray…. It drenches an Alaskan native who shivers on the Arctic shores before her parka begins to warm her. It glistens on the back of a Greek boy who tugs fiercely on fishing nets in the warm Mediterranean Sea…. Water connects your feet with every stream flowing into the oceans around the world…. You can reach up the rivers to the hearts of continents…. You can feel the tremor of the hippopotamus that just dove into an African river…. You can feel an alligator silently sliding toward a heron in the Florida Everglades…. You can feel beavers busily building a dam on a stream in Europe…. You can see water, thousands of tons of it, in great drifting fleets of heavy white clouds…. Your reach embraces all the whales, all the porpoises, all the sharks…. You are connected with the mythical creatures that live only in the minds of people in the past—mermaids, citizens of

*continued*

Atlantis, and the mythical monsters that swim in Loch Ness…. Your feet feel the flow of the current of the miles-wide Amazon River in South America, the ancient Nile River pushing north through Africa, the Colorado River thundering with a boatful of river rafters through the Grand Canyon…. Your watery embrace wraps all around the Earth…. And, of course, the water flowing over your feet connects you with everyone else who is now sitting, with feet dangling in a stream, wondering where the water goes…. It is time to come back…. Bring the limits of your senses back from the world's rivers and oceans…. back to the surfaces of your feet…. back to where you are…. When you feel ready, you may open your eyes."

3. Once the visualization is complete, ask the students to open their eyes. Explain that each student had his or her own private journey even though all students heard the same words. Explain to them that in a moment you will ask them to close their eyes again to find one place on the journey through the world's waters that was their favorite—and you will ask them to try to remember what that picture was like.

4. Ask them to relax again and have them try to recreate the picture in their minds. Tell them to look at the detail—the colors, the plants and animals—and to try to capture it all in one scene. Have them pay particular attention to the role of water in the lives of people, plants, and animals.

5. After several minutes, ask the students to open their eyes. Provide the art materials and ask them to quietly paint the picture of their favorite place.

OPTIONAL: Educators may want to provide an opportunity for some or all of the students to talk briefly about their favorite places.

6. Once the pictures are complete, ask the students to write various short forms of poetry that express some of their feelings about water and its importance. Here are a few examples of poetic forms that can be used.

*Haiku:* Haiku, a Japanese lyric verse form having three unrhymed lines of five, seven, and five syllables, traditionally invokes an aspect of nature or the seasons. Traditionally and ideally, a haiku presents a pair of contrasting images: one suggestive of time and place, the other a vivid but fleeting observation. Working together, they evoke mood and emotion. The emphasis is syllabic, not rhyming. For example,

> The fish swam by me
> Nothing left in the shimmer
> My heart beat faster

*Cinquain:* The word "cinquain" is derived from the French and Spanish words for five. The cinquain is a poetic form, originated by the American poet Adelaide Crapsey (1878–1914), comprising five unrhyming lines of, respectively, two, four, six, eight, and two syllables. Each line has a mandatory purpose and number of syllables or words. These are (1) the title in two syllables (or words), (2) a description of the title in four syllables (or words), (3) a description of action in six syllables (or words) (4) a description of a feeling in eight syllables (or words), and (5) another word for the title in two syllables (or words). Here are two examples, the first using syllables and the second using words:

> **Osprey**
> Fishing eagle
> Moves above dark water
> With graceful strength it finds its meal
> Seeker

> **Sea Otter**
> Mammal of living waters
> Swimming, sleeping, eating, diving, basking, playing,
> Sensitive indicator of the quality of continuing life
> Still here

*Diamante:* Diamante is a poem shaped in the form of a diamond. It can be used to show that words are related through shades of meaning from one extreme to an opposite extreme, following a pattern of parts of speech like this:

noun
adjective adjective
participle participle participle
noun noun noun noun
participle participle participle
adjective adjective
noun

For example,

Stream
Small, clear
Rippling, moving, growing
Life, plants, animals, people
Rushing, sustaining, cleansing
Connected, universal
Ocean

*Free verse:* Free verse is poetry in which the author is free to invent its form. It may or may not rhyme. For example:

Water strider
I watch you stand on glass
that bursts apart to my gentlest touch.
You dash, you dart and exhaust the eyes
that try to follow.
I think you are teaching me something
I will know
on some day like this —
but in a time long after
you are gone.

OPTIONAL: Display the pictures and poetry in a circle around a world map. With yarn, connect the pictures that the students painted of their favorite places to the sites where they appear on the map.

7. Discuss the "one body of water" metaphor. Emphasize the concept that all the waters of the world are interrelated and connected. Help the students see that the air is also part of that connection. It is the air that carries the waters back to the rivers from the sea.

Point out that watersheds are the places where the air rains its water back down on the Earth's surface and where it accumulates. Talk about the importance of water to people, plants, and animals.

8. End the activity with a description of the water cycle. Ask the students to describe how their favorite places, which they illustrated in their paintings, are a part of the water cycle. You might want to point out that the water they used in their paintings has evaporated from the pictures and is back in the water cycle again!

## Extensions

1. Find out the annual rainfall and climate in the area that you chose to paint.

2. Trace the migratory path of a salmon, tuna, or whale. Then describe the qualities of the different water environments that the animal experiences.

3. Choose a body of fresh water near you and trace its path to the sea.

## Evaluation

1. Describe the water cycle. Illustrate your description.

2. Describe how all of the Earth's water is connected and interrelated.

3. List at least 10 ways that you use water every day.

4. List as many examples as you can of why water is important to plants and animals.

5. Draw a picture showing how one drop of water can connect with a whale, a school, and a cactus.

# Puddle Wonders!

## Objectives

Students will (1) predict where puddles will form and how they will change, (2) observe and describe organisms that live in or near puddles, (3) measure and record the amount of water in puddles, and (4) make inferences about what types of organisms occupy puddles.

## Method

Students will observe water that accumulates in puddles and will measure the depth, area, and volume of the puddle.

## Materials

Pencils; data sheets; measuring instruments (yardsticks, metersticks, or tape measures); string (for use in making measurements)

---

**Grade Level:** 5–8

**Subjects Areas:** Science, Mathematics, Environmental Education

**Duration:** two or three 20- to 45-minute sessions

**Group Size:** small groups of three to five

**Setting:** outdoors and indoors

**Conceptual Framework Topic Reference:** AAIA

**Key Terms:** puddle, wildlife, area, depth, volume

**Appendices:** Outdoors, Field Ethics, Metric Conversion

---

## Background

When water flows down a hill, it sometimes stops flowing and forms a puddle, vernal pool, pond, or lake. Puddles form in low spots or depressions in the land's surface. Depending on the size of the puddle, water may be trapped for some time. If the puddle lasts for several days, there is a strong possibility it will be visited by wildlife.

Vernal pools—which are isolated and temporary puddles or ponds—provide the essential breeding habitat for certain animals. Fairy shrimp, for example, are small (about 1-inch) crustaceans that spend their entire lives in vernal pools. Females lay eggs on the puddle bottom and the eggs remain even after the pool dries. The eggs go through cycles of drying and freezing, and then hatch the next year when water returns.

One-celled animals, aquatic insects, frogs, and salamanders also use temporary puddles and ponds for reproduction. The eggs and larvae of those species must be capable of developing rapidly, and must be ready to move onto land before the pool of water dries up. The spadefoot toad is one example of a species that goes through rapid development to cope with the short life span of those puddles. Spadefoot toads spend most of their adult lives underground. They emerge at night during warm weather to feed on insects and other invertebrates. In extreme cold or hot weather, those toads stay hidden.

Immediately after the first heavy rains of summer, spadefoots emerge to mate. The female lays between 300 and 500 eggs in temporary puddles and ponds. The male goes into the puddle or pond and externally fertilizes the eggs. The eggs hatch and the tadpoles complete their development over 10 to 12 days to complete their growth before the water dries up.

Salamanders also rely on temporary puddles and ponds for reproduction. They spend most of their lives in burrows and under rocks on the forest floor and nearby streams. Mole salamanders are one species that gather in vernal pools after early spring rains for mating and laying eggs. The eggs develop in the pool, and by the time the pool dries up, the young have emerged to begin their life as terrestrial animals.

Many species of flying insects—such as butterflies, wasps, and flies—visit puddles and sip from the mud at the puddle's edge. They sip the water on the banks of the puddles where they can get vital salts and other minerals from the mud. Some species of swallows and mud-dauber wasps visit puddles for mud-building materials for their nests. Other animals may visit the puddle to bathe or drink.

An advantage of vernal pools and puddles is that many species that prey on amphibians or compete with them for food cannot live in this type of habitat. Predators such as fish cannot survive in temporary puddles or ponds because of the periodic drying.

Aquatic biologists study the life forms of ponds, vernal pools, and lakes. Students examining puddles can also duplicate some of the techniques these biologists use. Simple observations and measurements can determine size, depth, circumference, cause of accumulation, and identity of transient animal life.

NOTE: This activity should, if possible, be conducted at a time of year when rainfall is likely. Ideally, students investigate the study site before and after a rainstorm. In arid areas, puddles may be created with buckets or water hoses.

## Procedure

1. Begin with a discussion about rainfall and runoff. Where does the water come from? Where does the water go? When water ceases to run off a surface, a puddle forms. Tell the students that the class will make a study of the smallest body formed as water flows across the land—the puddle! If necessary in drier climates, a few puddles could be created by using buckets or a hose.

2. Divide the students into teams of three to five members. Send the teams outside on the study site to make observations and predictions about where puddles will form in a rainstorm. Have each team of students prepare a map of the school or other study site, showing the location of the predicted puddles. Also have the students make a comprehensive list of all the forms of wildlife that can be seen on the site. Look for birds, insects, rodents, worms, mammals, reptiles, and such. Ask the students to look beyond direct observation and to find indirect evidence of wildlife, like tracks, droppings (scat), slug trails, feathers, ant hills, and so forth. Keep those maps and wildlife lists for later use following the storm.

3. After a storm, when there are puddles on the study site, send the teams outside again. Have the teams map the study site again, this time locating the actual position and gross dimensions of the puddles on their maps. They need to find the area of one or more puddles.

Diagrams A and B show students how to measure the area of a puddle.

*continued*

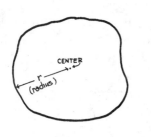

Diagram A

Round Puddles
Area = $\Pi r^2$
($\Pi$ = 3.14; it is a mathematical constant)
A = 3.14 x r x r =

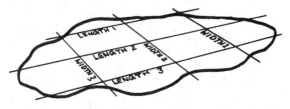

Diagram B

Area = Length (average) × Width (average)
Average Length (La) = $\dfrac{L1 + L2 + L3}{3}$

(3 is the number of measurements)
Average Width (Wa) = $\dfrac{W1 + W2 + W3}{3}$

A = La × Wa

The team should determine the volume of water in one or more puddles. Before that number can be calculated, the average depth of the puddle must be measured. There are many ways to determine the average depth. Either of two methods shown below can be used:

### Method 1 (Diagram C)

- Establish a grid on the surface of the puddle (lengths of string tied to rocks or nails pushed into the soil anchor the strings).

- Measure the depth at every place the strings cross (see the small arrows on the drawing).

### Method 2 (Diagram D)

- Imagine a grid on the surface of the puddle.

- Measure the depth every place the imaginary lines come together.

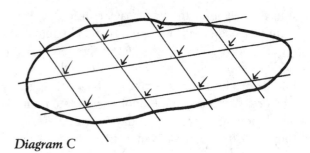

Diagram C

Use the following formula for average depth (Da). There are 10 measurements of depth shown in the example above.

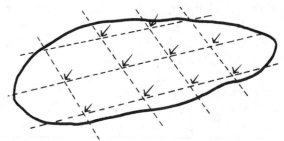

Diagram D

Da (average) =

$\dfrac{D1+D2+D3+D4+D5+D6+D7+D8+D9+D10}{10 \text{ (the number of measurements)}}$

Now the volume can be calculated:

Volume = La × Wa × Da

4. Once all the measurements have been taken for each puddle—or during the time while at a puddle—the team should make observations about wildlife. Each team should list any species of animal for which there is direct or indirect evidence of using the puddle in some way. Ask students to organize their observations in a written form. For example, they could list these:

- species

- evidence

- apparent uses of puddle by species

- estimated number of animals of this species using the puddle

5. After the activity, ask each team to report back to the other teams and discuss its findings. Compare similarities and differences in the teams' findings. Ask the teams to compare their early predictions about the puddles and wildlife with their actual findings. After all the reports are finished, ask each team to make a summary statement of one minute or less reflecting the inherently fascinating nature of the under-appreciated puddle!

## Extensions

1. Keep a record of these areas of accumulation over the seasons. What similarities occur? What differences? Ask the students to calculate how much water is "caught" each year by the puddle they studied.

2. Find relatively permanent puddles (small ponds), and carry out the same observations.

3. Biologists sometimes need to know where a pond is shallow and where it is deep. They use the same grid work approach used in the procedures above. The difference is that they keep a record of the change in depth along a straight line. See Diagram E.

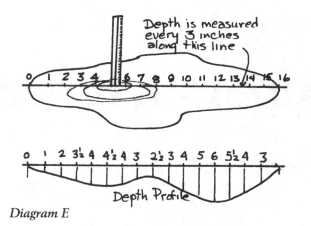

*Diagram E*

A good approximation of the shape of the puddle bottom can be achieved when this procedure is accomplished on all the lines.

4. Conduct the "Puddle Wonders!" activity using both English and metric measurements.

## Evaluation

1. Describe common characteristics of animals that use puddles. Explain the value of puddles to these animals.

2. How would you determine the amount of water in a puddle? Explain your method.

# Riparian Retreat

## Objectives

Students will (1) describe habitat characteristics of riparian areas, (2) identify animals that inhabit them, and (3) state the importance of riparian areas to wildlife and humans.

## Method

Awareness of a riparian zone is created through the use of a simulated field trip and art work.

## Materials

Art materials: water colors, acrylics, poster paints, crayons

## Background

Riparian zones are the green ribbons of life found on the edges of watercourses (streams, lakes, ponds, etc.). Riparian areas or zones are important and valuable in many ways, including hosting whole communities of life. Conditions within the zones support plant communities that grow best when their root systems are near the level of high ground water. These zones

range in width from narrow strips in desert and mountain settings to wide bands on the plains and lowlands.

Riparian areas provide space, shelter, and food for the plant and animal communities with which they are associated. For example, leaf litter and terrestrial insects falling from vegetation into a stream are a source of detritus, providing nourishment for some aquatic life. Vegetation may provide shade from the sun for aquatic plants and animals and land-dwelling creatures at the water's edge. Riparian areas are also transportation corridors for animals that depend on water bodies for food and shelter. The riparian plant community, especially shrubs and trees, provides shelter and food for many animals. Trees and marshy areas provide shelter for nesting birds, and the banks provide homes for burrowing animals.

The riparian zone may serve as a buffer between the uplands and the water. For example, rainfall dropping on uplands and flowing downhill can be cleansed as it flows through a riparian zone. The banks of riparian areas store water during periods of high flow such as rainstorms or snow melt and release this water to the stream during low-flow times. Riparian vegetation strengthens the stream banks. This tends to prevent erosion and maintains the stream channel, keeping the water clear.

Riparian areas have aesthetic and recreational values for humans. They are used for fishing, hiking, camping, picnicking, and resting.

---

**Grade Level:** 5–8

**Subject Areas:** Language Arts, Environmental Education

**Duration:** one 30- to 45-minute session

**Group Size:** any

**Setting:** outdoors or indoors

**Conceptual Framework Topic Reference:** AAIA, AAIB, AAIIA

**Key Terms:** riparian, ecology, habitat, value, buffer

**Appendices:** Simulated Field Trips

---

## Procedure

1. Ask the students if they have been to a stream or riverbank. What was it like? Were plants growing there? What did the area look like? Was it hot or cool? Encourage students to talk about and share descriptions of any area by a stream or riverbank they may have been to, or at least have seen pictures of.

2. Next, tell the students that the kind of area they have been describing has a special name: "riparian area." Riparian areas are important natural areas for people and wildlife. To learn more about these kinds of areas, the students will need to close their eyes and picture the things you will be describing. Invite the students to get in a comfortable position, close their eyes and do their best to picture what they hear.

NOTE: Educators may want to read the section about simulated field trips that appears in the Appendices for additional suggestions concerning use of this instructional strategy with students.

"It is a hot summer day. You are walking in a meadow filled with knee-high grasses. Here and there are masses of tiny blue wildflowers.... The ground beneath your feet is uneven, but you are in no hurry as you walk slowly toward a grove of trees. As you near the trees, you notice the changing colors of green.... A breeze whispers through, showing first a shiny green, then a dull green underside of the leaves.... As you step into the grove of trees, you are surrounded with a welcome coolness.... You immediately feel the protection of the canopy of green above your head.... A tap-tap-tapping sound breaks into your thoughts. Searching about among the rough-barked trunks, your eyes finally spot a bird, black and white with a touch of red on its head, clinging to a vertical tree trunk and bobbing its head in time to the rhythmic tapping.... Your eyes fill with the beauty of the setting.... Your skin welcomes the cool.... As you breathe deeply, the very scent of green comes to you.... The aroma of earth and growing things is strong,

and you detect here and there almost a memory of the sweet perfume of the flowers.... Once in a while, the pungent but not unpleasant odor of wet soil and last season's decaying leaves and grasses catches your attention.

"As you explore further, you notice that the tree trunks are not as crowded and close as before.... Grass, which earlier reached to your knees, is being overshadowed by chest-high bushes. Although these bushes have no thorns, they nevertheless snag your clothing.... Your arms are lightly scratched by the twig ends. Several of the bushes are covered with small berries, pink and pale green, ripening into red in the warm sun. The bushes become taller.... You find yourself pulling aside thick, tangled willows taller than your head.... You carefully choose a safe path along the precarious trail beneath your feet. Suddenly, your left foot drops six inches, and looking down to examine the terrain more closely, you notice that, where you stepped, the tunnel of a burrowing animal collapsed from your weight. Moving on again you feel the whisper of an abandoned spider web touch the side of your face.... Brushing it aside, you notice the slope of the land is steeper...You pause, listening... listening. You can hear the high drone of insects.... It has come upon you so gradually, you are surprised that you didn't hear it before.... Now it seems almost frighteningly loud.

"And beneath the buzzing drone, but lower in pitch and volume, is the sound of water gently spilling over rocks. Above the place where the water must be, you see thousands of tiny spots milling before your eyes, the creators of that high buzzing sound.... The spots are hundreds of swarming insects in a cloud too thick to picture.... A dragonfly flashes by with its iridescent pinks and greens, darting here, pausing, darting there, pausing, snatching dozens of the dots, relishing a meal in an unending insect buffet. You step aside, ducking beneath the swarming insects.... You smile as your eyes come to rest on the splashing waters of the stream a few feet below. As you proceed, you use your arms to open a space to walk between the graceful tan

*continued*

and green willows that bounce back undisturbed in your wake. As your eyes comb the scene for a place to rest, you notice a hip-high rock ahead of you—gray, warm, and not yet water-smoothed…. You pause before reaching the rock and bend toward the water, gathering a handful of pebbles from the stream bed. One leg anchors itself on the ground between two willows while the other reaches over the water. With the pebbles in your hand, you swing up onto the dry perch of the rock. You settle down and look at the still wet pebbles…. gray, pink, tan, and cool in your warm hand. After you examine them carefully, you toss the stones one at a time into the stream, listening to the pleasing plop of stone on water. Then your eyes drift downward to the waters of the stream near the base of your rock…. In an eddy you see a fish, hidden like an illusion in the stone and silt, waiting, waiting, unblinking and still, only the faint wave of a gill, a tail fin, showing any evidence of life at all.

"As you continue to look downstream you notice all kinds of small insects are now dancing across and above the water…. A small ripple occurs in the water, then another and another…. You realize that fish are rising from below and feeding on the surface insects…. Birds dart in and out of the tangle of vegetation…. Some fly through. Downstream a frog begins to croak…. Much nearer, another frog offers a reply. You look around quickly to see if you can find the nearer frog. For a moment, you think you spot it, but then you realize that, unless it sings again, you may never find it. Your eyes search for a moment as more frogs telegraph their messages back and forth. But then it seems time to leave…. You take one last sweeping look all around this beautiful setting…. You slowly get up from your rock along the streamside and head back home."

3. Ask the students to continue to sit quietly with their eyes closed and to review the whole experience. Have them pay particular attention to their favorite images. Tell them they will be asked to describe this setting as they saw it. Invite them to open their eyes.

4. Ask students to describe their favorite images. Once each student has done this,

invite all students to select art materials. Each student should draw or paint his or her favorite images on the paper provided. Once they are finished, have the students tape up their artwork on a display area.

5. Ask the students to identify some characteristics of riparian areas. What kinds of plants did they see? What kinds of animals? Was the environment different near the water than from farther away? If yes, what were some similarities and some differences? Ask the students to list, describe, and discuss some of the many reasons that riparian areas are important and have intrinsic value, as well as value to wildlife and humans.

## Extensions

1. Visit a riparian habitat. Look for things that you encountered in your visualization. List things there that you did not picture in your mind.

2. Develop a list of ways that would make it possible for people to visit a riparian area without damaging it.

3. Put your descriptions in writing. Combine words and pictures to convey some of the diversity in riparian areas.

4. Is a different word used in your region to describe those kinds of areas? If not riparian zone, what are they called?

## Evaluation

1. What is a riparian zone?

2. Identify four animals found in a riparian zone.

3. Why are riparian zones important to wildlife? To humans? Why are riparian zones intrinsically valuable? Write a poem to explain your response.

4. Describe your position on a plan to develop a riparian habitat for recreational use by hikers, birdwatchers, and other "low-impact" users. Consider a parking area, restrooms, walkways, garbage removal, and other needs.

# How Wet Is Our Planet?

## Objectives

Students will (1) describe the amount and distribution of water on the Earth in oceans, rivers, lakes, ground water, icecaps, and the atmosphere; and (2) make inferences about the importance of responsible water use.

## Method

Students calculate water volumes using percentages.

## Materials

Large display map of the world, 12-inch diameter globe (preferably one showing the ocean bottom), 5- or 10-gallon aquarium (or a 5- or 10-gallon bucket, trash can or other container), writing materials, calculators, 16-ounce plastic container, plastic cup (smaller than 16 ounces), tablespoon-measuring spoon, standard eyedropper (1 per 3 students)

---

**Grade Level:** 5–8

**Subject Areas:** Mathematics, Environmental Education, Social Studies

**Duration:** one 40- to 60-minute session

**Group Size:** any, individual and small group work

**Setting:** indoors

**Conceptual Framework Topic Reference:** AAIIA2

**Key Terms:** water cycle, fresh water, salt water, ground water, Earth, planet

**Appendices:** Ecosystems, Metric Conversion

---

## Background

The Earth has been called the water planet. Between two-thirds and three-fourths of its surface is water. The Earth's water can be seen in flowing rivers, ponds, lakes and oceans, locked in the northern and southern icecaps, and drifting through the air as clouds. Water that has seeped into the Earth's crust (ground water) is more difficult to see, yet all forms of water are part of the dynamic interrelated flow of the water cycle.

Water is continually moving around, through, and above the Earth as water vapor, liquid, and ice. The same water is continually being recycled all around the Earth.

Students tend to think of the water on the planet as being limitless, and yet simple calculations demonstrate the fact that the amount of water is limited. Scientists believe that all the water that we will ever have is on the Earth right now. Whatever amount is available to humans and wildlife depends largely on how its quality is maintained. Human beings have a responsibility to conserve water, use it wisely, and protect its quality.

## Procedure

NOTE: Refer to the table in the Variation section to adjust this activity for metric approximations.

1. Using a map of the Earth, begin a discussion of the amount of water that covers the Earth. Ask students why Earth is called "the water planet." Call their attention to the statistic that between two-thirds and three-fourths of the Earth's surface is covered with water. Following the discussion, provide students with these statistics:

*continued*

## Water on Earth

| Source | Percentage of Total Water (%) |
|---|---|
| Oceans | 96.5400 |
| Ground water | |
|    Saline/brackish ground water | 0.9300 |
|    Fresh ground water | 0.7600 |
| Surface water | |
|    Glacier/icecaps | 1.7400 |
|    Freshwater lakes | 0.0070 |
|    Saltwater lakes | 0.0060 |
|    Rivers | 0.0002 |
| Other | |
|    Ground ice, permafrost | 0.0220 |
|    Atmospheric water vapor | 0.0010 |
|    Marshes, wetlands | |
|       (mix of fresh and saline) | 0.0010 |
|    Soil moisture | 0.0010 |
|    Incorporated in organisms | 0.0001 |
| Total | 100.0000 |

NOTE: Total may not add up to 100 due to rounding

Source: Shiklomanov, I.A. 1993. "World Fresh Water Resources." In P.H. Gleick (ed.), Water in Crisis: A Guide to the World's Fresh Water Resources. Oxford University Press, New York.

2. Discuss the relative percentages. Ask students to calculate the estimated amounts of fresh water potentially available for human use:

### Fresh Water Amounts Potentially Available for Human Use

| Source | Percentage of Total Water (%) |
|---|---|
| Glaciers/icecaps | 1.7400 |
| Fresh ground water | 0.7600 |
| Freshwater lakes | 0.0070 |
| Rivers | 0.0002 |
| Total | 2.5072 |

3. In discussing these figures, emphasize that pollution and contamination reduce the useable percentage of existing fresh water. Also, all ground water is not available, and icecaps certainly are not readily available. Discuss our need for useable fresh water. Ask students to

consider what other life forms need both fresh and saline (salt) water.

4. Show students 5 gallons of water in the 5- or 10-gallon aquarium (or, a 5- or 10-gallon bucket, trash can, or other container). Provide them with the following equation: 5 gal = 1,280 Tablespoons (Tbs.).

5. Have students assume that these 5 gallons represent all of the water on Earth. Calculate, either as a class or individually, the volume of the other quantities provided on the table "Water on Earth." This step will require the use of decimals. Remind students that for multiplying percentages, the decimal must be shifted two places to the left prior to multiplying, so that 96.54 percent becomes 0.9654 (e.g., $0.9654 \times 1280$ Tbs. = 1235.71 Tbs.). The following amounts result:

### 5 Gallons (1280 Tablespoons)

| Source | Tablespoons (Tbs.) |
|---|---|
| Oceans | 1,235.7100 |
| Ground water | |
|    Saline/brackish ground water | 11.9040 |
|    Fresh ground water | 9.7280 |
| Surface water | |
|    Glaciers/icecaps | 22.2720 |
|    Freshwater lakes | 0.0896 |
|    Saltwater lakes | 0.0768 |
|    Rivers | 0.0026 |
| Other | |
|    Ground ice/permafrost | 0.2816 |
|    Atmospheric water vapor | 0.0128 |
|    Marshes, wetlands | |
|       (mix of fresh and saline) | 0.0128 |
|    Soil moisture | 0.0128 |
|    Incorporated in organisms | 0.0013 |
| Total | Approx. 1,280 |

NOTE: Total may not add to 1,280 due to rounding.

6. Once the values are obtained, ask students to calculate the volume of water, other than oceanwater and saltwater sources (approximately 32 Tbs.). Have students, working in teams of three, put 32 Tbs. of water in the 16-ounce container. This freshwater portion rep-

resents only about 2.5 percent of all the water on Earth! [See Table on "Fresh Water Amounts Potentially Available for Human Use] And, most is locked up in glaciers and icecaps covering Antarctica and Greenland, or is in deep groundwater aquifers.

7. Next, from the 32 Tbs. have students remove all accessible freshwater sources (fresh ground water, rivers and lakes—approximately 10 Tbs.), and place the amount in the smaller container.

8. Since most of the fresh ground water is located in deep aquifers and not readily available, ask students to remove from the small container the amount of water representing all freshwater lakes and rivers (0.0922 Tbs-approximately one-tenth of a tablespoon or 25 drops from a standard dropper.) Have them place this amount into the tablespoon-measuring spoon. Next, ask students to extract the amount representing rivers (two-thousandths of a tablespoon—less than a drop). Discuss the relative proportions with students. Then ask the students to extract the amount represented by rivers alone (about 2 one-thousandths of a tablespoon, or less than a drop). Discuss the relative proportions with the students.

9. Consider the fragile nature of the fresh water, wetlands and oceans of our planet. Discuss how all species depend upon this small percentage of water for their survival. Summarize the activity by using a globe to illustrate that if Earth were 12 inches in diameter, less than one-half cup (eight tablespoons) of water would fill all the oceans, rivers, lakes, and icecaps. And, of all the water on Earth, only 0.01% (one one-hundredth of one percent) is useable by humans!

## Variation

Do this activity using the metric system. If you use the conversion factor of 1 gallon = 3.8 liters, then all water on Earth represented earlier by 5 gallons would be equivalent to 19 liters, or 19,000 milliliters.

### 19 Liters (19,000 Milliliters)

| Source | Milliliters |
| --- | --- |
| Oceans | 18,342.600 |
| Ground water | |
|     Saline/brackish ground water | 176.700 |
|     Fresh ground water | 144.400 |
| Surface water | |
|     Glaciers/icecaps | 330.600 |
|     Freshwater lakes | 1.330 |
|     Saltwater lakes | 1.140 |
|     Rivers | 0.038 |
| Other | |
|     Ground ice/permafrost | 4.180 |
|     Atmospheric water vapor | 0.190 |
|     Marshes, wetlands | |
|       (mix of fresh and saline) | 0.190 |
|     Soil moisture | 0.190 |
|     Incorporated in organisms | 0.019 |
| Total | Approx. 19,000 |

## Extensions

1. Create a mural of the water cycle that graphically includes the statistics that represent the relative amount of water in each component of the cycle.

2. Calculate how much pollution is entering our waterways each year.

3. Calculate the size of a model of Earth that would accommodate all the water in the aquarium used in the demonstration.

4. Which wildlife habitats require the most water?

## Evaluation

1. Estimate the percentage of water that is distributed in each of the following areas of our planet: oceans, rivers, freshwater lakes, inland seas and saltwater lakes, ground water, icecaps and glaciers, and the atmosphere.

2. Explain why it is important that humans use water responsibly.

## Additional Resources

http://ga.water.usgs.gov/edu/

# Facts and Falsehoods

## Objectives

Students will (1) develop criteria for evaluating the quality, balance, and fairness of a presentation; and (2) evaluate the balance and fairness of presentations designed to represent specific points of view about an environmental topic.

## Method

Students analyze and evaluate print material according to criteria they establish for quality, balance, and fairness; as an option, they can then develop their own presentations using the same criteria.

## Materials

A collection of sample print informational brochures and publications concerning aquatic environments; sample advertisements and articles from popular tabloid publications; art materials, markers, poster paper; display boards, a display area; OPTIONAL: video or still cameras, darkroom facilities

**Grade Level:** 9–12

**Subject Areas:** Language Arts, Environmental Education

**Duration:** two or three 45-minute sessions

**Group Size:** any; part of activity has students working in small groups

**Setting:** indoors

**Conceptual Framework Topic Reference:** AAIIA1

**Key Terms:** balance, fairness, criteria, objectivity, subjectivity, bias, propaganda, accuracy

**Appendices:** Using Local Resources, List of Agencies and Organizations

## Background

People have many different points of view, particularly concerning issues they feel passionate about. At times it is difficult to discern fact from falsehood, objectivity from subjectivity, and accuracy from exaggeration. Sometimes people are knowingly selective in what information they present about a topic. Other times they do not realize that they are presenting only a narrow view of the topic.

Issues and concerns are subject to an individual's personal filters and perspective. Objectivity is one goal of science. Even in the precise world of scientific measurement, pure objectivity without some influence on the part of the observer may be beyond reach. So objectivity is a goal that is difficult, if not impossible, to achieve in a pure and technical sense.

If objectivity is so difficult to achieve, how do students develop the skills of objectivity? One technique is to become more discerning about balance and fairness. When a speaker is presenting information on a topic, particularly a controversial topic, ask if that person is making an effort to describe the topic as a whole. Or is the speaker selectively describing only his or her view? Does the speaker acknowledge that there are any other differing points of view? Is the speaker presenting accurate information or only opinion expressed as if it were factually based? These are some of the questions this activity is designed to address.

Information about the environment is provided in settings as varied as classrooms, national parks, government offices, reactor sites, industrial complexes, and wilderness preserves. Some information is provided through printed materials. In other cases, the information is provided through a presentation, possibly using many media and involving audience participation. Prepared lectures, exhibits, and handouts contain ecological, recreational, scientific, and historical information.

The main purpose of the organizations that prepare such materials and presentations is to inform the public. Part of the effort to inform may also focus on justifying the protection or development of a particular site. The result may be a mixture of information, entertainment, and subtle justifications of policy offered in a palatable form. Sometimes the exhibits, programs, and materials offered, even those under the administration of public agencies, become fairly one-sided and possibly even closed about other options or viewpoints. This approach may not be intentional, but the effect may be more to influence than to inform or educate.

In some situations, the lack of complete information may be intentional. At other times, the limitations are a reflection of emerging and conflicting perspectives about what is accurate concerning the topic. Science itself is not free from controversy. Physicists argue about whether light is a wave or a particle. Biologists debate whether wolves should be reintroduced to their former habitats, or whether Inuits should be allowed to kill bowhead whales. Aquatic biologists are on both sides of the fence regarding the introduction of exotic fish species; controversy exists about such fish introduced to North American waters from other parts of the world. Those who sponsor the construction of dams, canals, aqueducts, and locks, as well as those who propose large-scale diking and dredging projects, must wrestle with the impact that such projects may have on the aquatic habitat and its life forms.

## Procedure

*Before the Activity*

Assemble a file of sample informational brochures from various public or private agencies and organizations. The brochures may cover a range of topics. Make sure some address aquatic topics or issues. Examples might include acid rain, water pollution, conservation, sewage treatment, and hydroelectric power. Articles concerning water issues—including water quality, the development of aquatic resources, and water use—from local news media would also be of potential use.

Obtain several issues of popular, sensational, tabloid publications of the type widely available at the checkout counters of convenience stores and supermarkets. These publications will be used as a tool to evaluate balanced, fair, and accurate information. Articles, feature stories, and advertisements that deal with science, health, the environment, new products, or new inventions and discoveries are most suited to this activity. Next, prepare a list of questions similar to the ones given below. (Add others suited to the setting.)

- Does the article or advertisement cite or list facts? What are they?

- Does the item make a claim? Is the claim based on or supported by facts or by some sort of evidence? Describe the claims and the supporting facts and evidence.

- Does the item or article base its claim or story in some part on science or technology? Is a scientific law or principle used to support the claims? If so, what are they? Is a scientist or engineer cited as an authority? Who is he or she, and how is his or her expertise established? Which fields of science or engineering are used?

- Is there any indication that the writer of the article stands behind its accuracy or validity? Will the publishers or editors support the claims? Will the advertisers back up their products?

*continued*

- How could you go about checking or verifying the claims and facts in the article?

- What is your overall assessment of the accuracy of the article or advertisement? Exceptionally accurate? Generally accurate? Somewhat accurate? Generally inaccurate? Exceptionally inaccurate?

1. Divide the class into pairs or groups. Give each group an article from the tabloid and the list of questions. Ask the students to review the article or item and to answer the questions on the sheet. Encourage the students to develop any other questions that they think might be useful. Discuss the students' results. What do they think about the overall quality of the articles? Do they believe the article? Would they buy the advertised products? Why or why not?

2. Next, distribute the samples of informational brochures, handouts, or pamphlets that were collected and are related to aquatic and other environmental topics. Provide at least one brochure to each of the teams. Ask the students to analyze and evaluate these materials in the same way they did the tabloid items. Provide the students with another copy of the list of questions. Again, encourage them to add questions of their own. In addition, ask the students to consider the following:

   - Did the publication acknowledge different points of view or opinions about the topic; where did these views exist?

   - Was information or facts selected to support a view or develop a perspective? Did the material try to persuade the reader in some way, or was the reader invited to make up his or her own mind? What evidence can the students find to support their viewpoints?

3. Ask each group to report on its findings. Groups can summarize their findings by giving the brochure an overall rating—using the five categories from "exceptionally accurate" to "exceptionally inaccurate." Ask them to support their evaluations with some evidence and reasons for their views.

4. Now have the students work as a single group to develop a checklist that they can use to evaluate informational materials, exhibits, or presentations; name it Checklist for Quality, Balance, and Fairness in Informational Presentations. What, in their view, should be the characteristics of an informational presentation of quality? Of balance? Of fairness?

5. After the checklist has been drafted, open the discussion to a few more questions. For example, ask the students whether it is possible to be forceful and effective in expressing one's view without becoming unfair or biased. Is it possible to separate one's own viewpoint from a publicly neutral position? To what extent do government agencies, citizens' groups, businesses, interest groups and individual citizens have a responsibility to acknowledge other points of view concerning their policies and practices? After discussion, see if the students want to make any additional changes, to the checklist. Make those recommended changes, and post the final checklist. Provide each student with a copy of the final checklist for personal use.

OPTIONAL: Prepare a set of assignments in which groups of students are to act as the designers and developers of an informational brochure or program. Have the students draw assignments at random. Each group will prepare an informational presentation having two components:

- a verbal presentation (10 minutes maximum)

- a print brochure

In each case, the remainder of the class will apply the criteria from the Checklist for Quality to the presentations. Following each presentation, the other class members will suggest improvements and changes to enhance the quality.

## Extensions

1. Visit a site where environmental information is provided to the public. Using the established criteria, evaluate whether the programs, exhibits, and printed materials appear to be balanced and fair.

2. Choose an aquatic wildlife issue in the students' community. Write an article for a newspaper or develop a presentation to make in informal educational settings (garden club, Kiwanis, Chamber of Commerce, etc.). Make sure your article or presentation reflects your standards for quality, balance, and fairness.

3. What could the students do to enhance the public's understanding of aquatic wildlife and habitats without using propaganda?

## Evaluation

1. Select one of the following topics and describe the types of information that could be included in an informational presentation designed for students: recreation area, sewage treatment plant, whaling museum.

2. Why is it, or is it not, important for informational presentations to be accurate, balanced, fair, and of good quality?

3. The Big City Dam Visitor Center has two informational displays. One display explains how water is taken from the basin and used for irrigation for agriculture and for city water supplies. The second shows property damage from floods before the dam was constructed. What other information, if any, could be provided for visitors?

# Plastic Jellyfish

## Objectives

Students will (1) describe the potential effects of plastic waste on aquatic wildlife and habitat, and (2) identify specific actions they can take to help remedy the problem.

## Method

Students monitor the plastic waste production in their own households, research the effects of plastic waste on fresh water and marine life and propose various ways to lessen the problem.

## Materials

Plastic waste from home; a shallow tray or box (2 to 3 ft² in area) for each pair of students; soil (enough to cover the bottoms of all of the trays); re-sealable plastic sandwich bags, one for each pair of students; 1 tablespoon of tiny (1–5 mm diameter) multicolored beads for each pair of students (be sure that many are clear) placed in sandwich bags; clock; paper towels

Grade Level: K–4

Subject Areas: Environmental Education, Social Studies, Mathematics, Science

Duration: one 20- to 60-minute session or longer

Group Size: any

Setting: outdoors and indoors

Conceptual Framework Topic Reference: HIIA, HIIIA3a, HIIIA3b, HIIIB5

Key Terms: pollution, litter, plastic, biodegradable

Appendices: none

## Background

The United States disposes of more than 200 million tons of trash each year, and the amount continues to increase. Thanks to better resource conservation, source reduction, and efficiency, communities are disposing of less waste than they did 10 years ago. Despite this fact, certain waste materials continue to affect wildlife. One area of concern involves plastics. Of the total amount of waste disposed per year, plastics contribute only 9.4 percent by weight, or about 18.8 million tons. The issue surrounding plastic materials is that they do not decompose, and aquatic animals can mistake some plastics for food.

According to a 1997 report by the Marine Mammal Commission, entanglement and ingestion incidents have been reported for at least 267 animal species, including marine mammals, seabirds and sea turtles, several of which are listed as threatened, endangered or depleted. Leather-back turtles often mistake plastic bags or balloons floating in the sea for jellyfish, one of their favorite foods. As plastics accumulate in the intestines of such animals, starvation occurs slowly.

Plastic litter is not only a problem in ocean environments. Plastic holders for beverage cans, baling twine, plastic bags, and discarded fishing lines found in fresh water (e.g., ponds, lakes, and rivers) and on land also threaten wildlife.

One of the newer concerns about plastic materials are resin pellets, the raw materials that are melted and molded to create plastic products. Resin pellets may be formed into various shapes (e.g., spherical, ovoid, cylindrical); sizes (range: 1- to 5-mm diameter); and colors (most commonly clear, white, or off-white). An estimated 60 billion pounds of resin, most of which is formed into pellets, are manufactured annually in the United States. The most commonly produced resins include polyethylene, polypropylene, and polystyrene.

After being formed, the resin pellets are packaged and transported to processors for molding into plastic products. At many points in their creation, transportation, and use, the pellets may be spilled and carried by rain water and drainage systems into the aquatic environment. More recently, studies of aquatic debris conducted by the U.S. Environmental Protection Agency (EPA) revealed that pellets were among the most common items found in many harbors—13 out of 14 harbors sampled. Pellets make up half of man-made debris in storm water discharge, and 20,000 pellets can pass through some municipal waste water treatment plants each day.

Several documented accounts describe pellet and other plastic ingestion by wildlife, most notably by seabirds and sea turtles. However, the impacts or biological effects of the pellets have not been clearly defined or demonstrated conclusively in most wildlife. Seabirds ingest pellets more frequently than any other animal, and approximately one-quarter of all seabird species are known to ingest pellets. Pellets ingested by seabirds are suspected to cause false feelings of satiation (i.e., the birds feel as though they have eaten) and reduce the feelings of hunger. Ultimately, the loss of nutrients may result in a decrease in energy reserves and the ability to survive adverse environmental conditions. Suspected impacts on sea turtles, fish, and other aquatic life have been less frequently reported and studied.

Strategies to reduce the problem involve ways to prevent release of the pellets into the environment and ways to recapture them, including better employee education on handling procedures, better packaging, and more effective spill containment and cleanup. Regulations have been developed to specify compliance criteria. Many companies within the industry are already voluntarily implementing these EPA recommendations.

## Procedure

1. Ask the students to collect and save every piece of plastic waste produced in their homes for a 2-day period. Instruct the students to clean the items so they are free of leftover food or drink. Instruct the students to ask an adult to help them clean out containers that held household cleaners such as ammonia, chlorine bleach, and such. These containers should be emptied and rinsed completely. Either ask the students to bring these materials from home or have a sample of them available for this activity.

2. Ask the students to separate the plastic containers into categories. Have students classify them in terms of how the materials might affect aquatic animals if they were not disposed of properly and ended up in an aquatic environment. That is, might the items be perceived as food? Might an animal become entangled in an item? Which ones are likely to cause a problem for wildlife and which are less likely to cause a problem?

3. Explain to the class how plastics are produced as pellets that are transported to the manufacturers who create these plastic items. Sometimes the pellets are spilled and washed into aquatic environments. Because they are small and often colorless, they are difficult to recover. Ask the students to suggest ways this item might affect habitats and wildlife. Which animals do they think might be most affected?

4. Show the students the beads, and explain that plastic pellets are similar in size and color to the beads. Divide the class into pairs, and give each pair a sandwich bag containing a heaping tablespoon of beads and a tray of soil. Ask the students to sort the beads by color on a paper towel, label the color of each pile created, and count the number of each color. Have the students record the number for each color on the paper towel beside the corresponding pile of beads. Also record these amounts on a class data chart displayed on the board, flip chart or, overhead transparency (see example on page 131).

*continued*

5. Direct each pair of students to sprinkle the beads evenly over the soil in the tray. When all beads are in the soil, tell the students to jiggle their tray vigorously for 30 seconds. Emphasize that they must not lift the tray, but keep the tray on the table.

6. Next, ask the students to try to find all of the beads. Allow the students to look for 3 minutes precisely, placing the beads back on the paper towel in the original labeled piles. Time the students. When the time is up, have the students count the colors. Record these numbers on the paper towel and on the class data chart. Have students total the numbers of each color of bead.

NOTE: Older students may also be able to create a bar graph of these results. Have them list the colors along the bottom of the graph (X axis) and the number of beads up the left side (Y axis). Make two bars for each color: the original number of beads and the number of recovered beads.

7. Discuss the students' findings. Did they recover all of the beads? If not, why not? Which colors were the most difficult to recover? Why?

8. Tell the class that most of the pellets that are produced are clear. How could the characteristics of the pellets contribute to their being picked up by birds? How do the characteristics of the pellets contribute to difficulties in recovering spilled pellets?

9. Have the class brainstorm actions the plastics industry might be able to take to minimize loose pellets in the environment. Do students think it would be easier for them to recover spilled pellets or prevent the spill in the first place? Why? What actions could government take? Have the students brainstorm ways they might help reduce all types of plastic waste in the environment.

10. Make sure that the students wash their hands after working in the soil. Soil that still might contain beads should not be disposed outdoors where it may wash into streams or other bodies of water. Place the soil in trash bags and dispose. While the students are cleaning up, ask them to name any plastic products they used in this activity that help keep waste out of aquatic environments if they are correctly disposed of (the plastic sandwich bags and the trash bags).

## Extensions

1. Have the students investigate the difficulty of recovering beads from different media such as water, sand, and different shades of soil. Allow two or three teams to investigate each media type. Compare the results.

2. Invite the students to survey their school grounds or community for plastic litter. Look to see if and where it exists. Investigate its potential negative effect on animals in the community. If there is damaging plastic litter in the community, ask the students to create an action plan that will increase public awareness of the problem and help take care of it (e.g., setting up a plastic recycling depot). Help the students put the plan into effect!

3. Establish a litter patrol. Designate specific targets such as nearby beaches, lakes, and streambeds. Establish scheduled tours of these areas to pick up plastic and other forms of litter.

4. Write a plastic-consumption conservation plan. Is plastic recycled in your home or community? If so, how? If it seems appropriate, see if you can break some of your own plastic habits. Consider whether your own uses of plastics could be potentially damaging to wildlife and wasteful of natural resources. What courses of action might you personally take?

5. Take various types of plastic and put the items outdoors where they will not be disturbed for 1 month. Set up an observation schedule and a means of recording the date and the changes you observe in the plastic samples. What conclusions can you draw from your observations?

6. Research the latest technology for making plastic biodegradable. What progress is being made in this innovation?

7. Research any laws in your city, county, or state that attempt to address the problem of plastic pollution. What is the Marpol Treaty? Are there any bills before the state legislature? Before the U.S. Congress?

## Evaluation

1. Give three examples of ways that plastics could enter an aquatic food chain.

2. Describe the effects of plastic waste on aquatic animals.

3. List two things you can do to prevent harm to wildlife from plastic litter.

4. What are two ways that governments or industries can reduce the number of plastic pellets that enter aquatic environments?

## Additional Resources

www.csc.noaa.gov/

oceanlink.island.net/

www.epa.gov/ow/kids.html

www.oceanconservancy.org/nmdmp

www.vims.edu

## Sample Class Chart

### Teams

| Color | 1 | 2 | 3 | 4 | 5 | 6 | 7 | 8 | 9 | 10 | Totals |
|---|---|---|---|---|---|---|---|---|---|---|---|
| **Red** | | | | | | | | | | | |
| Starting number | | | | | | | | | | | |
| Recovered number | | | | | | | | | | | |
| **Blue** | | | | | | | | | | | |
| Starting number | | | | | | | | | | | |
| Recovered number | | | | | | | | | | | |
| **Clear** | | | | | | | | | | | |
| Starting number | | | | | | | | | | | |
| Recovered number | | | | | | | | | | | |
| **Green** | | | | | | | | | | | |
| Starting number | | | | | | | | | | | |
| Recovered number | | | | | | | | | | | |
| **Purple** | | | | | | | | | | | |
| Starting number | | | | | | | | | | | |
| Recovered number | | | | | | | | | | | |
| **Yellow** | | | | | | | | | | | |
| Starting number | | | | | | | | | | | |
| Recovered number | | | | | | | | | | | |

# Watershed

## Objectives

Students will (1) describe the characteristics of watersheds, (2) discuss the role of watersheds in providing wildlife habitat as well as human habitat, and (3) give examples of watershed conservation.

## Method

Students measure the area of a local watershed, calculate the amount of water it receives each year, and discuss the varied roles the watershed plays in human and wildlife habitat.

## Materials

Six stakes or markers, hammer; two 50-foot (15-meter) measuring tapes, two 100-foot (30-meter) measuring tapes, writing materials, clipboards, large pad of paper for display, local maps showing bodies of water

---

**Grade Level:** 5–8

**Subject Areas:** Environmental Education, Mathematics

**Duration:** one or more 30- to 60-minute sessions

**Group Size:** small groups of three to five students each

**Setting:** outdoors and indoors

**Conceptual Framework Topic Reference:** HIIIB3

**Key Terms:** runoff, precipitation, watershed, erosion

**Appendices:** Using Local Resources, Outdoors

---

NOTE: Twine or heavy string can be marked at intervals and used instead of measuring tapes.

## Background

A watershed is an area of land that allows water to flow over or under its surface into a particular body of water. The boundaries of a watershed are determined by the guiding contours of the land surrounding that stream, river, lake, or bay. Because precipitation and its runoff must flow somewhere, all land areas are a part of some watershed. Every home, school, office, business, and industry is part of a watershed.

A watershed is more than just a geological feature. It is a hydrologic system linking all living things within its boundaries. Not only does all plant and animal life depend on the water within each watershed, but also the watercourses are conduits that transport water, organisms, nutrients, and other materials within the system. What affects one watershed eventually affects other sites downstream.

One material moving through the watershed is soil. Because the rivers of a watershed are constantly engaged in the gradual erosion of the highlands that contain it, suspended sediments are part of the natural dynamics. However, human activities can accelerate this process through actions such as land clearing, dam building, farming, and industrial development. Runoff carries the loose soil into the water system, which may affect watershed quality. Significantly increased turbidity can interfere with sunlight transmission, fish respiration, and plant photosynthesis.

Of particular concern are contaminants in the water. Contaminants may be excessive nutrients that overload natural systems, or they may be harmful chemicals introduced into the water.

Both of these problems are often related to agricultural and industrial activities that result in the release of water back into the watershed that has been altered by their use. Fertilizers and pesticides are the major sources of agricultural contamination. Industrial wastewater can contain myriad contaminants from oil to heavy metals.

Contamination of watersheds is a serious problem for humans, but it is as great or greater a problem for wildlife. Most often it is the wildlife—particularly the aquatic wildlife—that suffers the most directly and immediately from contaminated water. Slight changes in pH (acidity) can destroy the natural balance in a body of water. Natural food chains can be damaged for decades by a single contamination.

Water contamination, like water, does not just remain on the surface. As part of the water cycle, watersheds both feed and are fed by ground water. Surface contamination can penetrate into the earth and contaminate water supplies. On a watershed's surface, water can move so rapidly it is often expressed in cubic feet (cubic meters) per second. Below the ground's surface, its movement might be expressed in inches (centimeters) per year. Contaminated ground water can negatively affect a watershed's quality for centuries. Most scientists feel that it is far more economical to prevent contaminants from entering water systems than to clean up pollution after it takes place.

Another human activity that affects watershed systems is the diversion of water from the natural flow of streams, ponds, rivers, and lakes. The growth of human populations in a watershed may result in greater and greater diversion. For example, the need for water and hydroelectric power often motivates the building of dams. Dams may radically alter stream habitat, yet they do provide predictable water supplies for agriculture, domestic uses, and industry. There are obvious benefits and liabilities to consider when making decisions affecting watersheds.

Because watersheds are natural units, they represent a logical basis for managing resources.

Traditionally, water quality improvements have focused on specific sources of pollution, such as sewage discharges, or on specific water resources, such as a river segment or wetland. While this approach may be successful in addressing specific problems, it often fails to address some subtle and chronic problems that might contribute to a watershed's decline. For example, pollution from a sewage treatment plant might be significantly reduced after new technology is installed. Yet the local river may still suffer if other factors in the watershed, such as habitat destruction or other sources of polluted runoff, are not also addressed. Managing the watershed unit as an integrated system provides a stronger foundation for uncovering issues that affect it, and it better equips resource managers to determine what actions are needed to protect and restore it.

## Procedure

*Before the Activity*

Select an outdoor site approximately 100 feet (30 meters) square that resembles a small watershed. If possible, there should be a visible drainage pattern. Look around the school or in a nearby park for a site that will suffice. There needs to be enough relief so the students will be able to visualize the watershed concept. OPTIONAL: Research the annual rainfall amounts for your area. Your State climatologist can be found online at **www.ncdc.noaa.gov/oa/climate/aasc.htm**

1.  Using local maps and local stream systems as examples, discuss the concept of a watershed. Topographical maps or raised-relief maps are valuable tools. Emphasize that the size of watersheds varies, from tiny tributaries to river systems as large as the Mississippi. Introduce the concept that a ridgeline is the border between two designated watersheds. Using local maps, show how the boundaries of a watershed can be determined by tracing the ridgelines between adjacent watersheds. To demonstrate this point, use a transparent overlay on a standard paper map, or use water-soluble marking pens on a plastic raised-relief map.

*continued*

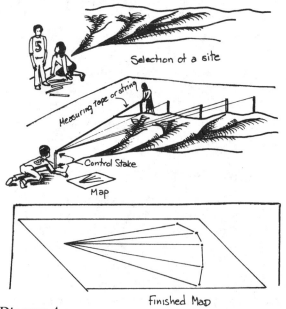

Selection of a site

Measuring tape or string

Control Stake

Map

Finished Map

*Diagram A*

2. Explain to the students that they will be going to a small watershed and will be measuring its area in much the same way large watersheds are measured. Show them the equipment that you will be taking along, and explain how five of the stakes will be used to mark the top of the ridgeline of the watershed. Indicate the "control" stake that will represent the bottom of the drainage system. Educators may choose to read the rest of the procedure and illustrate the process of measuring a watershed on the chalkboard before going to the site, or they may use a large pad and markers to review the procedures visually at the site.

3. Upon reaching the site, divide the students into teams of three to five. Determine the ridgeline of the watershed, and drive the stakes or markers along the upper boundary of their watershed. The ridge stakes should be 20 to 40 feet (6 to 12 meters) apart.

4. As a group, have the students determine the location of the control stake at the "bottom" of the watershed. The control stake is the one from which measurements to the other stakes are made. The control stake should be 60 to 100 feet (18 to 30 meters) from the ridge stakes.

5. Begin the measurements that will result in a map of the watershed. Each team should draw a map of this miniature watershed. Ask the students to record their results to scale on a large piece of paper (use about $1/4$ or $1/8$ inch [1 cm] on the map for each foot [meter] on the ground), as shown in Diagram A. The scale will depend on the size of the paper.

6. Have each team determine the area of the watershed, following these procedures (see Diagrams B and C):

• Turn each triangle segment into a rectangle, and then determine the area by multiplying length times width.

> L × W = Area of a rectangle
> (in square feet or square meters)

• Then divide by 2 because the area of the triangle will be $1/2$ the area of the rectangle.

• Repeat for each triangle.

• Add the areas of all five triangles together to get the area of the watershed (in square feet or meters).

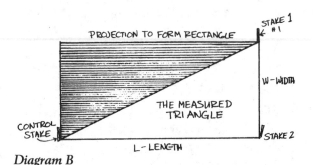

PROJECTION TO FORM RECTANGLE

STAKE 1 #1

W–WIDTH

THE MEASURED TRIANGLE

CONTROL STAKE

STAKE 2

L–LENGTH

*Diagram B*

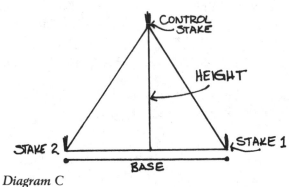

CONTROL STAKE

HEIGHT

STAKE 2

STAKE 1

BASE

*Diagram C*

Educators may want to use the formula for the area of a triangle: Area = ¹/₂ Base × Height

7. As an option, calculate the amount of precipitation that falls on the miniature watershed each year. This is where the value for the annual rainfall is needed. The rainfall value must be expressed in feet (meters) thus:

Rainfall × Area = Volume of Rain

8. Discuss the following questions with students. How does a watershed work? How does it affect humans? How does it affect wildlife? How is ground water affected by conditions in your watershed? What kinds of things can be done to protect, conserve, and improve watershed quality? What are some of the reasons, if any, to protect and conserve watersheds? What are some of the potential tradeoffs involved? When, if ever, might it seem inappropriate to protect and conserve a watershed? OPTIONAL: Explore an actual watershed where the students live. Identify locations of water diversion from natural pathways, determine the use of the diverted water, and describe the condition of the water when it is returned to the natural drainage.

## Extensions

1. Calculate the total area of an actual watershed in your area using county or state maps.

2. Calculate the total water that falls annually on your watershed.

3. Write a paper on the quality of your watershed.

4. Simulate a watershed. Have students stand in a circle with quart (liter) containers of water, and empty the containers on cue toward the center of the circle. Have the students trace the "natural" paths taken by the water, and see if they can trace the watersheds indicated by the diverse flow pattern.

5. Calculate the amount of rain in gallons (liters) that falls on your school or organization grounds each year.

6. Trace the watersheds of the major North American rivers. Use tracing paper or acetate overlays on large scale maps.

7. On a map, locate the habitat of specific life forms in your local watershed.

8. A noted scientist once remarked that "Human activities speed up the flow of water while nature slows it down." Is this true for the watershed in which you live?

## Evaluation

1. Describe and draw a watershed.

2. How are wildlife habitats related to watersheds? Why are watersheds important to people? Write a short essay in response to these questions.

3. Develop a plan on how to protect, conserve, or restore a watershed.

# What's in the Air?

## Objectives

Students will (1) describe acidic precipitation, (2) generate and test hypotheses concerning effects of acidic precipitation, and (3) make inferences about the potential effects of acidic precipitation on aquatic life.

## Method

Through simulations and direct measurement the students experience differing conditions of acidity in aquatic habitats and explore the consequences of acidic conditions on aquatic life.

## Materials

Vinegar, graduated cylinders, pH test kit or probe, six trays of grass seedlings in soil to be grown in the classroom (grass seed may be purchased at a plant nursery or hardware store), assorted containers

---

**Grade Level:** 5–8

**Subject Areas:** Science, Social Studies, Mathematics, Environmental Education

**Duration:** two 20- to 45-minute sessions, plus growing time of one or two weeks for seedlings to show effects of acidic precipitation.

**Group Size:** any

**Setting:** indoors

**Conceptual Framework Topic Reference:** HIIIB1, HIIIB4, HIIIB5

**Key Terms:** acidic precipitation

**Appendices:** Using Local Resources, List of Agencies and Organizations

---

## Background

Rain and other forms of precipitation that are normally slightly acidic can become more acidic because of pollutants in the air. These pollutants, sulfur dioxide and nitrogen oxide, combine with atmospheric water to produce a mild solution of sulfuric acid and nitric acid known as acidic precipitation. Scientists have discovered that air pollution from the burning of fossil fuels is one of the major causes of acidic precipitation. Nitrogen oxide is produced by the exhaust systems of cars, while electrical plants, industries, and smelters that burn coal and other fossil fuels generate sulfur dioxide. Other causes for acidic precipitation include mining, forest fires, lightning, and volcanoes. Acidic precipitation may come in the form of rain, snow, sleet, or fog.

Acid precipitation is thought to be carried long distances by air currents and storm systems. Understanding the movement of storm systems, high and low pressure movements, and fronts can help scientists discover where acid precipitation is coming from and where the precipitation is returning to the ground. By making projections of storm systems and air currents, researchers are also attempting to track where gases, fly ash, soot, and dust particles go.

The effects of acidic precipitation are visible in aquatic habitats. Most lakes and streams have a pH between 6.5 and 8.5 (a measure of the acidity or alkalinity of a solution, numerically equal to 7 for neutral solutions, increasing with increasing alkalinity and decreasing with increasing acidity). The pH scale commonly in use ranges from 0 to 14. However, some lakes are naturally acidic even without the effects of acidic precipitation. Lakes and streams become acidic when the water and its surrounding soil cannot buffer the acidic precipitation enough to neutralize it. In areas such as the northeastern United States, where soil buffering is poor, some lakes become even more acidic. Because of differences in emissions and wind patterns, the levels of acidic deposition are generally lower in the western United States than in the eastern United States.

As lakes and streams become more acidic the numbers and types of fish and other aquatic plants and animals may also decrease. Generally, the young of most species are more sensitive to acidic precipitation than are adults. Frogs may tolerate relatively high levels of acidity, but if certain insects are affected, the frog's food supply may be reduced. At pH 5, most fish eggs cannot hatch; at other levels, some adult fish may die. Conversely, some species of plants and animals are able to tolerate acidic waters. Even so, all organisms within an ecosystem are interdependent, and the loss of acidic-sensitive plants and animals will in time affect all the organisms in the ecosystem.

Scientists believe that acidic waters dissolve the nutrients and helpful minerals in the soil and then wash them away before the plants can use them to grow. At the same time, the acidic precipitation causes the release of other metals such as aluminum, cadmium, and mercury into the soil. Even if the soil is well buffered, modification in plant species can occur from acidic fog and clouds that surround mountains at higher elevations. Tree leaves are frequently bathed in fog or clouds, and the leaves are damaged and cannot produce the food the tree needs to grow.

Two methods are currently used by industries and power plants to reduce the amount of pollutants released into the atmosphere: smoke-stack scrubbers and electrostatic precipitators. Scrubbers are designed to remove various gases from the plant emissions, while electrostatic precipitators are designed to remove the visible soot from emissions. Also, cleaner vehicles are being manufactured that recirculate the automobile exhaust back to the engine to burn extra nitrogen oxide.

*Background Information on the Experiment*

This activity uses vinegar, distilled water, and grass seedlings to simulate the reaction that might occur in nature between acidic precipitation and plants.

Vinegar does not typically get into rain and water supplies, but in this activity it is being used to illustrate how something with similar characteristics—sulfuric acid—can affect plants. Students will use litmus paper to test the acidity of the vinegar and distilled water. Litmus paper is treated with chemicals so that it turns different colors depending on how acidic a liquid is. The measure of acidity is calibrated into a scale called pH. High acidity is designated by a low pH number (1). Conversely, a high pH number (14) means the solution is not very acidic. Vinegar, lemon juice, and sulfuric acid all have high acidity, thus a low pH.

Acids are chemical substances that are called "electrolytes." They furnish hydrogen ions in chemical reactions that create powerful reactions with other substances. There are strong acids and weak acids. Normal rain water is a weak acid. However, rain and other precipitation often come in contact with chemicals from pollution. When precipitation is exposed to these chemicals, it often becomes more acidic.

Using a simple experiment, this activity will aid students in identifying some potential consequences of acidic precipitation.

## Procedure

*Before the Activity*

Establish six trays of 50 to 100 grass seedlings each in a sunlit area of the room. Grass seedlings are used because of their fast growth and because the single blade makes height measurements less arbitrary. Trays should have the same type of soil. Label the trays 0 percent, 1 percent, 5 percent, 10 percent, 25 percent, and 50 percent.

*continued*

1. Begin by pouring a quantity of vinegar onto four or five sheets of paper towel. Place these towels around the class when students are absent. When the students return, note their discomfort with a bit of theatrical drama. Is something wrong? What could be wrong? Solicit their descriptions of what seems to be wrong.

2. Collect the paper towels, and discard them in a self-sealing plastic bag. Inform the students that you wanted them to experience the discomfort of a kind of "pollution" in their environment.

3. When the seedlings are just established, have the students begin to water the plants with the corresponding vinegar solution: 0 percent, 1 percent, 5 percent, 10 percent, 25 percent, and 50 percent. Place the corresponding amount of vinegar in a graduated cylinder and fill the remainder with distilled water. For example, a 5 percent solution would be made by pouring 5 ml of vinegar into a 100-ml graduated cylinder and then adding 95 ml of water. Have the students hypothesize which concentrations the plants will not tolerate. The plants should be watered regularly, and all plant trays should receive the same amount of liquid. If possible, use a spray bottle to spray several trays with the corresponding vinegar solution. What are the outcomes? OPTIONAL: Students should determine the pH for each solution each time they water, and they should record this number. Does the pH stay the same? How does it vary over time? Why? Explain that pH balanced refers to situations in which buffer systems "hold" the pH so it will resist change.

4. Each time the plants are watered, the number of living plants and their heights should be recorded as a reflection of their growth. Average the heights of all the seedlings in the tray. Qualitative observations should also be made on their appearance. Student should design and create the data sheets to record the data.

5. After 2 weeks (or whenever a difference in the plants becomes obvious), graph the average heights for each tray over that period. Allow students to create the graph if possible. The students can do one graph for each type of solution, or they can put all of the findings on one graph using a key to identify the symbols for each type of solution.

6. Why were each of the trays watered the same amount? Why did they all have the same kind and amount of soil? What else was the same for each tray? What might have happened if some of these conditions were different for some trays? What are the advantages of using grass when growth rates are measured? Why were so many plants used? Why were the heights averaged? How does using a large number of plants affect the reliability of the findings?

## Extensions

1. Collect water samples from several sites in the community and test the pH. Research local sources to discover if the pH level has changed in local aquatic habitats in recent years. Sources for this type of information might be water quality control offices or wildlife agencies.

2. Investigate the reported effects of acidic precipitation in the industrial northeast region of the United States. Compare your findings with those of the reported effects in the Rocky Mountain region.

3. Is there a relationship between acidic precipitation concentration and weather systems? If so, what is it?

4. Develop a hypothetical master plan for dealing with acidic precipitation. Is it feasible? Why or why not?

5. Research the ways acidic precipitation could be reduced, how much it could cost to reduce it, and how much it could cost not to reduce its effects.

6. Research the effects of buffering acidic lakes and streams with high pH materials such as lime.

## Evaluation

1. What is acidic precipitation? What are some of the causes of acidic precipitation? What are some of the effects of acidic precipitation? Write at least three paragraphs to respond.

2. Indicate true (T) or false (F) for each of the following statements:

- Acidic precipitation decreases pH.

- Acidic precipitation kills some fish populations.

- Acidic rain increases sulfate in some lakes and streams.

- Acidic precipitation increases alkalinity in rivers and lakes.

- Acidic precipitation causes toxins, like aluminum, to be released into waters.

3. Predict what might happen to each of the following as a result of acidic precipitation: plants, fish, soil, cars, buildings, aquatic insects, aquatic birds and mammals, aquatic habitats, and humans.

## Additional Resources

www.vims.edu/bridge/pollution.html

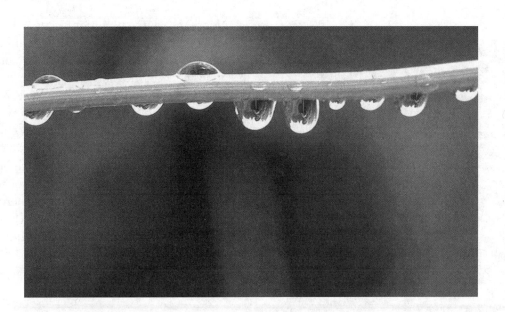

# What's in the Water?

## Objectives

Students will (1) identify major sources of aquatic pollution, and (2) make inferences about the potential effects of a variety of aquatic pollutants on wildlife and wildlife habitats.

## Method

Students analyze the pollutants found in a hypothetical river. They graph the quantities of pollutants and make recommendations about actions that could be taken to improve the habitat.

## Materials

Nine different colors of construction paper (two sheets each), writing or graph paper, Scotch tape or glue, paper punch, Pollutant Information Sheets (one for each student), $^1\!/_4$ tsp measure (for paper punch tokens), 1 Tbsp measure (for $^1\!/_2$ in. square tokens)

---

**Grade Level:** 5–8

**Subject Areas:** Science, Mathematics, Environmental Education

**Duration:** one 30- to 45-minute session or longer

**Group Size:** small groups of three students each

**Setting:** indoors

**Conceptual Framework Topic Reference:** HIIIB1, HIIIB4, HIIIB5

**Key Terms:** pollution, chemical, thermal, organic, ecological, point and nonpoint source pollution, ground water, toxic wastes

**Appendices:** none

---

## Background

Waterways such as rivers, lakes, and estuaries are important to humans and wildlife alike. Waterways are used for drinking water, transportation, recreation, and habitat for many wildlife species. Approximately 40 percent of our nation's rivers, lakes and estuaries are not fishable, swimmable, or potable because of pollution (source: American Rivers). Pollutants enter waterways from either point or nonpoint sources. Point sources are clearly defined, localized inputs such as pipes, industrial plants, sewer systems, and oil spills. Federal and state governments monitor and regulate pollution from point sources. Unfortunately, nonpoint sources are harder to detect and control, so they are, therefore, the major source of water quality problems. Nonpoint sources are indistinct inputs that do not have a clearly defined source, such as runoff of petroleum products from roadways or pesticides from farmlands.

Nonpoint-source pollution occurs when rainfall, snowmelt, or irrigation runs over land or through the ground, picks up pollutants, and deposits them into surface water or introduces them into ground water. Agriculture, forestry, grazing, septic systems, recreational boating, urban runoff, construction, physical change to stream channels, and habitat degradation are all potential sources of nonpoint-source pollution. Agriculture is the leading contributor to water quality impairments, degrading 60 percent of the nation's rivers and lakes. Runoff from urban areas is the largest source of water quality impairments to the nation's estuaries (Source: U.S. Environmental Protection Agency [EPA]).

The most common nonpoint-source pollutants are sediment and nutrients. These pollutants enter waterways from agricultural land, animal-feeding operations, construction sites, and other areas of disturbance. Other common pollutants are pesticides, herbicides, pathogens, oil, toxic chemicals, and heavy metals. Unsafe drinking water, fish kills, destroyed habitat, beach closures, and many other severe environmental and human health problems result from these water pollutants (Source: EPA Office of Water).

Pollution can be categorized into the following types:

- **chemical pollution:** the introduction of toxic substances into an ecosystem (e.g., acidic precipitation, contamination of water supplies by pesticides)

- **thermal pollution:** varying temperatures above or below the normal condition (e.g., power plant turbine heated water)

- **organic pollution:** oversupplying an ecosystem with nutrients (i.e., fertilizer inflow)

- **ecological pollution:** stresses ordinarily created by natural processes, such as

  1. Adding a substance that is not a naturally occurring substance in the ecosystem (e.g., extreme tides pour salt water into habitats ordinarily protected from salt water)

  2. Increasing the amount or intensity of a naturally occurring substance (e.g., abnormal increase in sediments in runoff water to produce silt)

  3. Altering the level or concentration of biological or physical components of an ecosystem (changing the amount of something that is already there) (e.g., introduction of aquatic plants via bird droppings, etc.)

In the definitions above, chemical pollution through the introduction of toxic substances is clearly caused by humans. Organic pollution in lakes and rivers typically results when chemical fertilizers used in agriculture enhance living organisms. Thermal pollution is predominately human caused through nuclear power plants, fuel-based electrical power production, and many industries. Some hydroelectric dams also produce unnaturally cooled water with bottom discharge of water.

Surprisingly, these three forms of pollution—chemical, thermal, and organic—can take place without human intervention. When pollution takes place without human intervention, it is most often ecological pollution. Natural ecological pollution may be beneficial, be harmful, or have no effect on wildlife and wildlife habitat. Examples include acidic precipitation resulting from volcanic eruptions, runoff from landslides and avalanches sometimes killing plant and animal life, hot springs and geysers heating water above normal temperatures in lakes and streams, and shifts in oceanic currents affecting water temperature and weather patterns.

The state and federal governments have made advances to control water quality by regulating, monitoring, and enforcing clean water programs. Some recent examples of federal government water pollution control programs are the 1987 Clean Water Act Amendments to the 1977 Clean Water Act and the 1990 Coastal Zone Act Reauthorization Amendments. Public and private businesses are using more pollution prevention and pollution reduction initiatives to control water pollution. More citizens are also practicing water conservation and participating in more community area cleanups (Source: EPA Office of Water).

## Procedure

*Before the Activity*

Make 100 tokens of each of the nine colors of construction paper for a total of 900 tokens. The construction paper may be folded in quarters to speed up the process of cutting or punching. For younger students, the tokens can be made by cutting construction paper into $1/2$-in. squares. For older students, simply use a hole-punch to make the tokens from construction paper. Put all the tokens in a container. Stir them so the colors are thoroughly mixed. Make one copy for each student of the Pollutant Information Sheet on page 144.

*continued*

1. List the four major categories of pollution (chemical, thermal, organic, and ecological) on the chalkboard and discuss each. Refer to the background for a description of each. NOTE: Humans primarily cause the first three types of pollution, although there are cases in which natural processes can cause them. Ecological pollution is typically natural, although there are cases in which humans cause it.

2. Pass out the Pollutant Information Sheets. Review each kind of pollution with the students. Discuss how some pollutants can fit into more than one of the four categories. Assign each of the pollution types a color. Then write a short description of the pollution and glue it to construction paper making sure it's the assigned color. (IDEA: Educators have simply copied the Pollutant Information Sheets, cut the descriptions apart, and pasted the appropriate paragraphs on construction paper.) Post each sheet of colored paper with its corresponding description of the kind of pollution it represents in a row in a convenient place.

3. Once all the kinds of pollution have been discussed and the students understand that each kind of pollution will be represented in this activity by one color of paper, have them divide into research teams of three students. Each team will analyze the pollution content of a hypothetical river. Supply each team with a piece of graph paper. Pass the container of colored paper tokens to each

research team to measure out their share ($1/4$ teaspoon of the paper-punched tokens or 1 tablespoon of the $1/2$" square tokens).

4. The teams first must separate the colored tokens into piles. Then, using the color key, they should identify each type of pollutant. Once this step is done, have students count the number of each kind of pollutant they identified and then use graph paper to construct a simple bar graph showing the whole array of pollutants. They should arrange the pollutants in the same order as displayed in the color key posted in the classroom. This step makes it easy to compare each team's findings. Remind teams that each has a different river. Their results are not likely to be the same.

5. When students have completed the bar graphs and compared results, tell them that any quantity above two units of each kind of pollutant is considered damaging to wildlife habitat. In their hypothetical rivers, what pollutants would likely cause the most damage to wildlife and wildlife habitat? Give examples, and discuss kinds of damage that could be caused.

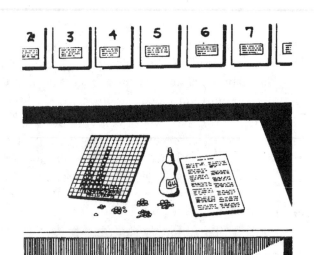

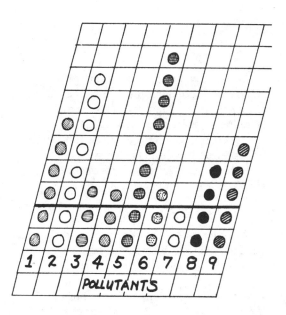

OPTIONAL: Invite the students to match the pollutants with the four categories of pollution listed at the beginning of the activity. Some seem to fit rather easily; others could fit in more than one category, depending on the source of the pollution. For example, is the thermal pollution human or naturally caused (power plant water effluent or thermal hot springs)?

## Extensions

1. List five things you can do to reduce the number of pollutants you add to the environment.

2. Conduct a field trip to a local waterway; attempt to identify what, if any, kinds of pollution are affecting it.

3. Get information about current national and state laws protecting water quality in the United States. Write a short history of the U.S. Clean Water Act.

4. Is DDT still being used, and where? Find out the current status of this pesticide's use in the United States and other parts of the world.

## Evaluation

1. Describe the effects that large quantities of the following things might have on an aquatic environment. Consider short-term and long-term effects of hot water, fertilizer, soil (silt), heavy metals, etc.

2. Water is taken from a river, treated, used by people of a community, sent to a city sewage treatment plant, and returned to the river. Is this aquatic pollution? Defend your response.

continued

# Pollutant Information Sheet

## Sediments

Particles of soils, sand, silt, clay, and minerals wash from land and paved areas into creeks and tributaries. In large unnatural quantities, these natural materials can be considered pollutants. Construction projects often contribute large amounts of sediment. Certain lumbering practices affect sediments in runoff. Sediments may fill stream channels and harbors that later require dredging. Sediments suffocate fish and shellfish populations by covering fish nests and clogging the gills of bottom fish and shellfish.

## Petroleum Products

Oil and other petroleum products such as gasoline and kerosene can find their way into water from ships, oil-drilling rigs, oil refineries, automobile service stations, and streets. Oil spills kill aquatic life (fish, birds, shellfish, and vegetation). Birds are unable to fly when oil loads their feathers. Shellfish and small fish are poisoned. If it is washed on the beach, the oil requires much labor to clean up. Fuel oil, gasoline, and kerosene may leak into ground water through damaged underground storage tanks.

## Human and Animal Waste

Human waste that is not properly treated at a waste treatment plant and then released into water may contain harmful bacteria and viruses. Typhoid fever, polio, cholera, dysentery, hepatitis, flu, and common cold germs are examples of diseases caused by bacteria and viruses in contaminated water. The main source of this problem is sewage getting into the water. People can come into contact with these micro-organisms by drinking the polluted water or through swimming, fishing, or eating shellfish living in polluted waters. Often unexpected flooding of barnyards or stock pens can suddenly increase the toxic effects of animal waste in water. Animal waste can also act as a fertilizer and create damage by increasing nutrients. (See Detergents and Fertilizers.)

## Organic Waste

Domestic sewage treatment plants, food-processing plants, paper mill plants, and leather tanning factories release organic wastes that bacteria consume. If too much waste is released, the bacterial populations increase and use up the oxygen in the water. Fish die if too much oxygen is consumed by decomposing organic matter.

## Inorganic Chemicals

Inorganic chemicals and mineral substances, solid matter, and metal salts commonly dissolve in water. They often come from mining and manufacturing industries, oil field operations, agriculture, and natural sources. Those chemicals interfere with natural stream purification; they destroy fish and other aquatic life. They also corrode expensive water treatment equipment and increase the cost of boat maintenance.

## Detergents and Fertilizers

Many of these substances are toxic to fish and harmful to humans. They cause taste and odor problems and often cannot be treated effectively. Some are very poisonous at low concentrations. The major source of pollution from agriculture comes from surplus fertilizers in the runoff. Fertilizers contain nitrogen and phosphorous that can cause large amounts of algae to grow. The large algae blooms cover the water's surface. The algae die after they have used all of the nutrients. Once dead, they sink to the bottom where bacteria feed on them. The bacterial populations increase and use up most of the oxygen in the water. Once the free oxygen is gone, many aquatic animals die. This process is called "eutrophication."

## Heated or Cooled Water

Heat reduces the ability of water to dissolve oxygen. Electric power plants use large quantities of water in their steam turbines. The heated water is often returned to streams, lagoons, or reservoirs. With less oxygen in the water, fish and other aquatic life can be harmed. Water temperatures that are much lower than normal can cause habitat damage. Deep dams often let extra water flow downstream. When the water comes from the bottom of the dam, it is much colder than normal.

## Acidic Precipitation

Aquatic animals and plants are adjusted to a rather narrow range of pH levels. When water becomes too acidic because of inorganic chemical pollution or from acidic rain, fish and other organisms die.

## Pesticides, Herbicides, and Fungicides

Chemicals that are designed to limit the growth of or to kill life forms are a common form of pollution. This pollution results from the attempts to limit the negative effects of undesirable species on agricultural crop production. Irrigation, ground-water flow, and natural runoff bring such toxic substances to rivers, streams, lakes, and oceans.

# Something's Fishy Here!

## Objectives

Students will (1) identify potential cause-and-effect relationships involving aquatic-related pollution, (2) generate and evaluate alternative solutions to problems of aquatic pollution, and (3) outline a plan to reduce the consequences of possible aquatic pollution in their communities.

## Method

Students read and discuss a story, inventing their own endings that lead to environmental action in their community.

## Materials

One copy for each student of the story "The Swimming Hole Tragedy" on page 148, writing materials

**Grade Level:** 5–8

**Subject Areas:** Language Arts, Environmental Education

**Duration:** two or more 30- to 45-minute sessions

**Group Size:** any

**Setting:** indoors

**Conceptual Framework Topic Reference:** HIIA, HIIIB4, HIIIB5

**Key Terms:** pollution, action, responsibility

**Appendices:** Using Local Resources

## Background

Individual citizens often feel helpless when an issue is presented in their community. Yet successful action to resolve community issues frequently begins with individual action. Students have initiated community projects that improved the safety of neighborhoods, created parkland, and preserved major habitats for wildlife.

Many issues face communities in the United States today. Reducing or eliminating pollution is one example of an area where individuals can make a difference. Significant aesthetic improvement can result from reducing the most common forms of water pollution: litter and siltation. Other forms of pollution are far more elusive and more difficult to detect and eliminate. Many organizations are working to identify and eliminate sources of pollution in ground water, brooks, streams, lakes, rivers, and oceans.

Pure water cannot be found in nature. Even as water falls from the sky, it picks up carbon dioxide and other gases and becomes more acidic. Water is known as the universal solvent, which means that it can dissolve many kinds of substances. Water also can carry suspended particles such as soil and plant materials to rivers, lakes, streams and so forth. These particles affect the penetration of light and, in turn, the plants living below the water's surface. Water temperature and the amount of dissolved gases also change and affect the life in it.

*continued*

Water pollution is usually described in relation to how humans use that particular body of water. For example, because trout are sensitive to many changes in aquatic chemistry, water in a trout stream may be labeled polluted for human use if conditions reach a point where trout die. However, the water could still support other types of fish and not be considered polluted for that species. In other words, water could be described as polluted for some purposes and not for others.

Adding chemicals to water affects certain organisms, depending on the concentration of the chemical. Some chemicals can be toxic to some organisms even at very low concentrations. Scientists usually measure concentrations of materials by comparing the parts of that substance to the parts of water containing it. When concentrations of materials reach critical levels, certain organisms die.

Aquatic organisms need the oxygen that is dissolved in water. When oxygen levels fall below certain points, those organisms die. The temperature affects the amount of dissolved oxygen that can be present in water. The warmer the water, the less oxygen it can hold. Some animals need more oxygen than others; therefore, warm water can be described as polluted for some kinds of fish and not polluted for others.

## Procedure

1. Have each student silently read the story "The Swimming Hole Tragedy" on page 148.

2. After all students have finished, discuss the story with them. Ask the students to think about as many different endings to the story as possible. OPTIONAL: Ask each student to write an ending for the story.

3. In small groups, ask the students to share their recommendations for how the story could end.

4. Ask each small group to decide on the ending they most prefer. It is fine if the students do not agree. Have each group report to the other groups the ending or endings they recommend. List the essential points of each recommended ending on the chalkboard.

5. Discuss the various endings with the entire class. Identify cause-and-effect relationships. Look for possible relationships between the story and problems regarding water use and the aquatic habitats that might or do exist in the students' own community.

6. Next, have the students generate a list of possible aquatic wildlife concerns or needs related to aquatic pollution that they believe exist in their own environment. Have them form groups that have a common interest in one or more of the concerns, and ask them to develop a plan to find out more about the situation in their community. That is, what will they need to know to address this need? (Will they need to know the history of the selected issue? Will they need maps of the area in question? Where can they get information to identify constituent groups or individuals?)

7. Once they have identified the needed information, they should devise a plan to collect it. (Who in the group collects what data? Where does each person acquire his or her assigned information? When can all students obtain their information?) Have each group report to the class the concern it selected and its plan to research the background information.

NOTE: Coach the students to choose problems that they might actually solve. For example, pollution in a nearby brook is far more realistic for them to address than that in an entire river system.

8. Allow each group time to research the aquatic concern it selected.

9. When the research is completed, ask each group to report its findings to the class.

10. After each presentation, have the entire class brainstorm 10 things that might be done to address that group's issue. Make sure each presenting group records the suggestions offered by the class. Allow class time for students in each group to discuss the various suggestions among themselves and to form an implementation plan.

11. Facilitate the class members' taking specific action by helping them establish time lines and specific assignments to carry out their implementation plans.

## Extensions

1. Follow through with class members on the implementation plans they created to address aquatic concerns or needs in the community.

2. Find a way to publicize what the groups have accomplished. Contact broadcast media, the city council, garden clubs, parent-teacher association, and so forth.

3. Work to raise interest among other students to address additional important aquatic wildlife and habitat-related issues.

## Evaluation

1. Identify potential types of aquatic pollution in the students' community. Identify the pollution source. Describe some of the issues associated with pollution.

2. Water is taken from a river, treated, used by people of a community, sent to a city sewage treatment plant, and returned to the river. Is this aquatic pollution? Defend your response.

3. Sam Smith and Jill Jones each caught a fishing line on a dead tree in a stream. They couldn't get their line loose, so they cut off about 15 feet of line. Is this aquatic pollution? Defend your response.

continued

# The Swimming Hole Tragedy

The swimming hole in the Creston River below Midvale was one of the most popular places, especially during the long, hot summer months. Even as early as May, groups of students would enjoy this special spot.

We had to drive 5 miles of unpaved road to a place where the river widened out and deepened. There we could take turns jumping off the overhanging branch of a big cottonwood tree into the cool dark waters. Most kids in town had known about this swimming hole since they were young. It was where most of us learned to swim. We went there to catch frogs and fish, and to float around on old inner tubes. That place brought back those special memories of childhood that still seemed as fresh as yesterday, even though years had passed.

On hot, lazy, vacation days, Midvale residents would be drawn to the wet oasis to play, relax, and learn some important lessons of life. It was there that I first learned that dragonfly "dive bombers" really didn't sting or sew up your lips. It's strange how those old stories get started. Sometimes I'm sorry that those myths have to die. They always added excitement and mystery to growing up and playing along the river. It was there that I learned that the best way to find stonefly larvae was to carefully lift a stone from the river bottom and scrape the clinging animals off with a leaf. It was easy to figure out how they got their name.

I reached the point where I knew almost every log that jutted out into the river's current below the surface. That was where those lunker bass were. I knew the locations of the best logs as I knew the back of my hand—at least until the next heavy rain and high water came along. I can still close my eyes and see the sparkle of sunlight on the rippling waters. I can feel and smell the dank moisture down under the big trees by the swimming hole. All of those memories and more made the swimming hole a special place—both in my head and in my heart. You probably know some special places in the outdoors that do the same thing for you.

No one could ever guess that such a paradise would turn our hearts so dark. This place took my sister's hearing away and came close to claiming her life. I was crushed, and I never will forget the feeling. Here's how I think it all happened. One day my sister Jenny, Jeff, and I went down to swim at our favorite spot. The swimming hole gradually had changed over the years. No one had been able to catch any big bass recently. More junk was floating downstream and the water wasn't as deep as it used to be. Fewer insects were hatching, and piles of trash were gathered around fence posts.

On the day we went swimming, the water was especially warm and it had a greenish tinge, but that didn't stop us. In fact, we invented a contest to see who could dive down and bring up the biggest rock from the bottom. We stayed longer than usual that day and made over 50 trips diving from top to bottom. A couple of days later, we all had earaches and had to stay home from school. There was little doubt how our pains came about. We had not told our families that we were going to go to the swimming hole. When my Mom found out, she said that the river had become an open sewer. She said that we had taken our last swim in the river. It was too late for my sister, Jenny. Jenny's ears got worse and, after an intense fever, she lost her hearing forever.

We called the health department and soon after someone came to the swimming hole to take water samples. In fact, they took samples all along a stretch of river that passed by three towns, including Midvale. I was there to watch them take the samples. The person from the health department told me that they suspected one or more of the towns might be dumping raw sewage directly into the river. The sewage treatment plants were all over 40 years old, and the towns had grown by leaps and bounds since then. Human sewage can carry germs that can cause more damage than just earaches, the official told me.

It was a long time before I could again return to the river, but when I did, I noticed that it was harder to find stoneflies and other creatures that lived in the river. I also noticed that the water color had become greener and murkier. It all had happened so slowly that, until our earache incident, I didn't pull all the pieces together. When I did, the conclusion was clear—even if the water in the river wasn't. The Creston River was polluted, and now I had a painful reminder that this was hurting the living things I cared about—including my sister.

It seemed ironic that the river that had taught me so much and had given me so much pleasure had now changed. What should I do about it? Could one person make a difference? I had some important reasons to try.

# Water's Going On?

## Objectives

Students will (1) record and interpret daily water consumption, and (2) make recommendations as to how to conserve water.

## Method

Students estimate and calculate water consumption; then they design and try ways to conserve water.

## Materials

Chalkboard, paper and pencils, a variety of liquid measurement containers

## Background

Almost every molecule of water that was present when the Earth's oceans were formed millions of years ago is still present in one of water's three forms: as a gas, liquid, or solid ice. Most of the fresh water in the world is frozen in the polar ice caps. The largest part of what remains is ground water—under-ground water that moves between layers beneath the ground's surface.

Approximately half of the water consumed by humans in the United States is drawn from groundwater sources—approximately 82 billion gallons a day. Much of the ground water used will not be returned to the water system for many human lifetimes. Shallow ground water may have a renewal rate of about 300 years; deep ground water, more than 3,300 feet (1,000 meters) deep, may renew itself in about 4,600 years.

Water is used by all the members of a community: schools, businesses, industries, and homes. Because water is important to all consumers, demands for this finite resource continue to grow, thus the need to conserve and manage supplies also grows.

Even though ground water supplies are slow to replenish, many rivers and lakes in the United States are cleaner than they were in the 1960s. Farmers have helped reduce ground water consumption through efficient water use practices such as planting crops that require less water, adopting water conservation irrigation methods, and capturing and reusing runoff.

Conservation and practical use of water can be used every day in every situation to prevent water shortages and to ensure long-term supplies. If sharers of a water source consider all the needs of all the water users, and if they plan and manage for those needs, then water of sufficient quality and quantity should be available for years to come.

---

**Grade Level:** 5–8

**Subject Areas:** Mathematics, Science, Environmental Education, Social Studies

**Duration:** two 30- to 45-minute sessions

**Group Size:** any

**Setting:** indoors

**Conceptual Framework Topic Reference:** HIIIA3, HIIIA3a, HIIIB

**Key Terms:** conservation, water

**Appendices:** Using Local Resources, Metric Chart

---

*continued*

## Procedure

1. Ask the students to estimate how much water each student uses each day in school. Have containers of different volumes for students to use for reference. Write their estimates on the chalkboard or on a chart. A chart may be made showing the class's estimates as follows:

| Gallons | 2 | 4 | 6 | 8 | 10 | 12 |
|---------|---|---|---|---|----|----|
| (or Liters) | 8 | 16 | 24 | 32 | 40 | 48 |
| | x | x | xxx | xxx | xxx | xxx |
| | | x | xxx | xxx | xx | |
| | | x | xxx | | | |

2. Ask the students to monitor their water consumption for a day. They can monitor the time spent at the water fountain and record it in a notebook. Ask them to do the same for hand washing. They should also record the number of times they use the restrooms, and any other water areas.

3. As a class, calculate the amount of water used (e.g., run water from the fountain to a container for 10 seconds and see how much water was used). Use this amount to calculate the amount per each drink that the students have recorded in seconds. Do the same for the sink faucets. Multiply a standard average of 3 gallons (12 liters) used per flush by the number of trips to the restroom. Have each student come up with an individual number of gallons or liters used per day.

4. Compare the estimates of water use to the actual water used.

5. Add all the individual gallons of water used to arrive at a total for the entire class. Divide this amount by the number of students in the class. In this way, individual students can compare individual usages against a class average to see if they are above or below average in their water use.

6. Ask the students if it would be possible to reduce the amount of water used and, if so, how. For example, cups could be used at the drinking fountain to reduce the amount of water that goes down the drain.

7. Put the students' suggestions into practice for 1 or 2 days. Then ask the students how water conservation practices changed what they did. What materials did they use or buy? Did their attitudes change? How? Which changes in their behaviors will they keep, as part of their personal lifestyles?

## Extensions

1. Where does our water come from? How does it get here? Do human exploration, transportation, and water consumption affect wildlife in any way? If so, how? After a discussion of the effects of water depletion and conservation on wildlife, draw two murals: one showing the effects of depletion and another the effects of conservation.

2. Monitor water use at home (showers, dishes, clothes washing, lawn watering, etc.).

3. Use this activity for paper and energy use conservation.

4. Incorporate use of elementary statistics in this activity.

## Evaluation

1. Estimate the number of gallons of water you personally use each day. Divide that usage into major categories. Present the data portraying your water use in the form of a graph.

2. What daily activity requires the most water per year?

3. Describe and explain three ways you can decrease your water consumption.

4. How do water conservation efforts affect people and wildlife now and in the future?

# Alice in Waterland

## Objectives

Students will (1) trace domestic water to its source prior to human use and to its destination after use, (2) identify potential effects from human water use on terrestrial and aquatic wildlife, and (3) develop and practice responsible water conservation behaviors.

## Method

Students use a simulated field trip, lecture-discussion, and student-gathered data to explore water use and its effects on wildlife habitat.

## Materials

One Water Consumption Chart (page 154) per student, several long sheets of paper for murals, art materials for the murals (poster paints, vivid pastels, or chalks, etc.)

---

**Grade Level:** 5–8

**Subject Areas:** Science, Environmental Education, Mathematics, Social Studies, Expressive Arts

**Duration:** two or three 45-minute sessions

**Group Size:** any

**Setting:** indoors or outdoors

**Conceptual Framework Topic Reference:** HIIIA3, HIIIB

**Key Terms:** water cycle, hydrologic cycle, conservation

**Appendices:** Simulated Field Trips

---

## Background

The hydrologic, or water, cycle is a model that traces the cyclical journey of water. This path involves (1) precipitation—such as rain or snow—on a watershed; (2) runoff that flows into streams, groundwater systems, lakes, reservoirs, estuaries, and oceans; (3) evaporation and evapotranspiration, which returns water to the atmosphere; (4) cloud formation; and (5) condensation as water falls again in the form of precipitation on a watershed (see Diagram A). The great storehouses of water—glaciers and ice-caps—are also part of this cycle. All forms of life on Earth are dependent upon and affected by this dynamic and continuing process. In between the watershed and the ocean, humans divert the water from its natural course to be used in a variety of ways. The most obvious use of water is for domestic purposes.

Human consumption of water affects wildlife. When water is drawn from its natural setting, wildlife and wildlife habitat may be affected. For example, building a dam may provide water for electricity, but it also modifies wildlife habitat in river and stream valleys. Wetlands modification can remove water from natural nurseries for wildlife. Once water is diverted from its natural path, it may return to the water cycle contaminated or polluted. If contaminated water is returned to human or wildlife habitats, the effects may be devastating.

Humans have choices in terms of how water is consumed. Water conservation can be adapted to daily life. Water conservation not only eases the stress on natural habitats by lessening the need for dams and other interventions, but also reduces the depletion of under-ground water supplies that provide moisture for many riparian and other habitats. Conservation of ground-

*continued*

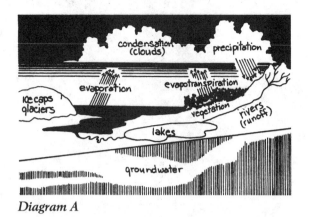

*Diagram A*

water supplies also benefits human populations that depend upon underground aquifers for municipal water supplies.

Conservation of both ground water and surface waters protects the continued availability of water for humans, wildlife, and the environment. Paying attention to what is put into water and the water cycle—being careful with pesticides, detergents, fertilizers, motor oils, aerosols, cleaning fluids and powders, and caustic acids, as well as fuels and their byproducts—is another way to conserve water resources.

## Procedure

1. Using a simulated field trip, ask the students to sit quietly, close their eyes, and imagine that they could shrink down to a size that would let them travel up through their faucet and into their water pipes. Ask the students to picture in their minds what you will describe for them in the following words.

NOTE: Educators may want to adapt the text so it will apply to local settings. Or, if many of the students have well water as their domestic source, educators can convert the simulated field trip to a school or other organizational setting. Even if this scenario does not apply exactly to the students' situation, it can be used to explore a typical source of water and its routes in the United States and other countries. Educators may want to refer to the Appendices for additional suggestions concerning use of simulated field trips for instructional purposes.

"Picture yourself small enough to climb into the faucet in your kitchen. See yourself with magic powers that allow you to travel through the water that comes from the faucet to its origins. You will be able to pass through all the pipes, valves, and other barriers on the way. The first part of the journey takes you through the pipes in your house to where they connect to your water source. If you live on a farm or ranch, the source would probably be a well or perhaps a spring.

"In the city, the water source for your home would probably be far away. First, you link into a water main. Then, you come to a pumping plant where water pressure is maintained. Past the pumping plant is a place where the water is purified. This structure may be very complex—a place with filters, chemical tanks, and treatment equipment.

"Beyond the purification plant, the water may be in an aqueduct or open channel coming from a reservoir. The reservoir is a huge lake where water is stored. There are often trees and bushes on its edges. Wildlife is common; fish are usually abundant; and people often use the site for recreation. Natural streams usually flow into the reservoir. They drain large areas of the land's surface, which are called "watersheds." A watershed is the land area that catches and transports water through streams, under-ground flow, and rivers. The water in a watershed contains all the water that is naturally available for use by all living things in that area. If you want, stay in the watershed. Try to see the plants and animals that live in the area. Or, follow your route all the way back through the reservoir, channels, treatment plant, and pumping plant to the water main and the pipes in from your house and out your faucet. Then, open your eyes."

2. After this simulated field trip, discuss the journey of the water from its source to the faucet. Identify the components of the journey. Emphasize the places where wildlife habitats are affected—positively, negatively, or with unknown effects—by the intervention of people as they consume the water or influence how the water is consumed.

3. Repeat the process for a journey down the drain into the wastewater system:

"Picture yourself small again. This time the journey will be down the drain in your sink. You move along through the used-water system to a treatment site. If you live on a farm, the site will probably be a septic tank. A septic tank is usually a large concrete box. Here bacteria break down the substances carried in the water. Once the water is partially cleansed, it flows out through drainage fields and back into groundwater sources or streams. If you live in a city much more water is being used, and large water-treatment plants must attempt to cleanse the water before it is returned to rivers and streams. In the treatment plants are great filters and holding tanks. The water must be held in place for solid substances to settle out by gravity. Air is often pumped through the waste water to increase the oxygen content so bacteria can break down the impurities more quickly.

"Eventually, the treated water is released into rivers and streams. It again re-enters the natural habitat for wildlife. There it provides an essential component for continued life. If all was done well, animals, plants and humans will safely re-use the water. It will nourish the crayfish caught by the raccoon. It will provide the pond for the box turtle. It will provide the refreshing drink for someone like you in some downstream city. After you have followed the water out into the environment, open your eyes."

4. Discuss the journey of the water through the waste-water treatment plant. Identify the components of the journey. Emphasize the places where wildlife habitats are affected—positively, negatively, or with unknown effects—by the intervention of people as they use water or influence how water is to be used.

5. Divide the students into two groups. Instruct one group to research the water cycle. Ask some students to find out details such as how much precipitation falls in their community and what kind of contaminant is likely in the precipitation. Instruct others to investigate runoff, where it goes, how much seeps into the ground, and how much travels overland. Why is it important for water to seep into the soil? Could this runoff pick up contaminants along its path? Which ones? How can runoff be reduced? Other students might look at evaporation. What conditions could accelerate or inhibit evaporation? How might changes in evaporation rates affect wildlife?

6. Ask the second group to research the waste treatment process. Some students might look up information on "primary treatment," some might research "secondary treatment," and others might find out about "tertiary treatment." Perhaps some students could find out how much water passes through the local treatment plant, which types of treatment it uses, and how much it costs to operate. Ask one team to compare the kinds of bacteria used in treatment plants to break down wastes with the bacteria that break down wastes in soil and in septic tanks.

7. Have the students in the first group create a mural on a single long sheet of paper, depicting the origins and journey of water through a natural system (i.e., emphasizing the water cycle and watershed processes). Have the students portray wildlife and habitat throughout the mural.

8. Ask the students in the second group to create a mural of the journey of water through a human system (i.e., emphasizing plumbing and waste treatment plant processes). Have them portray human effects along the way.

9. Look at the entire mural—natural and human. Identify, list, and discuss places in which the quality of the water may be affected by human activities, not just the quantity of available water.

10. Now shift the emphasis to the amount of water that people typically use. Pass out the Water Consumption Chart provided on page 154.

continued

11. Ask the students to keep track of how much water is used in their homes for 5 days. Suggest that the sheet be posted on the refrigerator and that each family member help by putting a mark in the section designated on the sheet after each water use. The miscellaneous section is for special uses not listed. Suggest that the students use empty 1- or 2-liter soda containers to estimate amounts.

12. After the water-use data have been gathered, make a master chart that summarizes the total use for the class for the entire week. Discuss places where water might be conserved. Challenge students to intentionally reduce their water consumption and invite their families to join in. Have them monitor use for another 5 days and tabulate the results.

13. Once the results are tabulated, discuss how wildlife, habitat, and humans can benefit from human water use conservation. Discuss the potential appropriateness and effectiveness of a variety of water conservation behaviors. Examine potential negative and positive effects. Discuss not only ways to reduce and conserve water use, but also ways to protect the quality of the water we use.

## Extensions

1. Conserving water supplies saves money. Drawing, storing, heating, and disposing of water can have economic costs. Calculate how much money your family would save in water and energy bills if you carried out conservation practices for a year.

2. Monitor water use by the school or organization. Identify ways to conserve water use.

3. Take field trips to water purification systems and waste-water treatment plants.

4. Modify the murals to show the effects of water conservation and improved water quality on wildlife habitat.

5. Design a closed-loop water system for a space station.

## Evaluation

1. Draw and label a flow chart tracing water in your community from where it comes—to your home—to where it goes after it leaves your home.

2. Estimate the number of gallons of water you use each day for personal use. What do you do that uses the greatest amount of water in a year?

3. Name three ways you might conserve water. How much water could you conserve using each method for a year? How might wildlife be affected by your water conservation actions? How might plants be affected?

4. Rank the following water uses from those that use the most water to those that use the least in the United States: domestic, industrial, agricultural or irrigation, recreational (1 = most).

5. What effect, if any, does human water consumption have on animals that live on the land? What effect, if any, does human water use have on animals that live in or around water?

6. Give examples of ways that water quality can be negatively affected by human consumption. Give examples of actions people can take to protect the quality of water.

### Water Consumption Chart
(all values are approximate)

| | |
|---|---|
| 3–5 gallons (12–20 liters) | Flushing a toilet |
| 3 gallons (12 liters) | Brushing your teeth and letting the water run |
| 5 gallons (20 liters) per minute | Shower |
| 8 gallons (30 liters) | Cooking three meals |
| 8 gallons (30 liters) | Cleaning house |
| 10 gallons (40 liters) | Washing dishes (three meals) |
| 20–30 gallons (75–115 liters) | Washing clothes |
| 30–40 gallons (115–150 liters) | Watering a lawn |
| 30–40 gallons (115–150 liters) | Taking a bath |
| 30–40 gallons (115–150 liters) | Washing a car |
| _____ | Miscellaneous use |

# The Glass Menagerie

## Objective

Students will describe the characteristics of oligotrophic and eutrophic aquatic habitats, emphasizing the effects of nutrient loading.

## Method

Students observe and describe changes in physical characteristics of several different experimental aquatic habitats that they create.

## Materials

Seven 1-quart (1-liter) glass jars; masking tape for labels; 1 gallon (4 liters) of distilled water; tap water; a small bottle of household plant fertilizer; a roll of aluminum foil; 1 gallon (4 liters) of recently gathered pond water (with abundant life forms); microscopes, both stereo and standard; soda straws; identification guides for pond life

---

**Grade Level:** 9-12

**Subject Areas:** Science, Environmental Education

**Duration:** four weeks for classroom observations

**Group Size:** any

**Setting:** outdoors and indoors

**Conceptual Framework Topic Reference:** HIIIB5

**Key Terms:** oligotrophic, eutrophic, nutrient loading

**Appendices:** Ecosystems, Field Ethics, Outdoors, Animals in the Classroom

---

## Background

A healthy body of water is a delicate balance of dissolved oxygen, nutrients, temperature, and transparency. The amount of plant and animal life in a pond or lake depends on the balance of these factors.

When the water of a young pond or lake is cold and clear, it supports very little life. Over time, erosion and runoff bring organic material into the lake. The organic material—drainage from surrounding watersheds (runoff), bottom sediments in the lake and organisms (living and dead)—are broken down by the bacteria and become food for nutrient loving algae. As the algae multiply, so do the number of fish that feed on the algae. Over time, as the lake fills with the silt from the erosion and runoff and as the water becomes warmer, marsh plants take root and fill the lake basin. Fish populations and other aquatic organisms decline because of the limited dissolved oxygen. When this change happens, a lake or pond supports more plant life than animal life, and its waters are rich in nutrients.

A pond or lake low in nutrients is called "oligotrophic." Low plant production and high transparency (clear water) characterize lakes that are oligotrophic.

The clarity of the water is correlated to the absence of an abundance of plant life. Oligotrophic lakes often have a relatively small surface area and greater depth. They also tend to have sand or gravel bottoms.

In eutrophic systems, the organic materials, or nutrients, can cause modifications to the

*continued*

lake such as algae blooms and small fish kills. A sudden bloom of algae uses up the nutrients rapidly and is often followed by an alga die-off. The algae that have died begin to decompose rapidly. Bacteria promoting the decomposition use up much of the available oxygen in the water. During the night, the algae continue to use oxygen that fish and other aquatic organisms need to breathe.

Human activity increases the rate of eutrophication in lakes. Domestic sewage, industrial wastes, and chemical fertilizers are some of the sources of human-caused nutrient enrichment. These "unnatural" nutrients are frequently introduced into lakes through municipal and industrial discharges.

Eutrophication can be good or bad, depending on degree and perspective. Usually, lakes in the early stages of eutrophication provide excellent recreation and fishing. In later stages, as nutrients build up, lakes can become obstructed with vegetation and covered with algae. This condition typically indicates that a lake or pond has a nutrient overload. Eutrophication is a natural process that can be accelerated by humans. This acceleration is called "nutrient loading," and it has complex effects on people, wildlife, and the environment.

## Procedure

NOTE: The following procedure is designed to have students explore the aspects of eutrophication. Further investigation and discussion of the characteristics of oligotrophic and eutrophic lakes in terms of depth, surface size, temperature, and turnover are encouraged.

1. Collect (with the students if possible) a gallon of viable pond water. The water must be a source of active organisms, both plant and animal. A microscope may be needed to verify how active the organisms are.

2. Label and prepare the seven jars as follows:
   - Jar 1 Control—3 cups (750 ml) distilled water.

   - Jar 2 Distilled Water—3 cups (750 ml) distilled water, $\frac{1}{2}$ cup (125 ml) pond water.

   - Jar 3 Tap Water—3 cups (750 ml) tap water, $\frac{1}{2}$ cup pond water.

   - Jar 4 Pond Water—3 $\frac{1}{2}$ cups (875 ml) pond water.

   - Jar 5 Distilled Water with Fertilizer—3 cups (750 ml) distilled water, normal amount of fertilizer (as on instructions), $\frac{1}{2}$ cup (125 ml) pond water.

   - Jar 6 Distilled Water with Fertilizer Overload × 10—3 cups (750 ml) distilled water plus 10 times the normal fertilizer, $\frac{1}{2}$ cup (125 ml) pond water.

   - Jar 7 Distilled Water with Fertilizer Overload × 20—3 cups (750 ml) distilled water plus 20 times the normal fertilizer, $\frac{1}{2}$ cup (125 ml) pond water.

NOTE: Be sure to agitate the pond water before introducing it into the other jars. It is best to have equivalent concentrations of life forms in each of the experimental jars. Save the leftover pond water for examination with the microscopes.

3. Cap the jars loosely with aluminum foil to prevent excessive evaporation. Place the jars in a cool, visible, and well-lighted place. Avoid placing the jars in direct sunlight. The students will now observe and record what takes place in the jars for a 4-week period. As a pre-assessment, ask the students to generate a hypothesis concerning the effects or outcomes in each of the jars. Tell them they will test their hypotheses against the evidence they gather during the 4-week observation period.

4. Have students use microscopes, either standard or stereoscopic, to examine the pond water not used in the experimental jars. Have them record their observations, including drawings or illustrations of the various life forms found in the water. Research the names of the animals in identification guides or other resource books on pond life.

5. Throughout the observation period, record daily entries on a data sheet for each jar. These observations may be completed with or without the use of microscopes, as changes will be visible to the eye without optical assistance. Have the students work on a rotation basis for the data recording.

6. Some changes will begin to appear during the second week of the experiment. When life forms begin to be visible, use an eye-dropper to remove some organisms carefully for study with a microscope.

7. Observe changes in the jars, and discuss the findings.

8. At the end of the 4-week observation period, discuss the role of nutrients and how they occur in nature. Label the jars with abundant organisms "eutrophic," showing nutrient loading. Label the jars without many organisms "oligotrophic." What is the role and impact of accelerated growth caused by introduced nutrient loads? What are the natural sources of nutrients and human-related sources? Compare the similarities and contrast the differences. How does nutrient loading change the number of life forms in the water? What are the indications of these accelerated changes? What kinds of effects might nutrient loading have on aquatic wildlife? On people? OPTIONAL: If possible, end the activity with a visit to the pond where the water was collected. If possible, visit lakes or ponds at various stages of eutrophication.

## Extensions

1. Investigate the role of temperature and dissolved oxygen in pond life.

2. Investigate the role of pollutants in pond life.

3. Find out whether a pond or lake in your community is directly affected, indirectly affected, or both by eutrophication.

## Evaluation

Code each of the following as a characteristic of eutrophic lakes (E), oligotrophic lakes (O), both kinds of lakes (B), or neither type of lakes (N) by writing one letter beside each statement.

_____ Deep, greater than 60 feet (18 meters)

_____ Have many species of plankton (both zooplankton and phytoplankton), but low number of each species

_____ High transparency (can see a long way down into the water)

_____ Large number of fish that many people consider desirable

_____ Large amount of decaying organic matter

_____ Little oxygen available

_____ Large amount of algae

_____ Taste and odor problems

_____ Bacteria mostly aerobic (oxygen using)

_____ A result of natural or human-caused erosion

_____ High total productivity

_____ Few plant nutrients (nitrates, phosphates, manure)

_____ Considered an old lake, in terms of succession

_____ High rate of nutrient cycling

# Fishable Waters

## Objectives

Students will (1) identify and describe the value of clean water and healthy fish populations in their community; (2) infer that populations and species compositions are not static but ever changing; (3) differentiate between harmful and positive impacts on water quality and fish populations, and know that human activities can accelerate natural processes such as runoff, sedimentation, and nutrient cycles; (4) know that management of aquatic species and their habitats is directly influenced by land-based activities in the surrounding watershed; and (5) learn that legislation, such as the Clean Water Act and fishing regulations, is a tool used to manage resources for the benefit of present and future generations.

---

**Grade Level:** 6-9

**Subject Areas:** Science, Social Studies, Environmental Education

**Duration:** one or two 45-minute sessions

**Group Size:** teams of 4-6 students

**Setting:** classroom

**Conceptual Framework Topic Reference:** ITIIA1, WMIA1, WMIIB2, WMIIIB4, BDIIA, BDIIB, BDIIC, BDIIIE, ECIIB1a, HIIB, HIIIC2, HIIIB3, HIIIB4, HIIIB5

**Key Terms:** biodiversity, Clean Water Act, dissolved oxygen, fishway (fish ladder), non-point source pollution, nutrients, point source pollution, riparian zone, runoff, turbidity

**Appendices:** Ecosystems, Taking Action, Agencies and Organizations

---

## Method

Students evaluate how healthy fish populations provide multiple benefits for their community, and they play a card game to explore the connection between water quality, habitat, and "fishable and swimmable" waters, as stated in the Clean Water Act of 1972.

## Materials

For each student, a copy of the "Sample Fishing Report" on page 165. For each group of 4-6 students, a copy of "Fishable Waters Game Rules" on page 166; copies of "Urban Fish Species & License Cards" on page 167 (2 copies if groups of 4; 3 copies if groups of 5 or 6); a copy of each page of "Fishable Waters Action Cards" (pages 168-171), cut apart; 40 "fish" tokens (e.g., poker chips, fish-shaped crackers, pennies, paper clips [see "Game Options" on page 164]); OPTIONAL: copies of state fishing regulations (free from natural resource management agency or sporting goods stores), pictures of common local fish, or field guides

NOTE: You may want to copy group sets of cards on different colors of cardstock and laminate them for easy tracking and repeated use.

## Background

Most major cities in the U.S. were established along water—rivers, bays, or large lakes. People settled along waterways for a variety of reasons: water-based transportation was easier and faster than traveling overland; water was easily accessible for drinking and other household uses, as well as for agriculture and livestock; and fish and wildlife found in or near water supplemented the diet and livelihoods of early communities.

The waters that supported such bounty also provided an easy way to get rid of waste. By the mid-1800s sewage in rivers caused water-borne diseases to reach epidemic proportions. By the 1960s many of our nation's waterways were so contaminated they were closed to swimming. Signs were posted along the Potomac River in Washington, D.C., warning the public not to inhale the air. Ohio's Cuyahoga River was so polluted with chemical wastes that it caught fire. The rivers, lakes, and bays that once sustained communities and provided welcome recreational opportunities had become places to avoid; our nation's fisheries were in trouble.

The Cuyahoga River fire sparked a movement toward regulating industrial pollution and resulted in the passage of the Clean Water Act of 1972. The Act called for a reduction in the direct discharge of pollutants into waterways and to achieve "fishable and swimmable" waters. The Act primarily addressed "point source pollution," pollution that can be traced to a definite point where it enters the environment, such as a factory or sewage discharge pipe.

With point source pollution regulated, water quality in many urban waterways improved dramatically. Today, there are nearly twice as many waterways that meet standards for fishing and swimming as there were before the passage of the Clean Water Act. Yet, approximately 44 percent of U.S. waterways that have been assessed are still too polluted for those activities. Where is all this pollution coming from? Urban sprawl and increasing populations require more energy, overload old sewage treatment facilities, and result in more paved and impervious surfaces. Storm water and snowmelt runoff from a variety of urban, suburban, and rural sources—from city streets, homes, construction sites, lawns, parking lots, and farms—is a form of general "people pollution" that results from activities people do every day. Because you can't necessarily point to any one source, we call this nonpoint source pollution or runoff pollution. The Environmental Protection Agency warns that unless communities take action, water quality is likely to return to pre-Act levels by the year 2016.

The major problem associated with runoff is the soil, nutrients, and pollutants it often carries. Soil erosion from agriculture and urban development causes fine silt to wash into waterways, where it may settle to the bottom, smothering fish eggs and covering up rocks that provide habitat for small aquatic organisms. When silt doesn't settle, the water will look muddy or turbid. Turbidity

## Discover an Urban Fishing Program Near You

To learn about urban fishing programs in your area, visit www.takemefishing.org. Click on "Fishing," then on "Urban Fishing," to see a list of states that offer urban fishing opportunities. Though information varies, clicking on the name of your state will yield information such as: highlights of fishing programs in different cities; recommended fishing sites organized by region; information about fishing clinics and free fishing days; links to state fishing license requirements and other fishing regulations; and contacts for tackle loaner programs.

US FISH AND WILDLIFE SERVICE

*continued*

Sustaining Fish and Wildlife Resources
..............................................................................................

Fishable Waters

## Assessment of U.S. Waterbodies

| Waterbody Type | Total Size | Amount Assessed* | % of Total | Assessed Good | Assessed Good but Threatened | Assessed Polluted |
|---|---|---|---|---|---|---|
| Rivers (miles) | 3,692,830 | 699,949 | 19% | 367,129 | 59,504 | 269,258 |
| Lakes (acres) | 40,603,893 | 17,339,080 | 43% | 8,026,988 | 1,348,903 | 7,702,370 |
| Estuaries (sq. miles) | 87,369 | 31,072 | 36% | 13,850 | 1,023 | 15,676 |

*Includes waterbodies assessed as not attainable for one or more uses.*
*Note: percentages may not add up to 100% because of rounding.*

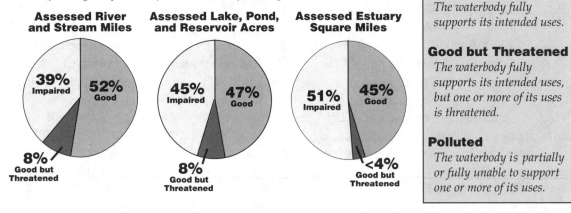

**Assessed River and Stream Miles** — 39% Impaired, 52% Good, 8% Good but Threatened

**Assessed Lake, Pond, and Reservoir Acres** — 45% Impaired, 47% Good, 8% Good but Threatened

**Assessed Estuary Square Miles** — 51% Impaired, 45% Good, <4% Good but Threatened

**Good**
*The waterbody fully supports its intended uses.*

**Good but Threatened**
*The waterbody fully supports its intended uses, but one or more of its uses is threatened.*

**Polluted**
*The waterbody is partially or fully unable to support one or more of its uses.*

*The data above were obtained from a fact sheet prepared by the U.S. EPA to summarize the* National Water Quality Inventory: 2000 Report, *prepared under Section 305(b) of the Clean Water Act. The Water Quality Report characterizes U.S. water quality, identifies widespread water quality problems of national significance, and describes various programs implemented to restore and protect our waters. Both the fact sheet and full report are available at www.epa.gov/305b/. United States Environmental Protection Agency Office of Water (4503F) EPA-841-F-02-003 • August 2002*

*Please note: www.epa.gov/305(b) also provides data from individual states through the 2002 National Assessment Database..*

*www.epa.gov/waters/ provides access to* WATERS, *U.S. EPA's* Watershed Assessment, Tracking & Environmental ResultS, *an interactive tool that connects water quality data from several databases and displays information by generating maps and reports.*

blocks light from reaching oxygen-producing aquatic plants, and fine silt particles may clog the gills of aquatic species.

Agricultural runoff, containing manure and crop fertilizer, is considered the main source of harmful nutrients (nitrogen and phosphorus) in our waters. Urban pet wastes and fertilizers from lawns and golf courses also contribute significantly. These excess nutrients fuel rapid growth of algae. Like turbidity, floating algal mats block sunlight needed by submerged aquatic vegetation. When algae and grasses die, the decomposition process consumes oxygen from the water, causing "dead zones" where few fish or other aquatic species can survive.

What can be done to address such a large and ambiguous challenge? Communities can "adopt" and clean up local waterways; citizens can vote for change, making tough decisions that balance local economics with sound resource management; and people can educate each other about nonpoint source pollution and how to take preventative action. Specific actions individuals can take to reduce runoff include planting buffer zones of trees and vegetation between homes and businesses and storm drains or bodies of water; replacing impermeable hardscape (concrete, asphalt, etc.) with gravel, vegetation, or other permeable materials; and installing ponds, wetlands, or rainwater catchment systems to collect excess water. To reduce the amount of pollution collected by runoff, individual citizens can limit fertilizer and pesticide use (especially before it rains), pick up trash and pet waste, and properly dispose of household and other chemical wastes.

Across America many citizens, and even entire cities, have taken action to improve waterways. Riverfront and waterfront revitalization projects have improved communities' water quality, as well as recreational access to these remarkable water resources. The recreation and tourism industry is the second largest employer in the nation, and a significant portion of recreational spending comes from water-related activities, such as swimming, boating, sport fishing, and hunting. Ensuring that local waters are fishable is a sound investment for any community.

## Procedure

1. Ask students to name species of fish found in local waterways and write the name of the species on the board. (Hint: Teachers can contact their State Department of Fish and Wildlife to learn about the types of local fish species.) Write the word "FISH" in the center of the board and draw several lines with arrows radiating outward from the word (similar to spokes on a wheel; see Diagram A). Ask student volunteers to describe the values of fish for the local community, and write or draw a different value at the end of each spoke. Encourage students to consider how certain species might be of cultural, religious, economic, or recreational importance in their community.

2. Next, draw a set of spokes with arrows pointing toward the "FISH" hub. Have volunteers indicate factors necessary for fish survival. Encourage students to describe specific water quality factors (e.g., pH, temperature, turbidity, concentrations of oxygen, nitrates, phosphorus, etc.).

3. Facilitate a discussion about the importance of good water quality for fish in your community. Describe the Clean Water Act of 1972, legislation that set a goal for "fishable and

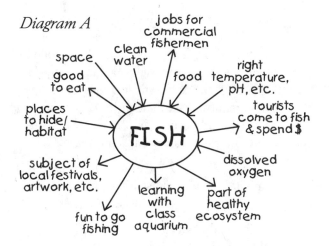

Diagram A

swimmable waters" (see "Background" on page 158). Ask students the following question: If waters are suitable for fishing and swimming, what other benefits —for wildlife and people—might be implied? Fish can be thought of as indicators of a healthy aquatic ecosystem that includes the food web necessary for survival and reproduction of fish and other species.

4. Divide the class into small groups of four to six students. Distribute copies of the "Sample Fishing Report" and instruct students to read independently or in their groups.

5. Facilitate a class discussion about the reading. Make sure students understand the connections between water quality, fish populations, and different natural and human impacts affecting both.

6. Explain that groups will play a card game to simulate the different ways human activity can impact water quality and fish populations in urban waterways. The challenge is to have the best "fishable waters" possible—indicated by lots of "fish" added to the waterway or by "fish" caught and distributed among players.

**Note:** Make sure students understand that results of actions on "Fishable Waters Action Cards" are presented solely from the perspective of impact on water quality, fish habitat, or fish populations. The cards are not intended to imply generalized judgment of any of the actions featured. For instance, hydropower

*continued*

dams generate power and store water for municpal and agricultural needs and also often adversely affect fish populations. Determining the pros and cons of building a dam in any particular area and determining whose water needs are most important are, of course, open for debate and beyond the scope of this simulation. This point can be made prior to or immediately following the simulation.

7.  Distribute a copy of "Fishable Waters Game Rules" to each group. Review and discuss the rules aloud.

8.  Distribute a set of cards, 40 tokens ("fish"), and other game materials to each group. See "Game Options" on page 164 for possible variations. Allow groups to start the simulation and play until at least one student from each group gets to "go fishing." Circulate among your students to make certain the game runs smoothly. You may pretend to be a fisheries biologist "stocking" waterways with fish. If you do stock fish, be certain to include the impact of stocking when discussing the results of the simulation.

9.  After 10 or 15 minutes (or after all cards have been read), stop the simulation. Ask groups to report the number of fish in their urban waterway, the number of fish in their lost fish pile, the number of fish "caught" and stored in their ice chests, and the number of people in their group who had the opportunity and chose to go fishing. Compile class data on the board.

10. Discuss the results of the simulation, including reasons for any differing results among groups. You may use the following questions to guide the discussion:

• What did a big pile of playing tokens represent?
  *A large, healthy (and diverse) fish population resulting from improved water quality and habitat, sustainable harvesting practices, effective stocking or some combination thereof—a large fish population indicates "fishable and swimmable" waters with a variety of community benefits.*

• What did a few tokens represent?
  *A small fish population (likely lacking in diversity) resulting from poor water quality, habitat destruction, overfishing or some combination thereof—indicating the need for habitat and community improvement projects and/or development of sustainable fishing practices).*

• Was obtaining fishable waters hard? How long did it take your group to have a "fishable" waterway?

• What happened as the game progressed and the deck got smaller?
  *More cards in the deck were fish and license cards, resulting in more opportunities to go fishing. Increased fishing without continued action projects or positive influences on fish populations causes fish populations to decline.*

• Which activities were more effective at improving water quality than others (more tokens added)?

• Which activities were more detrimental to healthy water and fish populations (more tokens removed)?

• How does this simulation represent the real world of water quality and fish populations?
  *Water quality and fish populations are not static: they change over time because of both natural and human influences.*

• How does this activity differ from the real world?
  *Resource managers and communities make and implement plans for managing water quality and fish populations, whereas actions in the simulation were more random; reproduction and other natural events would occur, causing fish populations to fluctuate differently.*

• How do fishing regulations influence the availability of fish?
  *Regulations serve to distribute and/or limit fishing opportunities for the purpose of maintaining viable and/or sustainable fish populations. Note: Some habitats have changed so*

*drastically that sustaining populations by natural reproduction alone is not possible. In other cases, the demand for fish is higher than the number of fish that is naturally sustainable. In both instances resource agencies may raise and stock fish to maintain populations.*

## Extensions

1. Students may conduct research on a recreationally or economically important local fish species. Are populations stable and sustainable? Have populations or biodiversity changed over time? If so, why? What management strategies (regulations, stocking, habitat improvement projects, etc.) are used to ensure viable populations? Or, invite a fisheries biologist to visit your classroom and speak about managing local fish populations and what they do to attain or maintain fishable waters.

2. Challenge students to identify and report on local water quality or fish population issues. After hearing student reports, encourage the members of the class to decide how they would like to take action. Sample projects include: raising fish in the classroom; organizing a river cleanup; monitoring water quality or fish populations; designing projects on runoff/erosion control (building and installing rain barrels, planting rain gardens and trees, etc.).

3. Plan a fishing trip. Most states have resources for urban fishing, including: tackle loaner programs; free "how-to" fishing clinics; lists and maps of places to fish; free fishing days; and print materials, such as fish posters or identification cards.

4. Have students quiz each other, using their state's fishing regulations booklet.

5. Conduct your own fishing simulation using "Backyard Bass" (by Ironwood Pacific). Children and adults learn to operate reels and cast a special weight that "hooks" (using a non-hooking device) a plastic fish. You may also make your own fish using felt and Velcro.

6. Work with your school's physical education teacher to apply for a grant to acquire fishing rods so students can practice the life skill of casting.

## Evaluation

1. Draw a new "fish wheel," highlighting areas of possible concern regarding fishable waters in your community.

2. List or describe a variety of reasons why fish are important to your community.

3. Identify and describe five negative impacts on water quality or fish populations.

4. Describe ways to address negative impacts on water quality or fish populations.

5. Relate how human activities are connected to water quality and how water quality is connected to fish populations.

*continued*

# Game Options

1. Use pennies as tokens to represent the economic value of "fishable and swimmable" waters in your community.

2. Use fish-shaped crackers or other snacks to represent an important product of "fishable and swimmable waters," food for wildlife and humans. If you use snack food as tokens, ask students to refrain from eating their "catch" until the end of the game and class discussion. This enables students to tally and compare their catches at the end of the simulation.

3. Enhance the sense of "fishing" by making fishing rods using a pencil, string (approximately 1 foot in length), flat thumb tack and small magnet. Use metal paper clips to represent fish. You might use both large and small paper clips, stipulating that large paper clips represent keeper-size fish and that small paper clips represent fish sized below the legal limit. Players should put back (or release) any small paper clips they "catch."

4. At times during the simulation a student may answer a question on a "Fishable Waters Action Card" correctly, but still be required to subtract a "fish" from his or her urban waterway because of the detrimental effect an action has on fish populations. If you feel your students will object to this, you might consider an alternative tracking and reward system to recognize students for providing correct answers to questions.

---

**Directions for making a fishing rod:**

A. Tie a small knot in one end of a string. Insert a thumbtack into the knot, and then push the tack into the eraser end of a pencil.

B. Cut a piece of magnetic tape about an inch in length. Don't take the paper backing off the tape—the adhesive is very sticky.

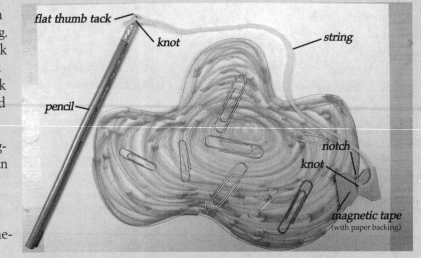

flat thumb tack
knot
string
pencil
notch
knot
magnetic tape
(with paper backing)

C. Cut two small "v" shaped notches on either side of the piece of magnetic tape.

D. Tie the string onto the tape, securing it in the notch. Make sure the knot is on the paper side of the magnet so that the magnet can work effectively to "catch" paper clips.

## Sample Fishing Report

# What's the Catch in the D.C. Metro Area?
## -A Fishing Report for April 2005 -

Cool spring water temperatures in the Potomac River and nearby tributaries mean fishing is "hot." Cold waters hold more dissolved oxygen than warm waters—meaning fish are breathing easily. In the Potomac, largemouth bass are hitting lures, including soft plastic jigs and vertically jigged spoons, with frenzy! D.C. and Maryland regulations limit a daily take of five fish measuring at least 12 inches (15 inches after June 15th), and conservation officers will ticket anglers over their limit!

The mouth of Little Hunting Creek (VA) is usually a great spot for catching bass, but runoff from a nearby construction project is washing soil into the river causing high turbidity (muddy water) even after light rains. To compensate for the turbidity, anglers are using dark lures. Later in the season, bass anglers know they can catch fish in the grass beds (submerged aquatic vegetation) near the Woodrow Wilson Bridge.

Yellow perch have spawned out, but a few are still being caught in Piscataway Creek (MD). Anglers reported strong bluegill action at Cameron Run (VA) when casting small jigs toward the grass edges, shoreline vegetation or under overhanging trees. This riparian zone provides shade that cools the water. Roots prevent bank erosion and are perfect structure for hiding or resting perch.

**TROUT IN WASHINGTON?** - Paint Branch Creek (MD) is a unique urban cold-water fishery with wild brown trout. Nonpoint source pollution from urban runoff continues to threaten these pollution-intolerant fish. Fisheries biologists and local conservation groups have educated people living along the creek about the need to reduce fertilizer use, especially before a rain. Nutrients in fertilizers, manure, leaky septic tanks, and pet wastes cause explosive algal blooms. Eventually, this algae rots causing a stinking mess that consumes dissolved oxygen—suffocating fish and other aquatic critters. To find trout, focus on riffles, the swift, bubbly areas that help oxygenate water.

The Anacostia Park (D.C.) is always good for channel catfish. Serious anglers fish right from the shore, using surf rods to get their lines into the river channel. A weighted line with cut bait works best. These fish are fun to catch, but D.C. has published a fish consumption advisory against eating catfish, as they may harbor harmful toxins.

U.S. FISH AND WILDLIFE SERVICE
*American Shad caught in net.*

This past spring biologists reported record numbers of spawning American shad just below Chain Bridge off Fletcher's Boathouse (D.C.). The return of this historic fish is due in part to the hundreds of students raising fish in the classroom and the fishway or ladder at the Little Falls Dam that helps spawning fish navigate the 12 foot dam upstream to their preferred habitat.

Other local improvement plans include a shoreline revitalization project along the Anacostia River. Once completed, people will be able to enjoy fishing piers, boardwalks, and parks—the perfect spot to grill up your catch. In the meantime, we encourage anglers to join a river cleanup organized by the Earth Conservation Corps—Riverkeepers. To date, Riverkeepers have hauled out 536 tons of trash and 8,103 tires.

### HOMEGROWN HEROES

Since 1989, the Anacostia Watershed Society–along with thousands of volunteers–has aimed to make D.C.'s Anacostia River more "fishable and swimmable." Their projects include:

- Wetland Nursery Project
- Urban Forests Project
- Streambank Stabilization
- Non-native Plant Removal
- Water Quality Flagging
  *(blue flags = water is safe for boating)*
- River Cleanups
- Stormdrain Stenciling
- Shad & Herring Awareness and Restoration Effort (SHARE)

Source: <www.anacostiaws.org>

### GOOD OLD DAYS? -

Old timers might remember when fishing our nation's rivers wasn't this good. Back in the 1950's, the Potomac ran foul with factory discharge and poorly treated sewage (point source pollution). The Clean Water Act in 1972 regulated this pollution, and now 60% of U.S. waterways are "fishable and swimmable"—twice the number of fishable waters as before the Act. Today, the Potomac is considered one of the nation's premier bass fisheries, and anglers can watch nesting bald eagles while they fish—an indication that water quality has improved. Biodiversity in a waterway is not just about lots of different fish species—but includes all other animals and plants living in or near the waterway.

*continued*

# Fishable Waters Game Rules

*Discover how human activities impact fish populations. Take turns drawing cards, answering questions, taking action, and going fishing. The group with the most "fishable" waterway at the end of the game wins!*

## Setting Up the Game:

1. Place 10 tokens (15 for groups with 5 or 6 players) in the center of your group. The tokens represent "fish" in your urban waterway. Place the deck of cards face down to serve as your Draw Pile.

2. Place remaining tokens in a Stock Tank. You will add these fish to your urban waterway, as directed on cards.

### Your group's goals are:

- **To improve your fishable waters—indicated by increasing the fish population (# of tokens) in your waterway**

- **To have each individual in your group collect three (3) fish cards and one (1) fishing license card in order to "go fishing"**

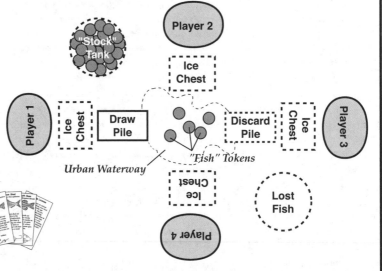

## Playing the Game:

1. Decide who will go first. Begin the game by drawing a card from the Draw Pile.

2. If the card has a ★, read it aloud and ask the player to your left to answer the question. Instruct the player to add or subtract fish from your urban waterway, as directed on the card. Subtracted tokens represent fish lost because of negative impacts on water quality and habitat. Make a separate pile of "Lost Fish" for later comparison. Place the used question card face up in a Discard Pile.

3. If the card has a ●, read it aloud and do what it says.

4. If you draw a **fish** or **license** card, read it aloud and keep it.

5. Play moves clockwise (to player's left). Take turns drawing cards, answering questions, and collecting **fish** and **license** cards.

6. When you collect 3 **fish** cards and 1 **license** card, you may "go fishing." Fishing regulations limit your "catch" to 5 fish. If using large and small tokens, only large fish may be kept; release small fish back into the waterway.

   Before going fishing, decide whether waters are "fishable."

   - What if there aren't enough fish in the waterway to take your limit of five?
   - Should you take fewer than five?
   - Should you take any?
   - What if you practice "catch and release" where you return all fish "caught" back into the waterway?

   Decide whether to take what's available or wait to go fishing until the waters get more "fishable."

7. If you do go fishing, shuffle your **fish** and **license** cards back into the Draw Pile. Keep all fish in your "Ice Chest" for later comparison.

8. If you draw an extra **fish** (you have more than 3) or **license** card (you have more than 1), shuffle it back into the Draw Pile and draw a new card.

9. If you draw a **Wild Card!**, you may go fishing right away. Keep any **fish** or **license** cards you have accumulated, but shuffle the **Wild Card!** back into the Draw Pile.

10. When your teacher calls time to end the game, count and record the number of fish in your Urban Waterway, Lost Fish pile, and Ice Chests. Also record how many people went fishing.

---

### RULES AT A GLANCE

- **You may go fishing only when you have 3 fish cards AND 1 fishing license (fish cards can be any species)—OR when you draw a Wild Card! After fishing, return your collected cards to the Draw Pile and reshuffle.**

- **When fishing you must follow regulations (possession limit of 5 fish), but you may take fewer if you choose.**

- **Players must immediately shuffle extra fish and license cards into the Draw Pile so that others can collect them.**

# Urban Fish Species & License Cards

## Yellow Perch
**Scientific Name:** *Perca flavescens*

**Bait/Lures:** Perch are delicious eating and easy to catch, especially during spawning season. Fish near structures using minnows, grass shrimp, or worms. Jigs, small plugs that imitate small fish (minnows or crayfish), are good lures.

*jig*

## Channel Catfish
**Scientific Name:** *Ictalurus punctatus*

**Bait/Lures:** Catfish are active mainly at night, during twilight hours, and during or right after a rain. These are bottom feeders, so fish them deep with a sinker. Cut bait, like herring or chicken liver, work great, but worms, stinkbait, and cheese are good, too.

*worm on hook*

## Bluegill
**Scientific Name:** *Lepomis macrochirus*

**Bait/Lures:** Fish for bluegill near "structure" (brush piles, weeds, docks), using worms you dig from your yard or small jigs and spinners. Using a sinker, fish about a foot from the bottom and attach a bobber so you can see when they hit.

*bobbers*

## Brown Trout
**Scientific Name:** *Salmo trutta*

**Bait/Lures:** Trout are smart predators, so you need to think like a trout. Is it winter? Then don't fish with grasshoppers. Your best bet is lures that mimic local baitfish: small crankbaits (crawfish and minnows), spinners, and flies (not *real* flies, ones made with feathers and fur).

*trout fly*

## Largemouth Bass
**Scientific Name:** *Micropterus salmoides*

**Bait/Lures:** Largemouth are predators that lurk in weedy, quiet waters and feed mainly on other fish. Minnows are great bait, but live or plastic worms work, too. Bass are often caught on spinner baits and crankbaits.

*spinner baits*

## Fishing License

Most states require an annual fishing license (check your local regulations for specific age requirements).

Did you know that license sales help fund fish research, restoration and stocking programs, access sites (parks, piers, docks, etc.), and education programs? By buying a license, you're not only obeying the law but also helping fish and habitat as well.

**Fishing license sales help fish.
(Add 1 "fish")**

## American Shad
**Scientific Name:** *Alosa sapidissima*

**Bait/Lures:** American shad live in the ocean but reproduce (spawn) in freshwater. The best time to fish for them is during their spawning run when they congregate near dams or fishways. Fish for shad with flutter spoons, shad darts, or small Clouser flies.

*flutter spoon*

## Fishing License

Most states require an annual fishing license (check your local regulations for specific age requirements).

Did you know that license sales help fund fish research, restoration and stocking programs, access sites (parks, piers, docks, etc.), and education programs? By buying a license, you're not only obeying the law but also helping fish and habitat as well.

**Fishing license sales help fish.
(Add 1 "fish")**

*continued*

# Fishable Waters Action Cards

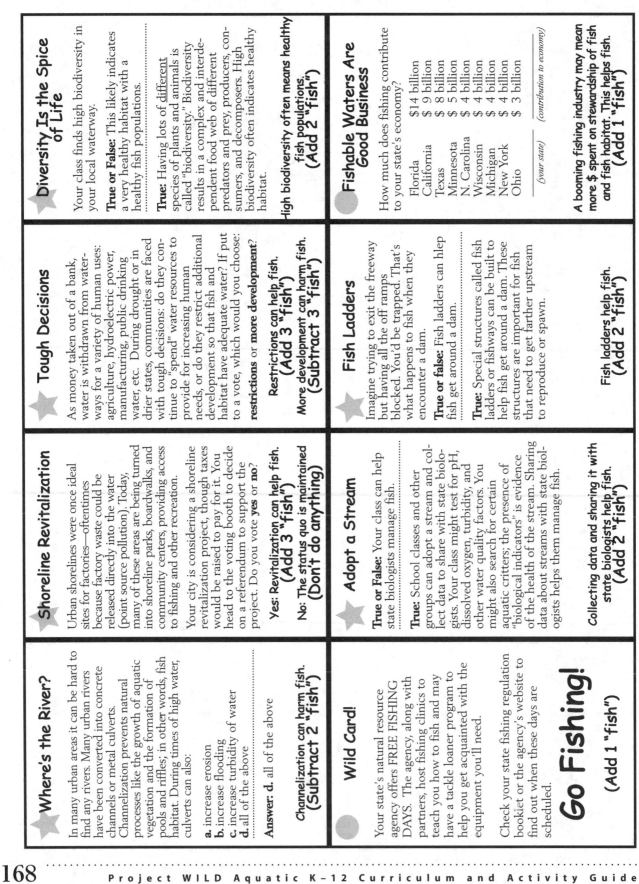

## ⭐ Diversity Is the Spice of Life

Your class finds high biodiversity in your local waterway.

**True or False:** This likely indicates a very healthy habitat with a healthy fish populations.

**True:** Having lots of different species of plants and animals is called "biodiversity." Biodiversity results in a complex and interdependent food web of different predators and prey, producers, consumers, and decomposers. High biodiversity often indicates healthy habitat.

High biodiversity often means healthy fish populations.
**(Add 2 "fish")**

## ⬤ Fishable Waters Are Good Business

How much does fishing contribute to your state's economy?

| | |
|---|---|
| Florida | $14 billion |
| California | $ 9 billion |
| Texas | $ 8 billion |
| Minnesota | $ 5 billion |
| N. Carolina | $ 4 billion |
| Wisconsin | $ 4 billion |
| Michigan | $ 4 billion |
| New York | $ 4 billion |
| Ohio | $ 3 billion |

_(your state)_ _____ _(contribution to economy)_

A booming fishing industry may mean more $ spent on stewardship of fish and fish habitat. This helps fish.
**(Add 1 "fish")**

## ⭐ Tough Decisions

As money taken out of a bank, water is withdrawn from waterways for a variety of human uses: agriculture, hydroelectric power, manufacturing, public drinking water, etc. During drought or in drier states, communities are faced with tough decisions: do they continue to "spend" water resources to provide for increasing human needs, or do they restrict additional development so that fish and habitat have adequate water? If put to a vote, which would you choose: **restrictions** or **more development**?

Restrictions can help fish.
**(Add 3 "fish")**
More development can harm fish.
**(Subtract 3 "fish")**

## ⭐ Fish Ladders

Imagine trying to exit the freeway but having all the off ramps blocked. You'd be trapped. That's what happens to fish when they encounter a dam.

**True or false:** Fish ladders can help fish get around a dam.

**True:** Special structures called fish ladders or fishways can be built to help fish get around a dam. These structures are important for fish that need to get farther upstream to reproduce or spawn.

Fish ladders help fish.
**(Add 2 "fish")**

## ⭐ Shoreline Revitalization

Urban shorelines were once ideal sites for factories—oftentimes because factory waste could be released directly into the water (point source pollution). Today, many of these areas are being turned into shoreline parks, boardwalks, and community centers, providing access to fishing and other recreation.

Your city is considering a shoreline revitalization project, though taxes would be raised to pay for it. You head to the voting booth to decide on a referendum to support the project. Do you vote **yes** or **no**?

Yes: Revitalization can help fish.
**(Add 3 "fish")**
No: The status quo is maintained
**(Don't do anything)**

## ⭐ Adopt a Stream

**True or False:** Your class can help state biologists manage fish.

**True:** School classes and other groups can adopt a stream and collect data to share with state biologists. Your class might test for pH, dissolved oxygen, turbidity, and other water quality factors. You might also search for certain aquatic critters; the presence of "biological indicators" is evidence of the health of the stream. Sharing data about streams with state biologists helps them manage fish.

Collecting data and sharing it with state biologists helps fish.
**(Add 2 "fish")**

## ⭐ Where's the River?

In many urban areas it can be hard to find any rivers. Many urban rivers have been converted into concrete channels or metal culverts. Channelization prevents natural processes like the growth of aquatic vegetation and the formation of pools and riffles; in other words, fish habitat. During times of high water, culverts can also:

**a.** increase erosion
**b.** increase flooding
**c.** increase turbidity of water
**d.** all of the above

**Answer: d.** all of the above

Channelization can harm fish.
**(Subtract 2 "fish")**

## ⬤ Wild Card!

Your state's natural resource agency offers FREE FISHING DAYS. The agency, along with partners, host fishing clinics to teach you how to fish and may have a tackle loaner program to help you get acquainted with the equipment you'll need.

Check your state fishing regulation booklet or the agency's website to find out when these days are scheduled.

## Go Fishing!

**(Add 1 "fish")**

# Fishable Waters Action Cards *(continued)*

## Storm Drain Stenciling

**True or False:** It is easier and more cost effective to prevent pollution from getting in our water than to restore water quality, habitat, and fish populations later.

**True:** Pollution prevention, including public education and storm drain stenciling, can help reduce the often enormous costs of restoring waterways after they have been polluted.

You can help by educating your community about the harm in using sewers as dumps by stenciling:

"all drains lead to
name your waterway here"

**Pollution prevention helps fish.
(Add 1 "fish")**

## Litter: Trash or Treasure?

**True or False:** Litter may look ugly, but it poses no harm to fish and other aquatic wildlife.

**False:** Many types of litter can cause great harm to aquatic wildlife. Litter may be mistaken for food and ingested, such as when sea turtles eat floating plastic bags, thinking that they are jellyfish. Wildlife can also become ensnared in plastic rings used to package beverages or in discarded fishing line.

**Litter harms fish.
(Subtract 2 "fish")**

## Stream Cleanups

We can't prevent all pollution from entering our water—but we can take action.

Your group decides to organize a local cleanup event to help get the trash out. You invite the local media so that your community can learn how they can help maintain "fishable and swimmable waters," too.

**Stream cleanups can help fish.
(Add 1 "fish")**

## Riparian Buffer Zones

How can trees, shoreline vegetation, and wetlands help fish and improve water quality?

**a.** Trees and shoreline vegetation trap runoff before it gets to our waterways.
**b.** Wetlands absorb and filter out pollutants and protect young fish.
**c.** Trees shade waterways, keeping them cooler.
**d.** all of the above

**Answer: d.** all of the above

**Riparian buffer zones help fish.
(Add 3 "fish")**

## Fishing Regulations

You know someone who keeps all the fish they catch—no matter how large or small the fish are. *What if everyone did this?*

How can you learn about current fishing regulations?

**a.** Read your state's current fishing regulations booklet.
**b.** Ask your fishing buddy.
**c.** Ask your uncle (he hasn't gone fishing in 5 years).
**d.** none of the above

**Answer: a.** Read your state's current fishing regulations booklet.

**Following fishing regulations helps fish.
(Add 1 "fish")**

## Fish in the Classroom

Native fish in your area are in trouble—they aren't reproducing at a rate that maintains a sustainable population.

Your class wants to help by hatching eggs and raising fish in the classroom and then releasing them back into your local waterway. Who might you work with to achieve this goal?

**a.** environmental education center
**b.** state fish and game offices
**c.** local fishing clubs
**d.** all of the above

**Answer: d.** all of the above

**Raising and releasing fish helps maintain fish populations.
(Add 3 "fish")**

## Algal Blooms

You discover algae growing out of control in your favorite fishing hole. It is beginning to rot and stink. You see a dead fish floating on the surface of the water and remember that the rotting process (called decomposition) uses up oxygen. This means there is less dissolved oxygen for aquatic animals, such as fish. What is the likely cause of this algal bloom?

**a.** too much sunlight
**b.** excess nutrients, including nitrogen and phosphorous
**c.** emptying aquarium water into the fishing hole
**d.** none of the above

**Answer: b.** excess nutrients

**Algal blooms harm fish.
(Subtract 3 "fish")**

## In Hot Water

Thermal pollution, adding warm water to a waterway, reduces dissolved oxygen, changes habitat, and can stress fish if the temperature rises too much. Which of the following cause thermal pollution?

**a.** direct discharge of warm water from factories and power plants
**b.** runoff from hot city streets and pavement
**c.** a summer heat wave
**d.** both a. and b.

**Answer: d.** both a. and b.

**Thermal pollution harms fish.
(Subtract 2 "fish")**

continued

# Fishable Waters Action Cards *(continued)*

## ★ Conservation Officer

**True or False:** Conservation officers can't ticket people.

**False:** Conservation officers are like police officers, but their main duty is to protect our natural resources. They ticket people who don't follow regulations and can arrest poachers—people who don't follow fishing or hunting regulations.

Enforcing fishing regulations helps fish.
**(Add 1 "fish")**

## ★ Clean Water Act

The Clean Water Act of 1972 did much to regulate point source pollution—pollution that can be traced to a definite point where it enters the environment. An example of point source pollution is:

**a.** chemicals leaking from a factory's discharge pipe
**b.** runoff from fields
**c.** sewage from a discharge pipe
**d.** both a and c.

**Answer: d.** both a and c. Both chemicals and sewage from discharge pipes can be traced to their sources. Regulating this type of pollution has led to a dramatic improvement in water quality in many waterways.

The Clean Water Act helps fish.
**(Add 3 "fish")**

## ★ Keep or Release?

Many anglers choose to practice "catch and release." After reeling in a fish, they carefully unhook their catch and gently return it to the waterway. When practiced properly, catch and release does not harm fish. There are no limits on catch and release fishing.

*Go fishing and practice catch and release!*

Catch and release helps fish.
**(Add 2 "fish")**

## ★ Fish Consumption Advisories

**True or False:** All fish are good for you to eat.

**False:** Some fish may contain high levels of mercury and other toxins, which make them unsafe to eat. Each state publishes "fish consumption advisories." Check your regulations to know which fish are listed as unsafe to eat.

Fish under consumption advisories are living in polluted waters.
**(Subtract 1 "fish")**

## ★ Permeable or Impermeable Materials

You are a member of the city planning commission. A vote has come up to decide whether new parking lots should be made of permeable or impermeable materials. Permeable materials allow some rain to seep into the ground whereas impermeable materials do not absorb water and can cause runoff. You know that controlling runoff helps reduce erosion, but permeable materials can be very costly. Which way will you vote? permeable or impermeable

Impermeable materials: Increasing runoff can harm fish.
**(Subtract 2 "fish")**
Permeable materials: Controlling runoff can help fish.
**(Add 2 "fish")**

## ★ Construction and Water Quality

Which of the following would help your construction company win a "*Water Steward of the Year Award*"?

**a.** Leaving as much native vegetation and trees on site as possible
**b.** Installing silt fencing or wattles to prevent erosion and reseeding after construction
**c.** Installing raingardens and catchment basins that take up excess storm water
**d.** all of the above

**Answer: d.** all of the above

Environmentally responsible construction helps fish.
**(Add 2 "fish")**

## ★ Water Conservation

Water conservation increases the availability of water for all life forms, but sometimes there just isn't enough to go around.

During times of drought, should your city restrict certain water uses, like watering lawns, washing cars, and filling swimming pools?

**Yes or No**

**Yes:** Conserving water, especially during drought, helps fish.
**(Add 3 "fish")**
**No:** Using water for nonessential purposes, especially during drought, harms fish.
**(Subtract 3 "fish")**

## ★ Aquatic Vegetation

**True or False:** Submerged aquatic vegetation, like grasses, is messy and should be cleaned out of rivers and lakes.

**False:** Fish need a place to hide from predators and to rest. If you've ever gone fishing, you know that many species of fish hang out near grasses and other aquatic plants. This structure is "home sweet home" to fish.

Submerged aquatic vegetation helps fish.
**(Add 2 "fish")**

# Fishable Waters Action Cards *(continued)*

## Hydropower Dams

**True or False:** A dam provides extra water, which is good for the native fish that lived in the river before it was blocked by the dam.

**False:** Large dams generate power and store water for municipal and agricultural needs. But most fish and other native species prefer their natural river environment—not a warm, still reservoir. Some dams drain rivers virtually dry, allowing only a trickle to pass below—not good for fish or other aquatic species.

Dams can harm fish.
**(Subtract 1 "fish")**

## Nutrient-rich Wastes

Excess nutrients in waterways can cause algal blooms, which in turn may cause "dead zones" and "fish kills" by depleting dissolved oxygen. How can we prevent excess nutrients from entering our waterways?

**a.** Maintain or upgrade wastewater treatment plants.
**b.** Limit fertilizer use on lawns, golf courses and farms, especially before a rain.
**c.** Scoop pet and livestock droppings.
**d.** all of the above

**Answer: d.** all of the above

Keeping excess nutrients out of waterways helps fish.
**(Add 2 "fish")**

## Off-season fishing

It's a week before bass season opens. Your buddy hooks a trophy-sized largemouth bass. This is:

**a.** illegal
**b.** called poaching
**c.** a great opportunity for his uncle, a taxidermist
**d.** both a. and b.

**Answer: d.** both a. and b. Poaching means fishing or hunting out of season, taking more than the legal limit, and fishing or hunting without a license. Seasons and limits are set by resource managers to prevent overfishing. License sales help pay for management and track the number of anglers.

Poaching harms fish.
**(Subtract 1 "fish")**

## Go Green!

Your neighbor removed trees and shrubs from her yard that were blocking her river view.

**True or False:** She can be fined and forced to replant.

**True.** In many areas setback laws require that business and residents maintain a "buffer zone" of trees and other plants along waterways. This vegetation filters pollutants and stabilizes banks, preventing erosion.

A single tree can keep more than 4,000 gallons of water out of the sewer each year. Just imagine what a whole shoreline of trees can do!

Setback laws help fish.
**(Add 2 "fish")**

## Impermeable Surfaces

An example of an impermeable surface is:

**a.** a wetland
**b.** a dirt road
**c.** a concrete parking lot
**d.** none of the above

**Answer: c.** concrete parking lot
Many urban and suburban areas are concrete: streets, sidewalks, parking lots, and buildings. These impermeable surfaces don't allow rain or snowmelt to seep into the ground. During heavy rains, city storm drains are often flooded by runoff that has picked up chemical pollution and street trash, too.

Impermeable surfaces on land can harm fish.
**(Subtract 2 "fish")**

## Attack of the Aliens

**True or False:** It's okay to dump or release your live bait when you're done fishing.

**False:** If bait is not native to your waterway, it is called an "alien species." Unfortunately, some aliens can become invasive, meaning they out-compete native species for food and habitat. They can take over and disrupt the natural ecological balance.

Alien species may harm fish.
**(Subtract 1 "fish")**

## Nonpoint Source Pollution

Which is an example of nonpoint source pollution?

**a.** oil leaking from a docked ship
**b.** chemicals seeping from a landfill
**c.** motor oil washing from driveways, streets, and parking lots
**d.** sewage overflow from a sewage treatment plant

**Answer: c.** When we can't point to the source of pollution in waterways—which may come from many different streets, lawns, construction sites, parking lots, and farms—we call it nonpoint source pollution. Most water pollution today comes from nonpoint sources.

Nonpoint source pollution harms fish.
**(Subtract 2 "fish")**

## Turbidity

Turbidity means:

**a.** cloudy or muddy water
**b.** still or slow moving water
**c.** cranking a fishing reel slowly

**Answer: a.** Another word for muddy water is "turbidity." Storms can stir up sediments that are "turbid." Storms can stir up sediments from the bottom of waterways, and heavy runoff erodes banks and washes soil into streams and rivers. Some fish have a hard time feeding in turbid, muddy water, and sediments can smother fish eggs as well as reduce resting and hiding places.

Turbid water may harm fish.
**(Subtract 2 "fish")**

# Turtle Hurdles

## Objectives

Students will (1) describe the life cycle of sea turtles, (2) identify specific mortality factors related to sea turtles, (3) make inferences about the effects of limiting factors on sea turtle populations, and (4) make recommendations to minimize the factors that might lead to the extinction of sea turtles.

## Method

Students become sea turtles and limiting factors in a highly active simulation game.

## Materials

40 to 60 feet of rope or string, two jump ropes or hula hoops, one paper or plastic bag per student, identity cards for each predator or limiting factor (can be drawn by students), wooden clothes pins, poker chips, dried beans

---

**Grade Level:** 5–8

**Subject Areas:** Science, Social Studies, Environmental Education

**Duration:** one 45-minute session

**Group Size:** 20 to 40 students or more

**Setting:** outdoors or large indoor area

**Conceptual Framework Topic Reference:** ITIB1, ITIIA1

**Key Terms:** life cycle, endangered species, prey, predator, limiting factors, sea turtles

**Appendices:** Simulations, List of Agencies and Organizations

---

## Background

Sea turtles are survivors of the great age of the dinosaurs and inhabit nearly all the oceans of the world. The best-known sea turtles are in the family Cheloniidae, which contains the green turtle, loggerhead turtle, hawksbill turtle, and ridley turtle. The huge leatherback turtle, the largest living turtle, is placed in Dermochelyidae, a separate family. Sea turtles live mostly in warm waters and have limbs modified into flippers. Female sea turtles crawl above the tide line to bury their eggs. Sea turtles leave the water only during these nesting periods. It is during this time that the turtles and their offspring are the most vulnerable to predation by humans and other wildlife.

As with most reptiles, turtles lay eggs. The eggs look somewhat like wet, pliable Ping-Pong balls. Using their rear flippers, female sea turtles dig deep holes on sandy beaches where they lay and bury their eggs. Mature female sea turtles may deposit several hundred eggs in one season. Once the eggs are buried, the females return to the sea or seek additional nesting sites.

The eggs incubate for nearly 2 months. If the eggs survive predation by raccoons, ghost crabs, foxes, dogs, and humans, then the sea turtles hatch, dig their way upward through the sand, and promptly head toward the sea. Predatory crabs, raccoons, and dogs, with gulls and other birds joining in, typically accompany the hatchlings' journey across the beach. Once hatched, only about 1 to 5 percent of the turtles survive the first year. In the sea, the turtles must mature for nearly a decade before returning to nesting sites as a natural part of their life cycle.

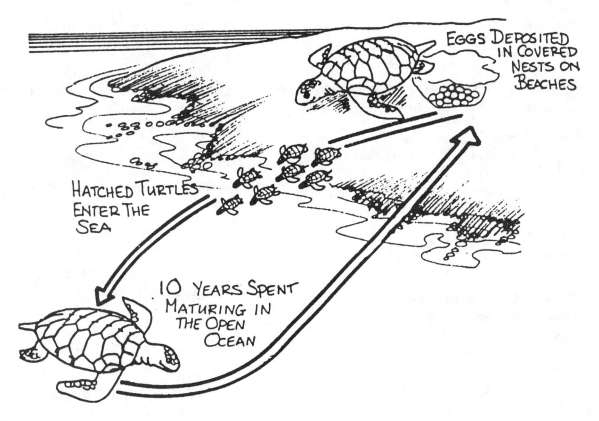

EGGS DEPOSITED IN COVERED NESTS ON BEACHES

HATCHED TURTLES ENTER THE SEA

10 YEARS SPENT MATURING IN THE OPEN OCEAN

*Diagram A*

Biologists are uncertain how long sea turtles reproduce and live. Diagram A illustrates the life cycle of a sea turtle.

The motives for human predation are based predominantly on products that are outlawed in many countries. Jewelry, leather, oil, and food are the primary uses. Turtle eggs are seen by some as a boost to longevity and vigor; tens of thousands of eggs are illegally harvested for vanity sales. Evidence suggests that a serious human threat to the turtles is the poaching of their eggs from their nesting sites.

There are other human-caused factors. Dune buggies may break the eggs buried in the sand. More damaging, given the scope of the impact, is commercial and private construction (condominiums, private homes, hotels, etc.) on coastal sites. This construction may create a barricade that prevents the turtles from reaching their traditional nesting sites and that eliminates many nest sites. Entanglement in discarded fishing gear and plastic waste cast into the oceans is a serious hazard, killing many sea turtles each year. Many turtles fall accidental victim to the nets of large fishing trawlers. Once caught in the nets, they drown. Efforts are being made to popularize special trawling devices that will prevent turtles from getting trapped in the nets. One of the turtles' favorite foods is jellyfish. Many turtles mistake the human-produced litter of floating plastic bags for this food. When eaten by the turtle, its digestive tract becomes blocked with the discarded plastic and it dies.

Six of the seven known sea turtle species are officially designated either endangered or threatened. The leatherback, olive ridley, Kemp's ridley, hawksbill, green, and loggerhead are all listed as endangered species by the U.S. Fish and Wildlife Service.

*continued*

## Procedure

1. Set up the activity areas as shown in Diagram B on page 176. Give each student a paper or plastic bag.

2. Divide the class into two groups.

### Group 1—Turtles
Each student counts out 50 beans to place in his or her bag. Beans represent turtles. Each bag of beans represents the turtles that hatch from a single nest.

### Group 2—Limiting Factors
Divide this group into two smaller groups, on-land and in-sea.

*On-land:* Predators (e.g., raccoons, dogs, ghost crabs, foxes, and gulls) and limiting factors from human activities (e.g., dune buggies, human egg collectors, shoreline development)

*In-sea:* Predators (e.g., sharks, killer whales) and limiting factors from human activities (e.g., entanglement in fishing gear, eating plastic litter, illegal killings by humans)

Give each student a sign that indicates what kind of limiting factor each one represents. Attach those identity signs to students' clothing with clothes pins.

3. Walk the class through the activity and explain these rules:

A. Turtles must hatch, cross the beach, and spend 10 years in the open sea. The turtles running between the year zones simulate the time in the ocean. They pick up one poker chip at a year zone and then run to the other year zone to pick up another poker chip. Each chip represents 2 years of successful ocean survival. After collecting five poker chips, turtles return to the nesting area to reproduce.

B. Turtles try to avoid limiting factors and predators. If tagged by a limiting factor, a turtle stops, counts out 10 beans, and places those 10 beans in the limiting factor's bag.

C. The ocean's sea grass areas are turtle safety zones where limiting factors cannot tag them. The teacher may set a time limit for how long a turtle may rest in a sea grass zone. OPTIONAL: The educator may eliminate the safety zones after the turtles have been in the ocean for a while. This change simulates the turtles growing too big to hide in the sea grass.

D. Limiting factors must obey the following rules:

- They cannot tag the same turtle twice in a row.

- They cannot tag turtles that are counting out beans to another limiting factor.

- They must stay at least four steps away from any turtle that is transferring beans to another limiting factor.

E. Any turtle that loses all 50 beans is dead. It must go to the beach and become a condominium. If the condominiums (sitting side by side) eventually block the access to the nesting beach, the remaining turtles die without reproducing and starting the next cycle.

F. The activity ends when all turtles are either dead or have returned to the nest area.

4. Review the rules two times to make sure the students understand their roles and the procedures. Students then become endangered sea turtles or limiting factors and conduct the activity.

5. After completing the activity, encourage the students to discuss the results. It is likely that some students will be disturbed by the high mortality of the turtles and will benefit from the realization that there are groups actively trying to diminish human contributions to such high mortality. However, it is also important to emphasize that natural limiting factors are built into the scheme of things.

If all sea turtle eggs survived, there might well be an overabundance of these creatures. Many animals produce more young than will survive, serving as food for other species as a part of nature's dynamic balance. Ask the students to briefly describe the life cycle of sea turtles.

6. Summarize the importance of the high numbers of turtles that result from reproduction. Ask the students to identify and discuss the factors that limit the turtles' survival. Because sea turtles are threatened with extinction, the limiting factors affecting their survival seem to be out of balance. What specific recommendations would the students suggest to increase the successful reproduction and survival of sea turtles?

## Extensions

1. Change the ratio of predators and hazards to turtles ($^1/_3$ predators or hazards to $^2/_3$ sea turtles), and replay the simulation. Describe and discuss the differences.

2. Set up a sea turtle information center.

3. Where possible, visit sea turtle restoration sites, and determine what actions may be taken to enhance the stability of sea turtle populations.

4. Replay the activity with all human factors removed from influence.

## Evaluation

1. Describe and illustrate the major stages of sea turtles' life cycle, beginning with the egg.

2. Name at least four limiting factors that prevent sea turtles from reaching the adult breeding stage.

3. Write a law that would help protect sea turtles. What would the law include? Who would enforce it?

*continued*

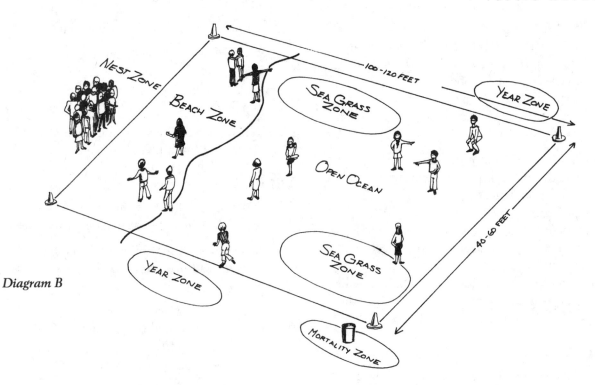

*Diagram B*

**nest zone:** the place where the eggs are laid and hatch (This is the zone to which the surviving turtles will return in 10 years. It is where the baby turtles hatch and begin their journey to the sea.)

**beach zone:** the zone the hatchlings must cross to get to the sea (It is a place of high predation and other limiting factors.)

**sea zone:** the area where the turtles must mature for a period of 10 years before returning to nest

**year zones:** the two zones that the turtles must visit to acquire the year cards necessary to "mature" to 10 years of age (One poker chip is awarded for each one-way trip between the zones. During the trip between the zones, the turtles are vulnerable to predators and other limiting factors. Turtles are safe from other limiting factors when they are inside either year zone.)

**sea grass zones:** places where the turtles are safe until they reach 4 years of age (At that age they are too large to hide from predators.)

# Aquatic Roots

## Objectives

Students will (1) trace the origins of various species of local aquatic animals, aquatic plants or both; (2) categorize them into native and exotic species; and (3) evaluate the appropriateness of introducing new species.

## Method

Students use reference materials to research various local aquatic plants, or animals, to find out whether they are natives or exotics and to investigate their effects on people, other animals, and the environment.

## Materials

A world map, yarn, paper, reference materials, and a list of local non-native plants and animals

---

**Grade Level:** 5–8

**Subject Areas:** Science, Social Studies, Environmental Education

**Duration:** two or three 45-minute sessions with additional time for student research and preparation of reports

**Group Size:** several small groups or individual students

**Setting:** indoors

**Conceptual Framework Topic Reference:** ITIIA2, ITIIA2b

**Key Terms:** exotic, native, introduced species, benefits, liabilities, tradeoffs, regulations

**Appendices:** none

---

## Background

A non-native species is a species that does not naturally occur in a specific location. While species have always migrated from one place to another, natural land barriers have prevented their indiscriminate movement. Over time, human modification has changed those barriers. For example, organisms, seeds, and animals can be transported in ships, in ballast water, on clothing, and on boats as people move from one place to another.

Zebra mussels and lampreys have made their way into the Great Lakes through modern canals and shipping lanes. Female zebra mussels are capable of laying over 1 million eggs each year. This population explosion is clogging the water systems of power plants and water treatment facilities, and is reducing the populations of native mussels. Lamprey eels, common to the ocean waters from Florida to Labrador, swim inland into fresh waters to spawn. Lampreys are parasitic on many native fish species, including paddlefish, lake trout, and whitefish, causing a reduction in the populations.

Intentional introduction of plants and animals can become unmanageable to state and federal governments. Purple loosestrife was brought into the United States from Europe in the 1800s for use as a garden perennial and an ornamental wildflower. With no natural predators present, the ability to reproduce rapidly, and the capability to benefit from land disturbances, purple loosestrife has modified wetlands, marshes, pastures, and riparian meadows. The result is the degradation of habitats where native plants grow, fish spawn, and wildlife live and breed. Another example of an introduced non-native species is the gypsy moth. French naturalist

*continued*

Leopold Trouvelot, who hoped to begin operating a New England silk industry, first introduced the gypsy moth, a large European moth, to the United States in Medford, Massachusetts, around 1868. During this time, the moths escaped and their larvae (which feed on leaves) became a serious economic menace by destroying fruit orchards. The gypsy moth has since spread to other parts of the United States where the caterpillars devour the foliage of numerous trees, especially oaks and birches.

Why do these invaders have such success? While not all non-native species succeed, those that do are aided by their ability to out-compete natives for resources and by the lack of natural predators.

NOTE: Local wildlife agencies, garden clubs, nature societies, and wildlife organizations may be able to assist in developing a list of invasive species. Look for information in reference materials under exotic species, introduced species, and species introduction.

## Procedure

1. Provide the students with a list of local non-native species. Ask them to predict which of the plants and animals are "native" and which are introduced, or "non-native." Establish clear working definitions of "native" and "non-native." A native species occurs naturally in an area. Any plant or animal not naturally occurring in the ecosystems of the United States is non-native.

2. If the students' predictions were not entirely accurate, identify the non-natives for the students on the provided list.

3. Next, ask each student or small group of students to research one species known to be introduced as a non-native to the area or state. Within the class, ideally a variety of introduced species will be studied, including aquatic species. Each student or group of students should prepare a written and oral report. Include in the research information concerning the origins of the plant or animal and its effects in the area. Has the introduction created more benefits or liabilities for the ecosystem? The students could create a two-column list of benefits and liabilities. In addition to simply listing benefits and liabilities, they could assess the importance of each item in the columns. Benefits and liabilities—positive and negative effects—may not have equal value. Some introductions may seem to have both positive and negative effects. This will be reflected when the students list items under both the "benefits" and "liabilities" columns. Some effects will be unknown so students might also generate a list of unknown effects or questions.

4. Ask each student or group of students to report to the class. Following the reports, encourage discussion and debate. Ask the students to identify and discuss potential benefits and liabilities involved. Then ask the students to evaluate the appropriateness of each of the introductions in their judgment, identifying and describing their criteria. They might also consider the potential introduction of a species that is common somewhere else but not yet in their area.

5. Using a world map, have the students connect their location with the original location of non-native species. Stretch a strand of yarn from their location to the site of origin of each organism, and place a tag on the yarn with the name of the plant or animal.

6. Preventing "accidental" introductions is also important. Develop a list of ways these introductions can occur and ways to help ensure that they don't happen. Discuss the importance of laws and regulations that prevent, control, or allow introductions of species.

## Extensions

1. Investigate and compare local, state, and federal laws pertaining to introducing exotics into aquatic environments.

2. Investigate how humans have reintroduced some wildlife species into their original habitat where the species had previously become extinct. Have students distinguish some differences and similarities between reintroductions and non-native species.

## Evaluation

1. Identify three native aquatic plants and animals in your area. Identify three exotic aquatic plants and animals in your area.

2. Give four reasons that an aquatic plant or animal might be introduced in an area. Are these reasons appropriate? Why or why not?

3. A local organization has proposed that a new fish be introduced into a state's rivers or lakes. List at least five questions that could be answered about the fish and its impact on the state's watercourses before the proposal is approved or rejected.

*continued*

# Where Have All the Salmon Gone?

## Objectives

Students will (1) interpret and make inferences about fluctuations in fish populations from actual data, and (2) analyze the effects of human use and habitat changes on a fish population.

## Method

Students graph and interpret actual fish population data in relation to historical events.

## Materials

Graph paper, copies of Fish Caught on the Columbia River worksheet on page 182 (Diagram A), information about each fish species (page 182), chart and historical data on fish caught on the Columbia River (page 183)

## Background

Research data gathered about a wildlife population in a similar manner over a period of time may be useful in detecting trends in that population. The data may be analyzed in a variety of ways. Because a fish population is influenced by many factors, it may be difficult to measure the effect of a single factor. Thus, assumptions must often be made that factors other than the ones being measured are not significantly affecting the population.

Usually, only a sample of the population can be obtained, and inferences about the total population must be made from this sample. Errors or inconsistencies in gathering the data over time may greatly influence the accuracy of the data. Despite the influence of unknown factors and possible inconsistencies in data gathering, regularly conducted counts or inventories of a population may still be the best information available, and decisions must be made from this information.

In this activity, actual data from fish catches from the Columbia River, Oregon, are provided for students to analyze. The fish species are all anadromous, or fish that migrate from the ocean to fresh water to spawn. Young fish live in the river from 1 to 3 years, travel to the ocean and grow to adults in several more years. The data are in pounds of fish caught in the river rather than in the ocean.

NOTE: This activity does not address ethical questions related to the appropriateness of catching fish for human uses. This dimension may be added at the professional discretion of the educator conducting the activity.

---

**Grade Level:** 5–8

**Subjects Areas:** Science, Mathematics, Social Studies, Environmental Education

**Duration:** one or two 40- to 60-minute sessions

**Group Size:** any

**Setting:** indoors

**Conceptual Framework Topic Reference:** ITIA, ITIB2, ITIVA

**Key Terms:** population, inventory, trend

**Appendices:** Using Local Resources

---

## Procedure

1. Provide students with the Fish Caught on the Columbia River worksheet and information about each fish species. Instruct the students to graph levels of each species caught from 1870 to the present. Educators may want to make an overhead transparency for students to check against and for use in discussions.

2. What inferences can the students draw from the data provided? Do the graphs show any long-term trends? Are there periods in which the rates of fish caught change rapidly in a short time? What inferences about population abundance of each species can be made from the graphs and fish information? What other factors may be affecting the number of fish caught or the population levels? Might the ways in which the fish are caught have changed? A new event or factor may take some time to have an effect on a population or to be detected. Do the graphs seem to show any of these situations in relation to a possible historical event? Are there different interpretations that individual students make from the same information? Does each of the interpretations seem to explain or fit the information and data? If faced with making a management decision on the basis of one interpretation, how would the students decide which interpretation to use?

3. Provide the students with the Historical Data on Fish Caught on the Columbia River worksheet. Have them review this new information in relation to what their graphs show. Integrate the actual data with the historical information by making notes on the graphs at the points where significant historical events occurred. What new inferences can be made? Must some of the old inferences or explanations be changed to fit the new data?

## Extensions

1. Contact the department of fish and wildlife in the state where the students live. Invite a fisheries biologist to review the class's data and make an analysis. Does it differ significantly from your own?

2. Have students write a short scientific paper explaining the data, analysis, and interpretations of the fish populations. Then have students present their paper to the class and defend their analysis.

## Evaluation

Study the graph below to answer these questions:

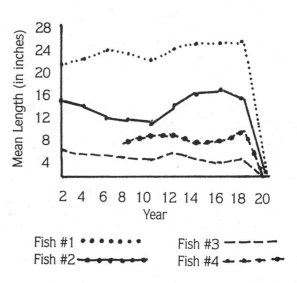

Fish #1 •••••••    Fish #3 – – –
Fish #2 •—•—•—•    Fish #4 ▲–•–▲–•

- Which fish population appears to be the most stable?

- Fish #3 appears to be a prey species for which fish?

- What would you think is the primary diet of Fish #1? Fish #2? Fish #3? Why?

- What natural and human events may have accounted for the decrease in Fish #2's size between years 2 and 4, and between years 16 and 18?

- What effect did the introduction of Fish #4 appear to have on the other fish species?

- What actions might the state fish agency have taken to maintain the populations of Fish #2?

- What natural and human events may have caused all the fish species to die in year 20?

*continued*

# Student Page

**Fish 1 (Chinook):** These fish are considered to be the most abundant and valued fish species for catching. They migrate the entire length of the river and are the largest in individual size of all salmon.

**Fish 2 (Coho):** These fish are second to Fish 1 in popularity and economic value. They migrate only up to the lower middle part of the river system.

**Fish 3 (Chum):** Never popular, this fish species does not bite a hook well, is found only near the mouth of the river, and is usually caught with nets.

**Fish 4 (Sockeye):** Smallest fish in the group, they migrate to the uppermost part of the river. They require lakes for successful spawning and rearing. This fish species does not bite a hook well and is taken mostly with nets.

**Fish 5 (Steelhead):** These fish migrate throughout the river system. Habitat requirements are more restrictive than others.

The data below are taken from actual fish catches. The accompanying historical data provide an overview of human activity in the river, plus developing regulatory and management efforts over time.

## Fish Caught on the Columbia River*

| Years | Fish 1 | Fish 2 | Fish 3 | Fish 4 | Fish 5 |
|-------|--------|--------|--------|--------|--------|
| 1870–79 | 22.7 | — | — | — | — |
| 1880–89 | 33.1 | — | — | — | — |
| 1890–99 | 24.1 | 3.2 | 0.8 | 2.4 | 3.0 |
| 1900–09 | 25.1 | 2.1 | 1.3 | 0.8 | 0.7 |
| 1910–19 | 28.1 | 4.3 | 3.6 | 0.9 | 1.9 |
| 1920–29 | 22.3 | 5.5 | 3.1 | 0.9 | 2.5 |
| 1930–39 | 17.2 | 3.2 | 1.2 | 0.3 | 1.9 |
| 1940–49 | 15.4 | 1.1 | 1.5 | 0.2 | 1.8 |
| 1950–59 | 7.4 | 0.6 | 0.2 | 0.3 | 1.1 |
| 1960–69 | 4.7 | 1.6 | 0.02 | 0.1 | 0.6 |
| 1970–79 | 5.9 | 1.9 | 0.01 | 0.2 | 0.4 |
| 1980–89 | 5.4 | 1.9 | 0.01 | 0.06 | 0.3 |
| 1990–99 | 0.05 | 0.019 | 0.001 | 0 | 0.18 |

*Figures are in millions of pounds. The 1990–1999 figures are from the Idaho Department of Fish and Game.

*Diagram A*

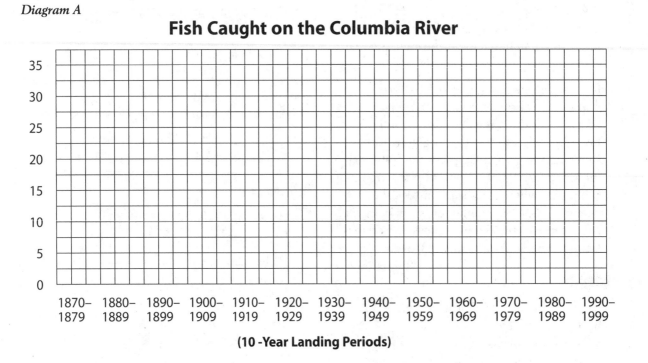

## Fish Caught on the Columbia River

(10 -Year Landing Periods)

Adapted from an activity in "Water, Water Everywhere," Corvallis, OR; Oregon State University Extension Sea Grant Program, 1985. Used with permission.

# Historical Data: Fish Caught on the Columbia River

**1866** Opening of first fish cannery on the Columbia River.

**1869–1883** Canning of Fish 1 jumped from 100,000 to 630,000 cases.

**1877–1878** First efforts to regulate fisheries by state. Enforcement was limited but control of amount and type of fishing gear helped.

**1880–1889** 43 million pounds of Fish 1 taken from river by commercial fishers.

**After 1883** Canneries begin to use other species of fish (2, 3, 4, 5).

**1900–1909** 30 million pounds of all fish taken.

**1915–1920** 40–44 million pounds of fish taken as World War I inspired intensive use.

**1920** Approximately 1,000 commercial trollers operating in the Pacific Ocean. At least that many boats in the river with gill nets, seines, and traps.

**1933–1938** Construction of first dam on lower part of the river.

**After 1935** Only gill-netters allowed on the river. All other commercial fishing techniques banned.

**1941** Second dam built in upper river. No fish ladders installed.

**1930–1950s** Extensive logging in lowest part of river systems.

**1940–1950** Four new dams built on the river between existing dams.

**1950s** Six dams built on the major tributary of the river.

Government launches a massive hatchery program for Fish 1, 2, and 5.

**1953** Another dam built on main river.

**1957** Another dam built.

**1950–1960s** Ocean harvest rather than river harvest of Fish 1 and 2, increases greatly.

**1968** Another dam built.

**1968–1973** Extreme nitrogen supersaturation in river from dam spill of runoff water. Many small fish killed.

**1960–1980** Fish hatchery techniques greatly improved on Fish 1, 2, and 5.

**1970s** Commercial use of Fish 5 is banned.

**1980s** Intensive regulation of ocean fishing on Fish 1 and 2.

**1990s** One of the dams is removed.

*continued*

# To Dam or Not to Dam

## Objective

Students will evaluate potential positive and negative effects from constructing a dam on a river.

## Method

Students portray individuals representing differing perspectives and concerns related to a complex issue.

## Materials

Role-Playing Cards on page 187

## Background

Educators: Make a copy of the situation summary on this and the next page, and distribute to the students or read aloud to the group.

---

**Grade Level:** 5–8

**Subject Areas:** Social Studies, Environmental Education

**Duration:** two or three 45-minute sessions, depending on whether time is used to develop position papers and write essays.

**Group Size:** developed for 30 students, can be modified for smaller or larger groups

**Setting:** indoors

**Conceptual Framework Topic Reference:** ITIA, ITIVA, ITVA, ITVA1

**Key Terms:** dam, river, costs, benefits, tradeoffs

**Appendices:** Simulations, Using Local Resources

---

*Situation:* The town of Rocksburg, population 900, is located along the scenic Jones River, approximately 60 miles from the closest city. The city's mayor and city council have proposed that a dam be constructed 2 miles upriver from Rocksburg. In the Environmental Impact Statement written by the city engineers, the following information was identified:

- The dam would meet the area's electrical power demand for 10 or more years.

- The dam would provide some water for irrigation and would help with flood control.

- The dam would be of rock-earth fill construction, and it would be 75 feet high and 300 feet across. Seven miles of river would be turned into a lake.

- The dam construction would take 5 years to complete and would employ more than 2,000 workers. After the dam was finished, approximately 150 employees would be needed to operate the facility.

Wildlife would be affected in the following ways:

- 20 percent loss to the deer herd that browses the lands alongside the river due to lost forage

- 20 percent loss to small mammals living in the river valley due to loss of habitat

- 20 percent loss to the area's songbird population due to lost riverbank nesting sites

- blockage of the migration of fish due to the creation of the lake and dam

- increase of the area's wintering bald eagle population

- reduction and possible elimination of fish species adapted to cooler or flowing water, including trout, minnows, and darters

- increase in warmer, nonflowing water habitat suitable for bass, bluegill, and carp

- growth in the economy resulting from the new tourist industry

The people of Rocksburg are concerned about the challenges and benefits from the people that would come to their town during and after the construction of the dam. As mentioned, they project the addition of 2,000 employees, plus their families, during construction for 5 years and those 150 permanent employees, plus their families that would stay after the dam was finished. They are concerned about effects on schools, sewage disposal, roads, home sites, property values, and the rural atmosphere, as well as police, fire, and hospital emergency capacities. They see potential benefits from the development, such as new recreation opportunities for the people of Rocksburg and the city that is only about an hour away (water skiing, sailboarding, motorboating, swimming, fishing, camping, picnicking, and other lake-related sports).

Other impacts could include these:

- flooding of American Indian archeological sites;

- cultural changes for local American Indian tribal people who have fished the river for generations;

- water for irrigation at a lower cost;

- potentially less expensive power when compared to other forms of power production (e.g., nuclear, coal, oil, fossil fuels);

- potential increase in total power bills that may be necessary to pay for construction of the dam; and

- loss of 7 miles of prime whitewater, plus private and commercial raft, kayak, and canoe trips would be gone.

## Procedure

1. Provide students with the situation background information. Generate an initial discussion with them about some of the possible costs and benefits from the construction of this dam, considering it from a variety of perspectives.

NOTE: Educators need to copy the Role-Playing Cards on page 187, cut them out, and distribute to the students. Create any additional roles that illustrate a variety of major perspectives and interests.

2. Ask students to research their roles and to develop a short position paper for use as a presentation for the county council.

3. Arrange the room to represent a meeting room for the Rocksburg County Council. Students role-play their positions and make presentations to the five-member council. This council will ultimately make a recommendation to the Federal Energy Regulatory Commission on a siting permit for the dam. (For more detail on procedures that can be adapted for use in this activity, see "To Zone or Not to Zone" in the Project WILD K–12 Activity Guide.)

4. After all the students have made their presentations, ask the county council to work together to form a consensus plan that attempts to compromise the various positions.

*continued*

5. Following the council's decision, have a brief class discussion to summarize the pros and cons that emerged from the students' presentations. Identify and list the benefits, if any, and the costs or liabilities, if any, as a result of building the dam. Include effects on people, plants, and animals. The pros, cons, and effects can be listed visually on a chalkboard.

6. After the role play and class discussion, ask each student to write a brief essay describing his or her personal recommendation for whether to build this dam. The students might expand their position papers in writing their essays.

## Variation

Describe a hypothetical community debating the removal of a dam. Have students role-play representatives of the various interest groups, research the issues, present findings, and attempt to determine a consensus plan.

## Extensions

1. Change roles and conduct the council meeting again. Note any differences in the results, as well as in the perceptions of the process and experience.

2. Inquire at a local regulatory agency to see if there are any proposals to create new dams or any other proposals that will affect wildlife habitat in your region. If so, investigate the benefits and challenges of one or more of those proposals.

3. Is there a dam in your area? Visit it. Find out about its positive and negative effects on people.

## Evaluation

1. If a dam were constructed on a river, what would be the benefits to wildlife?

2. If a dam were constructed on a river, what would be the challenges to wildlife?

# Role-Playing Cards

**A. G. "Rick" Ulture:** a representative of the local farmers' coalition interested in the dam's potential for protecting crops from floods, as well as in its ability to provide water for irrigation.

**Lotta Power:** a lobbyist for the municipal electrical power company interested in developing the dam.

**Rob or Marta Kanu:** kayaker concerned with the loss of the whitewater stretch for canoeing and kayaking.

**Sam N. Fish:** a local sporting goods storeowner and avid fisherperson concerned with the loss of migration routes for the fish on the river.

**Dan D. Lion:** the president of the "Save Our Native Plants and Wild Animals" organization.

**Pat "Pottery" Brusher:** an archeology professor from the local university who has done extensive research on the archeological sites of American Indian fishing camps along the river.

**Lynn Dripper:** the director of the municipal water quality authority responsible for providing quality drinking water for the city. Believes in the dam's potential for providing a reservoir of high-quality water for the long, hot summers.

**H. M. Owner:** a representative of all homeowners in the river valley below the dam who would like to see more flood control.

**Bobbie Lawkeeper:** the local Rocksburg sheriff concerned about maintaining police protection, peace, health, and safety with only a one-person staff as the sole legal authority in the region.

**T. M. Burr:** the owner of a lumber company whose land would be inundated by the reservoir.

**I. M. Floaten:** an owner of a whitewater rafting company who uses the river for commercial rafting. Concerned about loss of the "best 7 miles of the river," I. M. argues that the lake would submerge the best rapids.

**"Sky" Soarer:** the president of the local bird club who has organized eagle-watching trips to the river every winter for the past 15 years.

**Sam Slalom:** an avid water skier who sees the new lake as a real boon to skiing interests.

**Velma or Virgil Vigil:** a local representative of the Gray Panthers, a group of retired people who are concerned about any rise in power bills.

**"Boater" Cartop:** an older fisherperson who enjoys throwing the boat on the top of the car and putting in at the closest float spot—especially lakes!

**Marshal or May Flyfisher:** a long-time resident who champions the purity of fly-fishing and insists on pristine habitat, noting the necessity of whitewater riffles.

**Col. "Bull" Winkle:** the president of "More Moose Now," who believes that the lake will provide more moose habitat.

**Lap Larson:** the president of W.O.W. (Watch Our Waves).

**Cy or Sy N. Tist:** a respected biologist who is prepared to testify about potential effects on wildlife from the building of the dam.

**O. L. Slick:** a salesperson for motor boats, water skis, and other recreational equipment.

**Forest or Park Site:** a trained forester who has worked in the woods in the area for more than 50 years.

**Running Waters:** a tribal leader who is concerned about loss of native heritage from flooding the region for the dam.

**E. Conomy:** a local businessperson who is concerned about the long-range business potential of the area.

**C. D. Minium:** a wealthy land developer who has architects working on designs for lakeside condominiums and resort homes.

*continued*

# Aquatic Times

## Objectives

Students will (1) identify a diversity of issues related to aquatic organisms and habitats, and (2) develop their own opinions concerning some issues involving aquatic life and habitats.

## Method

Students investigate, write, and produce a newspaper that features aquatic information and issues.

## Materials

Research or library resources, current nature magazines (*Ranger Rick*, *National Geographic*, etc.), writing and art materials; OPTIONAL: Cameras/film, tape recorders, computers, video equipment (Educators may want to invite a local newspaper editor or writer to come to the class to discuss the mechanics of newspaper production.)

---

**Grade Level:** 5–8

**Subject Areas:** Language Arts, Environmental Education

**Duration:** several sessions or longer

**Group Size:** small groups or individual activity as part of a class project

**Setting:** indoors

**Conceptual Framework Topic Reference:** ITIA, ITIB

**Key Terms:** newspaper, issue, aquatic

**Appendices:** Using Local Resources, List of Agencies and Organizations

---

## Background

The production of a newspaper requires an array of skills that include design capabilities, writing, composition, research, and decision making. This activity provides an opportunity for the students to coordinate newspaper production with information, issues, and recommendations about aquatic organisms and their habitats.

## Procedure

1. Using an actual newspaper as a model, discuss the various parts of a newspaper. Help the students recognize that in addition to news articles, other departments exist in most newspapers. Comics, sports, editorials, employment opportunities, political cartoons, food and nutrition, entertainment, business, advertisements, weather, obituaries, and many other sections are featured in a newspaper. Ask each student or team of students to choose one section of the newspaper to develop and write.

2. The theme of this newspaper is aquatic animals and plants, aquatic habitats, or aquatic-related issues. Ask the students to gather information and ideas for their chosen section. Show the students how to properly acknowledge and credit any sources they use.

   NOTE: If using the optional materials listed above, familiarize the students with any resources they can use, such as the tape recorders, computers, software, cameras, and so forth.

3. The articles in the newspaper could be both playful and serious. For example,

   • Water Strider Upends at Soap Spill in Stream

- Oil Spill Threatens New Hampshire

- Crayfish Die in Silt Avalanche

- Too Many Wells Deplete Local Aquifer

- Snoopy aboard the *Calypso* (cartoon)

- Dear Abalone (advice column)

- Aquatic Recipes

- Tidal Waves in History

- An interview with three grandparents about how local aquatic resources used to be

- Fish Race to Spawning Beds! (sports)

4. Once the students have accumulated their research and begin writing their articles, encourage them to share their work. In this way, interests can merge and different talents can be called on. Keep the students on track, making sure their writing is accurate even though they may have chosen humor or satire as their approach.

5. When most of the articles have been written, assign a small group of students to begin the production phase of the paper. The artwork can be photographs or drawings that illustrate a particular point in the article. Computer graphics can also be used to highlight specific articles. This phase of the newspaper can be produced using a computer, a typewriter, or by students neatly handwriting the articles using a specified column format (3 ½ or 4 inches wide works well). Most computers have software that includes a newspaper template.

6. Once the newspaper is complete, copies can be made for the class or for distribution throughout the community.

7. Summarize the activity with a discussion of each article or feature, emphasizing what the students learned about aquatic life and habitat from this activity.

## Extensions

1. Have an aquatic poster contest.

2. Establish a current events corner about wildlife.

3. Convert the newspaper to a video news format.

4. Visit a local newspaper and offer your articles for submission to the newspaper.

## Evaluation

1. Identify three issues involving aquatic animals, aquatic plants, or aquatic habitats.

2. Explain why it is important to accurately report environmental information to others.

3. What are the characteristics of a good environmental reporter?

*continued*

# Silt: A Dirty Word

## Objectives

Students will (1) describe how sand, silt, or both affect water flow; and (2) identify human activities that add sand, silt, or both to surface water.

## Method

Students create a model to simulate changes to a stream and its water flow when silt, sand or both are added to the system.

## Materials

For each group of four students, a clear plastic 1-gallon container such as a storage box, enough pea-sized gravel to cover the bottom of the container, enough water to fill the container to 1 inch from the top, 1 cup coarse sand, 1 cup silt (silica powder from the edge of a stream), three straws per person; OPTIONAL: brightly colored beads (pea-sized or larger), plastic tablecloth, paper towels

---

**Grade Level:** 3–4

**Subject Areas:** Science, Environmental Education

**Duration:** one hour

**Group Size:** small groups of four

**Setting:** indoors or outdoors, must have source of water

**Conceptual Framework Topic Reference:** WMIIB2

**Key Terms:** silt, habitat, spawning.

**Appendices:** none

---

## Background

Sedimentation is excess amounts of silt and other particles entering streams and rivers from the surrounding watershed. Sediments enter water in two main forms: (1) surface erosion sends small amounts of particles into the water and (2) mass erosion (e.g., landslides) dumps huge amounts of dirt into water. Causes of surface erosion vary. They can include anglers walking trails to favorite fishing spots or cattle trampling and consuming streamside vegetation that holds soil in place. Logging, mining, and road construction can also contribute to surface erosion. Mass erosion, such as mud slides or earth slumps, occurs more frequently on hillsides altered by human activity, such as clear-cut logging, road construction, or home building.

Regardless of its source, sedimentation may affect aquatic wildlife by reducing nutrients, diminishing sunlight to plants, and altering stream energy and velocity. One important effect of sedimentation is to block the flow of water to organisms residing in bottom substrates. The flow of clean water is important in most aquatic environments because flowing water often carries dissolved oxygen that aquatic animals need for respiration. Depletion of oxygen in bodies of water affects organisms even at early stages of development. For instance, some fish lay their eggs in gravel that receives a flow of clean water, either from a stream or river or from spring water percolating up from the lake bottom. As the water flows over the eggs, it delivers dissolved oxygen to them. If the eggs do not receive enough oxygen, they die.

Silt and sand enter streams through erosion. Silt and sand act like concrete to block water movement and thus diminish the amount of oxygen reaching the developing eggs. Once the erosion-causing activity is stopped, streams may cleanse themselves. (Depending on the extent of the problem, self-cleansing can take from 1 to 50 years.)

The major purpose of this activity is to show that aquatic wildlife and its habitat can be influenced by land-based activities in the surrounding watershed. Students experience what happens to a stream and its flow of water when sand, silt or both are added to the water.

## Procedure

1. Before class, set up a demonstration—a container with gravel covered by water— so that the students can see how to proceed. Post a large sheet of paper on the wall for groups to record their results. (See Diagram A.)

2. Place students into groups of three or four. Ask each group to gather the supplies and set up its demonstration. Ask the students why oxygen is important to aquatic animals. Explain the three parts of the procedure (Steps 3, 4, and 5 below), and ask students to predict what will happen as each sediment type is added to the water.

3. Each person in the group should simultaneously blow bubbles into the water with a straw. Make sure the straw is at or near the bottom of the container so that the end is pushed into the layer of gravel. The group then discusses the ease or difficulty in blowing the bubbles and records its observations on the sheet on the wall. Remind students that the blowing of bubbles is meant to demonstrate how things move through water in different situations.

4. Instruct the groups to add 1 cup of sand to the water and then to blow bubbles again. Be sure that the straw is pushed through the sand so that it reaches the gravel. The group then discusses the difficulty level and records its observations on the master sheet on the wall.

5. Now add 1 cup of silt to the water, allow to settle, push the straw end into the layer of gravel, and blow bubbles again. The group then discusses the difficulty level and records its observations on the master sheet on the wall.

6. Conduct a class discussion about the demonstration and results, and describe what these results might mean to aquatic organisms and their need for clean water. How do sand and silt get into the water in nature? Which of these sources are human and which are natural? What can happen to fish and other aquatic organisms if too much sediment gets into aquatic systems?

## Extension

1. Add brightly colored beads to the container to represent fish eggs.

2. Research and discuss ways to minimize the addition of sand or silt into natural aquatic systems.

## Evaluation

1. Write on a chart or blackboard all the observations and ideas generated by the students; engage them in a discussion about the meaning of these results.

2. Ask each group to create two illustrations: (1) a healthy stream that could support a variety of aquatic life and (2) a human activity that causes siltation in that stream.

*Adapted from "Wild About Salmon, An Educators Guide," Idaho Department of Fish and Game, 1999.

*continued*

# Sample Observations Chart

Each group of students selects one difficulty level for each water type by placing a check in the appropriate box in its column. They may record additional observations in the boxes as well.

| Difficulty Levels | Group 1 | Group 2 | Group 3 | Group 4 |
|---|---|---|---|---|
| **Clean Water** | | | | |
| Easy to blow | | | | |
| Less easy to blow | | | | |
| Hard to blow | | | | |
| | | | | |
| **Sand in Water** | | | | |
| Easy to blow | | | | |
| Less easy to blow | | | | |
| Hard to blow | | | | |
| | | | | |
| **Silt in Water** | | | | |
| Easy to blow | | | | |
| Less easy to blow | | | | |
| Hard to blow | | | | |

*Diagram A*

# Dam Design

## Objectives

Students will (1) identify problems experienced by salmon in migration; (2) evaluate the social, political, economic, and ethical consequences of an environmental concern; (3) identify mitigation projects that have worked and those that have not; and (4) identify and propose strategies and technologies to address an environmental concern.

## Method

Students will design and draw a dam appropriate for salmon survival.

## Materials

For each group of students, paper and drafting equipment

## Background

In the northwest section of the United States, salmon populations are declining. One of the reasons for this decline is that dams block salmon migration routes. Biologists and engineers have tried a number of ways to help salmon move through and around the dams. For a time, these methods seemed to work. Unfortunately, salmon numbers continue to decline—a sign that the salmon populations are not stable and something new must be tried.

Some agencies and organizations have proposed removing some of the dams. Even if this change occurs, some dams will need to remain if both the needs of people and wildlife are to be considered. So new ideas are needed to help the salmon around these dams. Who is better to begin the work than tomorrow's biologists and engineers?

The purpose of this activity is to demonstrate the complexity of many wildlife management decisions that must consider political, social, economic, and biological concerns. Wildlife management also applies scientific knowledge and technical skills to protect or conserve wildlife and its habitat.

## Procedure

1. Write the following topics on a board, large sheet of paper, or overhead transparency:

   - Salmon migration—downstream and upstream

   - Location of dams in a river system such as the Columbia or Snake River systems (see Diagram A)

   - Designs of current dams, including turbines

   - Purpose of dams in the system

   - Problems that dams create for migrating salmon

   - Modifications to help the fish (their efficacy, cost, and benefits)

   - Roles that salmon play in the watershed

**Grade Level:** 9–12

**Subject Areas:** Science, Social Studies, Language Arts, Environmental Education

**Duration:** semester project

**Group Size:** small groups

**Setting:** primarily indoors

**Conceptual Framework Topic Reference:** WMIB, WMIIB2, WMIIC, WMIIC2

**Key Terms:** migration

**Appendices:** none

*continued*

2. Divide students into small teams of three or four. Instruct the teams to decide who will research which topic. To cover all topics, teams may need to choose more than one topic.

3. Allow sufficient time for the groups to conduct their research, compile a bibliography, and present their information.

4. Reassign the students into new small groups so that each group contains an "expert" on each topic above. The group then synthesizes and organizes the information into a documented paper on the problem of declining salmon as it relates to dam construction and design. Students analyze and evaluate the costs, benefits, and consequences for various options.

5. Instruct the new teams to design a dam that will produce electricity efficiently or store irrigation water and that will provide safe passage for salmon. The teams may draw or construct the model.

6. Have each team present its design to the class, noting important features that address the needs of humans as well as wildlife.

## Evaluation

1. Each presentation needs to include a diagram or model of the dam and its migration features.

2. Encourage students to question the design and conclusions of each group, and remind them that constructive criticism demonstrates understanding of the problems.

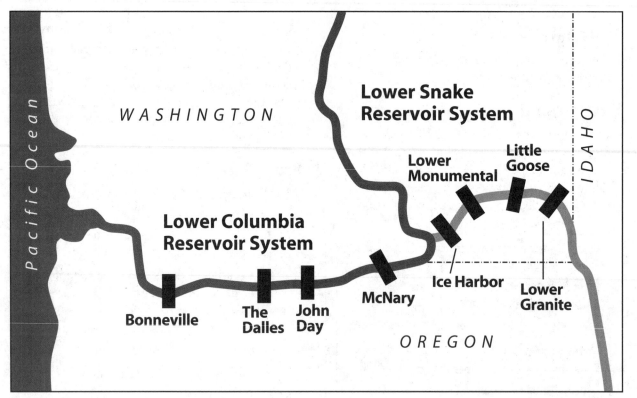

*Diagram A\**

* Adapted from "Wild About Salmon, An Educators Guide," Idaho Department of Fish and Game, 1999.

# Kelp Help

## Objective

Students will list and describe different ways that kelp can be beneficial to humans, wildlife, and the environment.

## Method

Students research kelp, create a mural, and report to the class their findings.

## Materials

Writing materials, references, art materials for a mural

## Background

Aquatic plants that are visible at the surface of the oceans are called "seaweed." In aquatic habitats, seaweed will play a role central to the rhythm of life in water.

Seaweed are algae. Algae are not restricted to the sea. They live in profusion in lakes, rivers, and streams. Algae are as important to aquatic animals in marine and freshwater environments as grass is to cows, horses, and other grazing

animals. Some algae are microscopic. Others, like kelp, are very large. Kelp, a seaweed, is an example of one of thousands of different plant forms found in aquatic habitats.

Kelp is often found in great forests in the sea. Other forms of kelp are smaller and more solitary. The Pacific Ocean varieties of kelp often grow to be more than 100 feet long. The plant is held to the bottom by a structure called a "holdfast" (see Diagram A). The holdfast anchors the plant to cobbles, large rocks, or debris in sandy bottoms. It looks like a root but is not. The holdfast cannot absorb nutrients the way true roots do. It serves only to keep the kelp in place during storms, tides, and normal wave action. Nutrients are absorbed through most of the kelp's surface area.

The kelp plant grows rapidly in crowded waving forests, adding as much as 1 foot of growth per day. The growing tip of a kelp plant is called a "frond" (see Diagram B). As the frond grows upward toward the surface, it forms a long string of leaf-like structures called "blades." Each blade has a float bulb that is attached to the growing main stem or stipe. As the frond grows toward the surface, the kelp plant's stem or stipe becomes the anchor for dozens of these floats and blades. When the frond reaches the surface, the growth rate slows down and soon forms its last blade called the "terminal blade."

Some marine biologists suggest that kelp forests provide habitat for as diverse a variety of wildlife as does a tropical rain forest on land. Both kelp forests and rain forests do support a tremendous diversity of wildlife. Worms, snails, crustaceans, and mollusks abound in kelp forests. Fish live at all levels within the protection of the kelp forest.

> **Grade Level:** 5–8
>
> **Subject Areas:** Science, Environmental Education
>
> **Duration:** two or three 45-minute sessions
>
> **Group Size:** groups of four to five students
>
> **Setting:** indoors
>
> **Conceptual Framework Topic Reference:** RAII
>
> **Key Terms:** kelp, algae, seaweed, algin
>
> **Appendices:** Ecosystem

*continued*

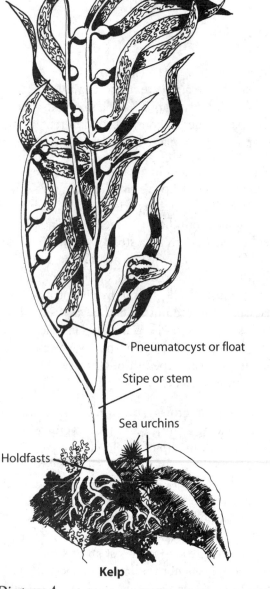

Pneumatocyst or float

Stipe or stem

Sea urchins

Holdfasts

**Kelp**

*Diagram A*

Bottom fish thrive at the base of a kelp forest. The dozens of aquatic species that live in kelp beds attract predators. Sharks, seals, and sea otters find these forests to be attractive hunting areas. Kelp is commercially harvested for dozens of products that are used by people. For example, within kelp is a chemical called "algin."

Algin is used as a thickener, stabilizer, and emulsifier. Thickeners increase a substance's density by making the substance less watery. Stabilizers prevent deterioration of foods, and emulsifiers help keep ingredients from separating. Algin from kelp is used in ice cream and a variety of other dairy products, as well as in many kinds of processed foods, beverages, and medicines. Algin is also used in the production of paper, cosmetics, ceramics, paint, and insecticides. Small amounts are used directly as food.

## Procedure

1. Divide the class into groups of four or five students. Assign (or have the students choose) topics such as the following to research related to kelp:

   - algin
   - kelp as a habitat for wildlife
   - kelp as a food source (kelp recipes)
   - emulsifiers
   - medicinal uses of kelp
   - aquatic weeds of the world (both marine and fresh water)
   - the Sargasso Sea
   - algae and the oceanic food chain
   - sea otters
   - sea urchins

2. Once the research is finished, have each group visually summarize its findings on a large sheet of paper.

3. When all groups are finished, have them place their art work on a wall and verbally report on their findings. The art work should be placed so that the edges of the paper overlap, producing a mural related to kelp.

4. Lead a class discussion about kelp, algae, and the other fresh water and marine plants, inviting the students to react to the information and insights shared by each group.

## Extensions

1. Investigate other aquatic plants and their role in aquatic habitats.

2. Draw an accurate portrayal of a kelp "forest" food web. Keep the animals and plants to their proportionate sizes in the drawings.

3. Visit a beach where kelp can be found. Identify its parts. If a beach is not available, make a small collection of aquatic weeds from a local pond or stream, and identify each.

4. Visit an aquarium that exhibits a kelp habitat.

5. Plan a Kelp Appreciation Day, including a potluck meal where kelp is a part of each dish.

6. Turn part of your classroom into a kelp forest. Use crepe paper, balloons, and construction paper to depict the habitat and its inhabitants.

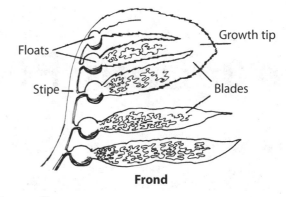

Floats — Growth tip

Stipe — Blades

**Frond**

*Diagram B*

## Evaluation

1. What is kelp? Write a paragraph and draw a picture to illustrate your response.

2. Describe two ways that kelp is helpful to each of the following: humans, wildlife, aquatic habitats.

*continued*

# Dragonfly Pond

## Objectives

Students will (1) evaluate the effects of different kinds of land use on wetland habitats, and (2) discuss and evaluate lifestyle changes to minimize damaging effects on wetlands.

## Method

Students create a collage of human land-use activities around an image of a pond.

## Materials

For each team, scissors, masking tape, paper, 2 sets of Land-Use Patterns (page 202), 1 Map of Dragonfly Pond on page 203, a large piece of paper (18" × 24")

**Grade Level:** 5–8

**Subject Areas:** Environmental Education, Social Studies

**Duration:** one to three 45- to 60-minute sessions

**Group Size:** designed for several small groups; can be modified to be an individual activity

**Setting:** indoors

**Conceptual Framework Topic Reference:** RAIC2, RAIC3

**Key Terms:** land-use planning, wetlands, trade off, lifestyle

**Appendices:** Using Local Resources, Ecosystem, Observations and Inferences, Simulations

## Background

Since the earliest times, humans have deliberately planned the arrangement of housing in regular, rectangular patterns and the prominent location of civic and religious buildings along main thoroughfares. These patterns have not only given structure to American cities, but also they have affected wildlife habitat and populations. Sometimes people perceive undeveloped areas of the natural environment as raw material for human use, while others believe that the natural environment is to be preserved without regard for human needs. Still others yearn for a balance between economic growth and a healthy natural environment.

Growth is at the core of land-use issues. Growth in natural systems has inherent limits that are imposed by a balance of energy among all parts of the system. Energy in natural systems is translated into food, water, shelter, space, and continued survival. The vitality of natural systems is expressed by the ability to be self-regulating. This capacity for self-regulation of all the life and plant forms of an ecosystem is equally important. The microbes in the soil are just as necessary to a habitat as the plants and predators. It is this natural dynamic balance, with all its inherent and essential parts, that much of human land use has tended to disturb. Growth in human activities can often go beyond the natural limits of a setting. Humans have the ability to import energy sources and other resources that allow a system to exceed its natural limits or to remove energy sources that are necessary for a system to stay in balance.

Wetlands, for example, can be perceived by some humans as swamp land that does not have any value. Yet biologists see wetlands as a nursery for hundreds of forms of wildlife. Fish, frogs, toads, migrating birds, snakes, insects, and a remarkable variety of plants all inhabit wetlands. Wetlands are highly vulnerable to development, pollution, and a variety of forms of human interference with the natural flow of water. Hundreds of thousands of acres of valuable wetlands are lost each year—for example, to draining, dredging, filling, and pollution.

One of the major challenges now facing our society is how to regulate growth and conserve open spaces. How can we develop the awareness, knowledge, skills, and commitment that are necessary for humans to take responsible actions affecting open spaces? How can we develop the necessary understanding to restore a more natural dynamic balance in places where human disturbance has existed?

Students will struggle with the arrangement of overlapping and conflicting land uses in an effort to preserve a wetland habitat. When the students reach some kind of agreement about the local issues, the activity shifts to how what they have done affects other "dragonfly ponds." The activity ends with consideration of the idea that the planet is, in fact, a single "Dragonfly Pond."

## Procedure

1. Begin by explaining to the students that during this activity they will use "Dragonfly Pond" as a microcosm of environmental concerns involved in making land-use planning decisions.

2. Divide the class into teams of three to five, with each group representing one of the interest groups described below. Students will stay in these groups until the end of the activity. Possible interest groups to include are these:

   - Residents—want to live in the area

   - Farmers—want to use the land to raise food and livestock

   - Conservationists—want to maintain the land as wildlife habitat

   - Business interests—want to use the land for commerce and economic growth

   - Gas station owners—want to make a living in servicing and repairing cars

   - Parks and recreation department personnel—want people to have a place for recreation

   - Highway department personnel—want to maintain access in the area

   - Factory representatives—want to preserve jobs and commerce

NOTE: Add other interest groups that may be locally important.

3. Distribute the 18″ × 24″ piece of paper that will serve as the base map for each team's pond and its associated land-use activities. Have the students cut out the Land-Use Patterns and Map of Dragonfly Pond. All the land-use patterns must be used. Patterns may be cut to smaller sizes and may touch, but may not overlap. The students may include additional land-use patterns. Suggest to the students that they may not want to adhere the land-use patterns to the base map until the team is in agreement.

4. When the students are ready to begin the process of making land-use decisions, have them create a list of pros and cons for each land use. Guide the class discussion so that they consider the consequences of each land use. Record these lists on the chalkboard. The following are only a few of the many possible examples:

**Farms:**

*Pro*
- produce food
- add economic value
- provide jobs through seasonal employment

*Con*
- use pesticides (herbicides, insecticides) that may damage people and environment
- become source of natural soil erosion
- sometimes drain wetlands for farm lands

*continued*

**Businesses:**

*Pro*

- provide employment
- provide commerce
- create economic stability

*Con*

- produce wastes and sewage
- may contaminate water (detergents, pesticides)
- use chemical fertilizers (lawns, etc.)

**Homes:**

*Pro*

- provide shelter
- provide a sense of community

*Con*

- generate wastes and sewage
- use water
- contribute to loss of wildlife habitat

5. Have the students work in the teams for 30 to 45 minutes.

6. Display each team's base map, and report on its work in progress. Encourage discussion of the students' choices emphasizing that

   - no land use can be excluded, and

   - consensus must be built around each decision.

   Look for the consequences of the students' proposed land-use plan. Be firm about the issues, but fair about this being a very difficult set of choices.

7. Continue the discussion by asking more teams to share their proposed plans. Again, be firm in discussing the consequences. What would happen if the factory and businesses were to close? Abandoning the farm would have what effects? Do farmlands provide habitat for some wildlife? What happens if wetlands are drained to create farmland?

8. Give the students additional time working in their teams to decide on the best possible land-use plan under the circumstances. Being sensitive to their frustrations, display all the final land-use plans. Analyze and discuss the merits of each of the approaches. Point out that although their solutions may not be perfect, they can minimize the damage to the Dragonfly Pond.

9. Choose one of the team's base maps and continue Dragonfly Creek downstream. The students may have dumped effluent below Dragonfly Pond and let it flow downstream. Show the route the stream might travel. On the drawing, have the downstream part of Dragonfly Creek become another pond and wetland, and label the new area Laughing Gull Lake. Continue the drawing to Sea Oats Estuary and finally into Whale Gulf. (See Diagram A.) You may also connect several of the teams' maps together, one above another, to indicate the flow downstream.

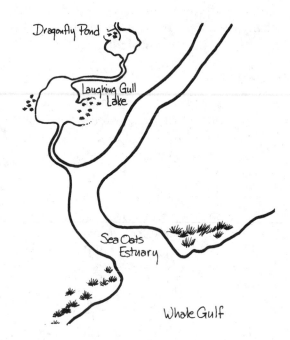

*Diagram A*

10. Ask the students to brainstorm possible problems that could be faced within each of these aquatic systems as a result of the human activities at Dragonfly Pond. Make inferences and predictions about the potential consequences of such activities. For example, you could emphasize the effluent from the factory. How will it be treated? Where? By whom? Where will it go? With what effects?

11. Ask the students to examine all of the land uses in this activity. If they had been considering any of them as inherently bad, have them consider a different question. What could the people who are actually in charge of those various land uses do in their practices to minimize the damage to Dragonfly Pond? Have the activity end with an emphasis on solutions rather than on problems. Point out, for example, the revolution taking place in the "mining" of industrial effluents through "scrubbers" to extract wastes as profitable resources. (Perhaps the students need to make a "scrubbing filter" for the factory.) Agricultural practices are changing, reducing the use of potentially harmful pesticides and herbicides. Petroleum wastes are being recycled, and industrial and community awareness regarding uses of harmful chemicals is evolving.

## Extensions

1. Do the activity again up to Step 6. After each interest group has presented its plan, form new groups with each one having a representative from each interest group. Have the new groups devise plans that all of the interests can agree on. Discuss how, if at all, this is a realistic experience in working to balance various community interests.

2. Locate a dragonfly pond in your community. Determine the overall quality of the wetlands with which it is connected.

3. Trace any stream or river system that passes through your community from its source to its entrance into the ocean. List all the sites that you can identify that lower the quality of the waters in their journey, and suggest how to reverse the process.

4. As a current events activity, collect newspaper articles concerning local water-related and land-use issues.

5. Learn more about environmental impact statements. Obtain actual copies of statements about wetlands in your area. What concerns are addressed in those documents?

6. Learn about the national wildlife refuge system. Are there any wildlife refuges in your area? What animals find refuge in them? Visit a national wildlife refuge.

7. Research private organizations that work to protect wetlands, such as The Nature Conservancy and Ducks Unlimited. What do those organizations do, and how do they do it?

8. Research zoning laws and land-use regulations in your area. Would the plan your group proposed for Dragonfly Pond be allowed in your community?

## Evaluation

1. Identify three actions that people can take to reduce or prevent damage to wetlands.

2. Under what conditions, if any, do you think these actions to reduce damage to wetlands would be appropriate? Inappropriate? Select any action that you think would be appropriate and that you could take to reduce or prevent damage to wetlands. Write a one-page paper about your plan.

*continued*

# Land-Use Patterns

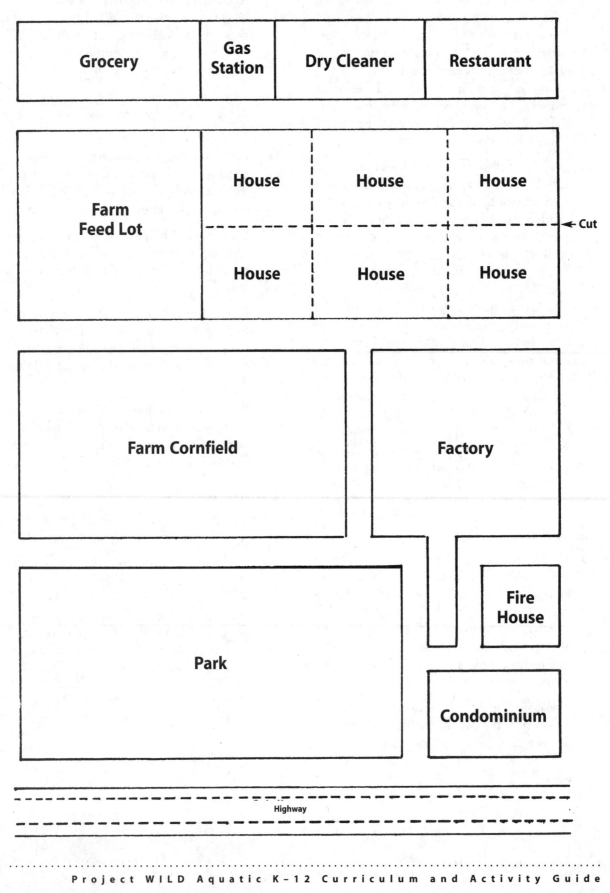

# Map of Dragonfly Pond

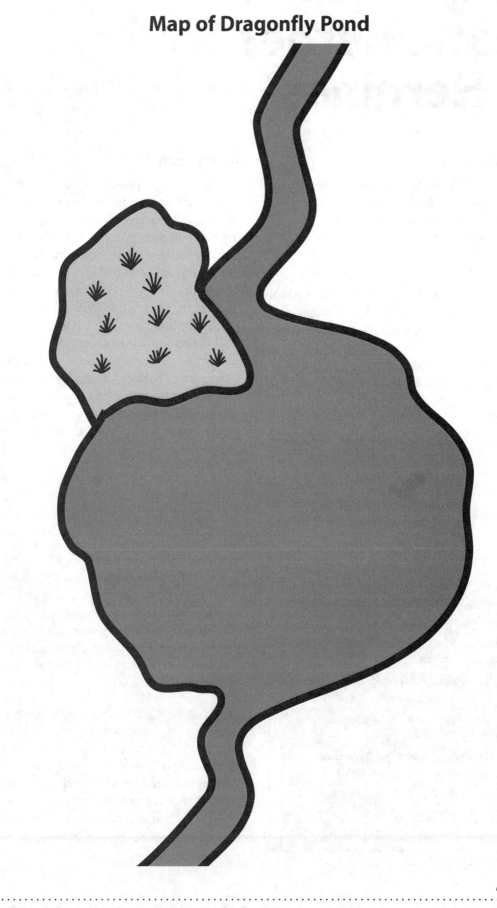

continued

# Living Research: Aquatic Heroes and Heroines

## Objective

Students will describe the importance of the accomplishments of local people who have contributed to conserving or preserving aquatic environments.

## Method

Students identify people—through news media, personal contacts, or other means—who have made contributions to conserving or preserving aquatic environments; research their contributions, including a personal interview; and then write a biography of the person.

## Materials

Writing materials, envelopes, postage, telephone; OPTIONAL: tape recorder, video recorder, camera, film, darkroom

---

**Grade Level:** 9–12

**Subject Areas:** Social Studies, Language Arts, Environmental Education

**Duration:** several sessions of 30- to 60-minutes each

**Group Size:** groups of three or four students each

**Setting:** indoors and in the community conducting interviews

**Conceptual Framework Topic Reference:** RAIC, RAIC1, RAIC2, RAIC3, RAIC4, RAIC5

**Key Terms:** efficacy, citizenship, heroes

**Appendices:** Using Local Resources, Interview

---

## Background

Students are frequently called on to write reports about people who are world famous or who have attracted a lot of attention in major media. This attention can give students the impression that active, committed people are very removed from real life. Yet there are people who work tirelessly, year after year, to contribute to the quality of life in local communities. Some of those people focus on issues involving wildlife and the natural environment. State or local governments employ some of these people. Some are in business and industry. Others work through conservation and wildlife organizations. Many are simply interested and dedicated private citizens, volunteering their time to work on issues of concern.

Efficacy is a word used in political science when talking about whether or not people think they can make a difference. People who believe they can make a difference feel a sense of efficacy.

Some people make a significant difference in local communities. These people feel or see something they care about, and they work to accomplish a goal. Every community has people who contribute to the improvement of the wildlife habitat, local planning regulations, conservation of open spaces, and many other quality-of-life issues.

The people who are the objects of this research are not likely to be well known—at least not in major media at national and international levels. Some may be members of local chapters or groups affiliated with national organizations. Others may be involved with purely local groups such as natural history clubs, botanical organizations, bird-watching societies, wildlife organizations, or outdoor recreation groups. Others may choose to have no organizational affiliations whatsoever. Still others may be people whose employment entails a day-to-day focus on environmental conservation and protection. Students will have to develop what may be new research strategies and skills in order to undertake this activity. In a sense, they become investigative reporters seeking a local story, using whatever local resources are available—including firsthand interviews and direct contact with people as sources of information. This approach requires sensitivity and skill on the part of students. Educators may find it helpful to refer to the "Using Local Resources" appendix in this guide.

## Procedure

1. Introduce the activity by explaining its purposes, with emphasis on the fact that the students will be doing some firsthand biographical research on people in their own community.

2. Brainstorm possible sources of information that could be used to find out about people in the community who have contributed to conserving or preserving aquatic environments. Examples might include public libraries and librarians, school libraries, city hall, government offices, the telephone book, local newspapers and magazines, reporters or editors on the staff of local papers, local television news directors, and the presidents or executive members of local groups or clubs. The group might even place an advertisement in the paper or enlist the aid of a reporter to write a story about the class project.

3. Once a list of names has been compiled, students in teams of three or four draw a name at random from the list. Each group will now become a biographical research team to prepare a biography or living history of the person. In some cases, the person may have been important in the community as

a conservationist, but is now deceased. In those cases, the team will have to identify relatives, friends, former employers, and other potential sources of information to interview and research.

4. Have each team develop a research plan. It could include the outline of any interviews they may want to conduct, whether with the person directly or with others who know or knew the individual. Discuss each team's plan with the group, and consider suggestions for improvement. After the plans have been discussed and refined, have the teams contact the people they want to meet and interview. This contact could be accomplished by sending a letter to the interviewee, stating the purposes of the research and stating that the students will follow the letter with a telephone call.

5. Once the teams have confirmed the willingness of the people to be interviewed, the teams need to meet with them and conduct the interviews. The basic format for the interview could include any personal history details, but the major questions to be addressed might include these:

   • How did you become interested in the aquatic environment?

   • What prompted you to take action?

   • How did you decide on the course of the action you took?

   • What difficulties did you encounter, and how did you overcome them?

   • What do you think your contribution has been?

   • What are your personal dreams and goals for aquatic habitats?

   • What would your advice be to citizens wanting to take positive action to improve the aquatic environment?

   NOTE: The list of questions could be modified to include personal interests of the students and to reflect particular circumstances.

*continued*

6. After the interviews and additional research are complete, have each team write a biography of its person. Once completed, ask each of the teams to give a brief oral report. Make copies of the biographies, and send each biography with a letter of thanks to the people who were interviewed and others who assisted. It is recommended that letters of thanks be sent to all who assisted in the process. OPTIONAL: Create a visual display of all the completed biographies, complete with photographs and news clippings. Invite the local aquatic heroes and heroines to the school for a public recognition of their contributions. They could be given letters of thanks and copies of their biographies at this time. The news media could be invited, including local television, radio, and newspaper reporters.

## Extensions

1. Form a group in the school to address problems related to the conservation and protection of aquatic resources and habitats. What have you learned from the biographical research that can assist the group to formulate some action plans?

2. View films or other media presentations to find out about other aquatic conservationists.

3. Present a copy of the biographical reports to the school library or the public library to include in its collection. These reports may be important contributions to local history.

## Evaluation

1. Identify two people who have helped protect a local aquatic area, and describe what each did. Why are their actions important?

2. What can you do—working alone or with others—to conserve or protect an area of aquatic habitat in your community?

# Appendices

# Conceptual Framework

This framework serves as the conceptual basis for activities in the *Project WILD* and *Project WILD Aquatic K–12 Curriculum and Activity Guides*. Every concept statement in a topic area is directly addressed by the activities listed for that topic. Activities under other topics may also support the concepts directly or indirectly.

## Ecological Knowledge

### Wildlife Populations (WP)

I. Characteristics

    A. Wildlife comprises all nonhuman and nondomesticated animals. Wildlife includes but is not limited to insects, spiders, birds, reptiles, fish, amphibians, and mammals.

        1. Wildlife is all around, although it may not be seen or heard or its presence otherwise sensed.

        2. Wildlife varies from forms that are microscopic to those more than 100 feet in length, and it occurs in a variety of forms, colors, and shapes.

    B. All living things go through a series of orderly changes in life cycles. Some species have distinct changes; the young of other species resemble their parents.

    C. Living things all need food, water, shelter, and a suitable place to live.

    D. Animals can be classified according to life needs, behavior, and physical characteristics, including body appearance, movement, habitat type, and relationship to humans (wild/domesticated).

II. Population Dynamics

    A. Wildlife numbers and species compositions are not static but are constantly changing.

        1. Systematic inventory of wildlife populations did not become a common practice until the 1930s, although journals of early explorers reflect considerable variation in historic population levels.

        2. Some wildlife populations exhibit cyclic patterns over time.

            a. Living things tend to reproduce in numbers greater than their habitat can support.

                (1) Carrying capacity is the dynamic equilibrium expressed by the availability of habitat components and the number of animals the habitat can support.

                (2) Each area of land or water, and ultimately the planet, has a carrying capacity of plants and animals.

                    (a) Carrying capacity is determined by climatic, geological, biological, or behavioral factors, along with human activities.

                    (b) Carrying capacity may fluctuate from season to season and year to year.

                    (c) Carrying capacity affects and is affected by wildlife behavior.

                        i. The numbers, health, and distribution of wildlife are related to carrying capacity.

    ii. Carrying capacity limitations can result in competition between and among domestic animals, wildlife, and humans.

  b. A population tends to increase in size until limited by one or more factors.

    (1) When one or more limiting factors exceed the tolerance range for an animal, population, or species, it directly affects the well-being of the animal(s) and may result in death or extinction.

    (2) Limiting factors include life history parameters such as food, water, shelter, space, disease, predation, and climatic conditions, as well as human activities such as development, pollution, and hunting.

B. Natural laws are ultimately as binding on human populations as on wildlife.

## Habitats, Ecosystems, and Niches (HN)

I. Distribution

  A. Wildlife is present in nearly all areas of the Earth.

  B. Each environment has characteristic life forms.

    1. The environment—created and shaped by natural forces or modified by humans—shapes life forms that occupy it.

    2. Each species occupies a niche within the range of environments in which it is found.

II. Importance

  A. Good habitat is the key to the survival of humans and wildlife.

    1. Habitat is composed of many integrated components including food, water, shelter or cover, space, and the suitable arrangement of these in relation to each other.

    2. In addition to supporting wildlife, ecosystems must furnish the products humans need to survive.

  B. Wildlife may be used as an indicator of the environmental health of an ecosystem.

## Interdependence (ID)

I. Commonalities

  A. All living elements of an ecological system are interdependent.

    1. All forms of life depend on food, water, shelter, and space in a suitable arrangement.

    2. Humans and wildlife have similar basic needs.

      a. Humans and wildlife share environments and are subject to essentially the same environmental conditions.

      b. The health and well-being of humans and wildlife depend on the quality of the natural environment.

  B. Plants and animals in ecological systems live in a web of interdependence, in which each species contributes to the functioning of the overall system.

*continued*

II. Interactions

    A. All living things are affected by and interact with their environments.

    B. In a naturally functioning ecosystem, life forms and environmental factors interact to keep wildlife populations in long-term dynamic equilibrium with each other and with their habitats.

        1. Many interactions result in a flow of energy and matter throughout the system.

            a. Energy takes a one-way course through an ecosystem and dissipates at every trophic level.

            b. Material substances, such as water, nitrogen, carbon, and phosphorus, cycle through ecosystems.

        2. Food webs illustrate the interrelationships of all living things.

            a. Either directly or indirectly, plants support nearly all forms of animal life, including humans.

                (1) Energy from the sun and organic matter enters the animal world through herbivores, those animals that eat plants.

                (2) A relatively large quantity of plant material is required to support herbivores (primary consumers), and herbivores can support only a smaller number of carnivores (secondary consumers).

                (3) Decomposers complete the cycle by breaking down organic matter formed by photosynthesis.

            b. Trophic relationships in an ecosystem may be complex and may vary depending on environmental conditions.

    C. Wildlife interacts with other wildlife and thereby affects the functioning of the ecological system.

        1. Interactions exist between different populations.

            a. Competition is a major determinant of community structure.

            b. Predation can be beneficial or harmful to a population as a whole.

            c. Symbiotic relationships may benefit or harm one or both of the partners.

        2. Interactions exist among members within a population, including competition and cooperation.

### Changes and Adaptations (CA)

I. Environmental Changes

    A. Variation and change occur in all ecological systems.

    B. Succession is an orderly, gradual, and continuous replacement of one natural community of life by another.

        1. Succession influences what kinds of plants and animals live in an area.

            a. New communities arise when ecosystems change through succession.

            b. Newer communities may have less diversity.

            c. Species present in new communities will have traits that allow them to survive in the new environment.

            d. Over time, species diversity may increase in a new community.

        2. Natural events and human activities affect the rate and direction of succession.

    C. All forms of life are affected by changes in the quality, quantity, and distribution of their habitats.

II. Organism Adaptations

    A. All life forms exhibit adaptations to the environments in which they live.

        1. Fish and wildlife are adapted to their environment in ways that enable them to survive and maintain their populations.

            a. Many physical and behavioral adaptations, such as body coverings, hibernation, and migration, are associated with climatic conditions.

            b. Adaptations to predator and prey relationships may include behavioral (e.g., signaling, flight, freezing) as well as physical (e.g., camouflage, mimicry) variations.

            c. Reproductive strategies are adaptations that maximize species survival.

        2. Fish and wildlife species differ in their ability to adapt to changes in their habitats.

    B. Each habitat is suitable only to those life forms that are adapted to its ecological conditions.

    C. Isolated ecosystems are more vulnerable to environmental change.

## Biodiversity (BD)

I. Types

Biodiversity can refer to a variety of natural systems, a variety of species in an area, or a genetic diversity within a species.

    A. Ecosystem Diversity

        1. Ecosystem diversity is affected by many influences, such as climate and level of disturbance.

        2. Ecosystems undergo successional changes that are usually gradual.

        3. Species that are not able to adapt to ecosystem change may become extinct.

        4. A biologically healthy ecosystem is diverse over the range of the ecosystem, not necessarily within each community.

    B. Species Diversity

        1. Climate and habitats influence species diversity.

        2. Organisms that are not able to adjust to ecosystem changes will die.

        3. New ecosystems and ecosystems that are harsh tend to have relatively few species.

        4. Species diversity tends to be higher in the transition zone between ecosystems.

    C. Genetic Diversity

        1. Genetic variability is important to health within a species.

        2. Diversity facilitates adaptation to change and provides sources of new genetic material.

II. Human Influence

    A. Some wildlife species are not native but have been introduced to the area they presently occupy. Such introductions can be beneficial, harmful, or both to other species in the ecosystem.

    B. Adding or subtracting members from a community affects other members of the community.

    C. Human activities can affect the rate at which wildlife becomes threatened, endangered, or extinct.

*continued*

III. The Importance of Habitat

A. Habitat is the key to wildlife survival.

B. Improving habitat improves wildlife populations.

C. Reintroduction of wildlife into its former range may be possible if suitable habitat and suitable wild stock are available, and if such other conditions as weather and predator levels do not substantially interfere.

D. Management of one species will affect other species in a community.

E. For a wildlife population to sustain itself, there must be suitable habitat to support a viable breeding population, not just a few individuals.

# Social and Political Knowledge

## *Cultural Perspectives (CP)*

I. Cultural Development

A. Human cultures and societies, past and present, affect and are affected by wildlife and its habitat.

B. Values, ethics, and historical traditions of cultures and societies are reflected in their treatment of wildlife and other resources.

 1. Human and wildlife relationships are expressed through legends, myths, religious teachings and writings, symbols, protocols, ceremonies, and other cultural and societal activities.

 2. Appreciation of wildlife is often portrayed through creative expression of human relationships with wildlife in historic and contemporary times.

II. Appreciation

Societies and cultures within societies may have different attitudes toward wildlife and its uses, formed and transmitted by family, community, and other social groups in a variety of ways.

A. The aesthetic and spiritual values that humans place on wildlife vary from person to person and culture to culture.

B. Different cultures may disagree over certain uses of and rights to wildlife and its habitat.

C. Wildlife and its habitat are interpreted and treated differently by people viewing them from various cultural perspectives and frames of reference.

 1. Increasing separation of people from direct contact with the natural world has influenced human actions and attitudes toward wildlife. Therefore, actions and attitudes toward wildlife may be positive, negative, naïve, or misguided.

 2. Formal and nonformal education and the media shape the attitude of people toward wildlife and its habitat.

## *Economic, Commercial, and Recreational Considerations (EC)*

I. Economic Considerations

A. Natural resources include water, air, minerals, soil, fossil fuels, and plant life, as well as aquatic and terrestrial wildlife.

 1. Nonrenewable natural resources are those available on a finite basis.

 2. Renewable natural resources, including wildlife, can replenish themselves independently or with human assistance.

B. The distribution and abundance of wildlife can affect the economy of an area.

   1. Some wildlife provides products of commercial value or subsistence needs to humans.

   2. Members of some cultures still depend on wildlife to supply a portion of their requirements for food, shelter, and clothing.

   3. Human use of wildlife directly and indirectly creates job opportunities for people.

C. Economic trends, in addition to increased human population and mobility, have important influences on wildlife and its habitat.

D. The human culture and economic condition of an area affect and are affected by the available resources, including wildlife and its habitat.

II. Commercial, Recreational, and Other Economic Considerations

A. Historically, when conflict between recreational and commercial harvest of a wildlife species became severe, the commercial use had been eliminated.

B. Recreational trends affect wildlife and its habitat.

   1. Wildlife-based recreation is of major importance to many millions of North Americans.

     a. Consumptive wildlife-based activities, such as hunting and fishing, provide U.S. and Canadian citizens with millions of days of outdoor recreation each year.

     b. Nonconsumptive activities, such as wildlife photography, painting, feeding, and observation, also provide millions of days of recreation annually.

   2. More leisure time and the growing popularity of outdoor activities are increasing the pressures on wildlife and habitat.

C. Funds provided by consumptive users, not general tax dollars, historically have been the primary source of income for most state wildlife management programs and some federal programs.

   1. Charging an access fee to hunt, fish, camp, play, or trap on private land is common.

   2. Reductions in income from direct consumptive uses of wildlife (hunting, fishing, etc.) and nonconsumptive uses (camping, bird watching, etc.) have resulted in a loss of revenue for natural resource agencies.

### *Historical and Geographic Development (HG)*

I. Development of Society

Historically, wildlife affected the development, movement, and size of human societies.

A. Human societies and cultures developed in various ways, partly because environmental factors produced different types of plants and animals in different places.

B. Wildlife has played a significant role in the development of human culture through its influence on art, religion, and commerce.

C. Wildlife questions and issues have influenced alliances and conflicts between and within communities, societies, states, and nations.

*continued*

II. Development of Commerce

Throughout history humans have used wildlife for food, shelter, clothing, and other products.

A. All livestock and pet animals were domesticated and developed from wildlife species as humans sought to provide themselves with food, shelter, medicines, and companionship, and to satisfy other needs or wants.

B. The ways in which humans value wildlife and natural resources have changed over time.

C. As human populations have grown and pressures on wildlife populations have increased, people have developed systems to study wildlife and to regulate human impact on wildlife and habitats.

### Political and Legislative Frameworks (PL)

I. United States

A. Political trends affect wildlife and other natural resources.

B. In the United States, wildlife is considered to be a public resource. Ownership of land or water alone does not secure ownership of wildlife on that land or in that water as it does in some other countries.

1. Public decisions that affect wildlife and the environment are made through social and political processes designed to represent the wishes of the society.

2. Primary responsibility for most wildlife conservation programs in the United States is delegated to governmental agencies.

   a. States are considered to have a greater responsibility for wildlife conservation programs than does the federal government. State wildlife agencies are legally responsible for managing most wildlife on public and private lands within their geographic jurisdictions.

   b. Federal agencies, in cooperation with state agencies, are legally responsible for managing wildlife affecting national interest, such as most threatened and endangered species and migratory wildlife.

3. Nongovernmental institutions play significant roles in influencing environmental policy and direction.

   a. Wildlife interest groups use judicial, legislative, and regulatory systems in reaching their objectives.

   b. Private organizations, industrial interests, and individual citizens also conduct wildlife conservation activities.

C. Societies develop programs and policies relating to wildlife and its habitat through a variety of social mechanisms.

II. International

A. Other nations and governments have different policies and philosophies relating to wildlife ownership and protection and to habitat management.

B. Many wildlife species regularly move across national boundaries, necessitating the adoption of international agreements and the formation of international agencies and organizations to ensure protection and management of these species.

# Sustaining Fish and Wildlife Resources

## *Attitudes and Awareness (AA)*

I. Awareness

   A. Humans may find peace and inspiration through study and observation of wildlife, or simply through knowledge of its existence.

   B. Citizens benefit from experiencing and enjoying their natural resources.

II. Values

   A. Wildlife has intrinsic value, although humans often recognize only values based upon human wants and needs.

   1. The value placed on wildlife is commonly an issue in resource management decisions because value is often intangible and varies from person to person.

   2. Various groups interested in wildlife represent a wide range of philosophies and ethics concerning wildlife and how best to ensure its long range health and viability.

   B. Ecosystems have a finite capacity to provide for wildlife and human needs and wants. Sustainable living requires humans to live within the limits of the ecosystem capacity.

## *Human Impacts (HI)*

I. The Importance of Impacts

   A. Human effects on fish and wildlife and their habitats are a driving force affecting environmental quality worldwide.

   B. The presence of people affects wildlife in positive and negative ways.

II. Impacts

   A. Humans have the capacity to sustain themselves and wildlife.

   1. Although all organisms affect their environment, only humans have the capacity to consider the effects of their actions and to develop a community that is sustainable into the future.

   2. A sustainable community is one that is in balance with a healthy environment and perpetuates a healthy environment for future generations.

   3. The development and adoption of sustainable human lifestyles and social decisions can change the negative effects of human activity on wildlife.

   a. Individual lifestyle decisions including recreational choices, transportation options, housing selections, vocation, food, clothing, and energy use affect wildlife directly and indirectly.

   b. Community conservation practices, plus social, cultural, and economic values affect environmental programs and activities.

   B. Human populations and technologies often require space and activities that are detrimental to wildlife and its habitat.

   1. Human development encroaches on wildlife habitat, decreasing the amount of available habitat.

   2. Wildlife habitats are being fragmented by urban sprawl, resulting in restricted wildlife movement.

   3. Some habitats are being altered by human development activities such as water storage and landscaping.

*continued*

4. Contaminants and their bio-accumulative risks to both wildlife and humans threaten sustainable environments.

5. Pollutants fall into a number of categories including acid rain, terrestrial runoff, biological (exotics, disease, waste), industrial waste and spills, post-consumer petroleum products, sewage, silt or sediment, thermal pollution, and radioactive and solid waste. Each of these pollutants creates particular effects on habitats and, if severe enough, may cause habitat loss.

C. Loss and degradation of habitat are considered the greatest problems facing wildlife today.

1. Wildlife habitat loss because of natural trends or human activities is a condition common in nearly all nations.

2. One specific cause of habitat degradation is pollutants, which can negatively affect environmental quality.

3. Many critical habitats have been, and are, under pressure from historic and current development. Many have been damaged or lost.

4. Remaining critical habitats can be, and in some cases are being, protected and maintained; damaged habitats can be, and in some cases are being, rehabilitated.

## Issues and Trends (IT)

I. Global Perspectives

A. Current wildlife issues and trends are complex, involve alternatives, and affect the environment.

B. Many problems, issues, and trends involving wildlife in other parts of the world are similar to those in this country.

1. Wildlife issues can affect global and international as well as national, regional, and local political activities—particularly regarding human harvesting practices, transmission of pollutants and their secondary impacts, migratory species, and aquatic habitats.

2. Consumptive uses of wildlife have been excessive in some settings and continue as a persistent problems in other parts of the world.

3. Commercial sale of wildlife and wildlife products is controversial and has worldwide implications.

II. Wildlife Populations

A. Human activities increasingly determine which species of plants and animals will flourish and which will decline or disappear.

1. Most species that are endangered or threatened became so from natural or human-caused changes in their habitat and their inability to adapt or adjust to such changes.

2. Exotic species introduced into a community can change the functioning of that system.

a. Evaluation of the impact of non-native plants and animals on ecosystems is important to the management and conservation of those ecosystems.

b. Citizens must be aware of their potential role in the dispersal of non-native species and the transmission of disease, and must take steps to avoid contributing to these problems.

B. Private landowners play an important role in sustaining and improving wildlife habitat.

III. Land Use

    A.  As human populations increase and become significantly urban, land usage is altered dramatically.

        1.  Individual transportation systems that allow increased accessibility spearhead development and drive land-use changes.

        2.  Natural areas are being converted to agricultural, recreational, residential, and commercial purposes.

        3.  Fragmentation of biological communities, caused by human activities, affects wildlife diversity and populations.

    B.  Consumer changes lead to agricultural production changes.

IV. Human Perspectives

    A.  Wildlife issues involve conflicts between different interest groups.

    B.  Issues involving wildlife and its habitat are often products of cultural differences and priorities.

    C.  Well-informed individuals can assist resource management through increased involvement.

V. Consumptive and Nonconsumptive Uses

    A.  Conflicts exist within and between consumptive and nonconsumptive resource users. Any resolution must consider the needs of all groups and the sustainability of the resource.

        1.  Whether uses of wildlife should be consumptive or nonconsumptive is of concern to many people.

        2.  Among consumptive groups, conflicts often involve how, when, and how much wildlife populations are used.

    B.  Nongame species have begun to receive greater and more specific management attention.

### Wildlife Management (WM)

I. Basic Concepts

    A.  For management purposes, wildlife often has been divided into categories, including game, nongame, endangered, and threatened.

        1.  Game species are those that are hunted, fished, or trapped for recreational or economic purposes by humans.

        2.  Nongame species are those that are not hunted, fished, or trapped for either recreational or economic purposes by humans.

        3.  Endangered species are those in danger of extinction throughout all or a significant portion of their ranges.

        4.  Threatened species are those likely to become endangered.

    B.  Wildlife management is the application of scientific knowledge and technical skills to the protection, preservation, conservation, limitation, or enhancement of wildlife and its habitat.

    C.  Conservation is the use of natural resources in a way that assumes their continuing availability to future generations through the wise use or protection of natural resources.

*continued*

II. Management Considerations

   A. Wildlife resources can be managed and conserved.

   B. Wildlife species are important components of a larger ecosystem and should be managed within the context of that ecosystem.

      1. Management of one species of wildlife may have positive or negative consequences for other species within the same ecosystem.

      2. Management of aquatic wildlife and its habitat is directly influenced by land-based activities in the surrounding watershed.

   C. Wildlife management considers the needs and desires of people as well as wildlife.

      1. Humans differ in how they value wildlife and its habitat, and the total demand on each may exceed the supply.

      2. Wildlife management decisions must consider political, social, economic, and biological concerns; such decisions should involve all interested or potentially affected constituencies.

      3. These same factors may limit the scope and effectiveness of wildlife management activities.

   D. Philosophies and practices in wildlife management have been both supported and criticized by individuals, as well as by public and private organizations.

   E. Most wildlife exists on land or in waters that are not directly controlled by state or federal wildlife management agencies.

III. Management Practices

   Wildlife managers combine an understanding of species biology and of ecosystem structure and function with population- and land-manipulation techniques to accomplish management goals.

   A. Wildlife management is based on natural sciences such as biology, ecology, geography, and soil science, as well as on many other disciplines.

      1. Wildlife management practices have been developed through extensive research on ecosystems, through both observation and experimentation.

      2. Habitat management practices are often intended to mimic the effects of natural ecosystem processes, especially disturbance.

   B. Wildlife management practices involve population and habitat inventory and monitoring, direct management of wildlife species through manipulation of populations, indirect management of wildlife species through protection and manipulation of habitat, and public regulation and education.

      1. Surveys of wildlife populations and their habitat provide important baseline information to guide management decisions.

      2. Wildlife populations are manipulated through practices such as artificial propagation, stocking, transplanting, predator and damage control, and regulated harvest.

      3. Acquisition, protection, improvement, and restoration of habitat are considered to be the most successful and cost-effective long-range techniques for managing wildlife species.

4. Regulations are necessary for wildlife conservation, but they cannot substitute for the availability of suitable habitat, nor can they maintain the population of a species whose habitat has been depleted or destroyed.

5. A public that is well educated about wildlife management issues is critical to the long-term success of wildlife management programs.

C. Scientific knowledge of all aspects of wildlife, including biological and social, is growing.

1. Technology changes affect environmental management decisions by allowing more sophisticated science-based analysis.

2. Wildlife agencies employ persons with a variety of scientific training and vocational skills.

### Responsible Action (RA)

I. All plants and animals (human and wildlife) must live within the limits of their natural resources.

A. Both consumptive and nonconsumptive resource uses by people can strengthen their sense of responsibility toward the environment and encourage ethical actions.

B. It is the responsibility of citizens, government, and industry to avoid waste and destructive exploitation of natural resources, including wildlife.

C. Communities can learn to live in a sustainable manner by understanding the effects of their actions on the long-term health of the environment.

1. Citizens must understand their rights, privileges, and responsibilities, plus the consequences of their actions. That is, they should be aware of methods to help protect and improve the resource and should have the opportunity to practice and apply them.

2. Private decisions that affect wildlife and the environment are made through personal judgments. Each person makes such decisions each day, including use of time and energy, consumer choices, and vocational and leisure time activities.

3. Citizens can become involved in the management of wildlife, habitat, and the environment by direct participation in the political process or through local, state, national, or international organizations.

4. Individuals can influence public processes by voting, demonstrating, lobbying, seeking office, and supporting compatible interest groups.

5. All users of wildlife must respect the rights and property of others, consider effects on the habitat, and observe rules and regulations relating to wildlife.

6. Communities can learn to live in a sustainable manner by understanding the effects of their actions on the long-term health of the environment.

7. Education can help landowners so that they can prosper while maintaining environmental quality and integrity into the future.

D. Each individual has a responsibility to act in ways that can directly or indirectly reduce the impact of the pollutants on the environment.

II. Conservation, restoration, and enhancement of natural resource habitats benefit humans.

# Aquatic Extensions to Project WILD K–12 Activities

The following are aquatic extensions to activities that appear in the *Project WILD K–12 Curriculum and Activity Guide*. Aquatic extensions are not suggested for all existing Project WILD activities. The activities for which extensions are suggested are listed below in alphabetical order. This list is included to encourage use of both *Project WILD K–12* and the *Project WILD Aquatic Curriculum and Activity Guides* in a complementary manner to expand on concepts or to develop thematic units of study.

## Adaptation Artistry

1. What species of birds live near and depend on aquatic environments? Create a bulletin board display of aquatic birds according to the habitats in which they live.

2. Have students list as many aquatic mammals as they can think of in 3 minutes. Next, have each student pick a mammal to learn more about, then prepare a brief oral and written report using visual aids.

3. Have the students invent an aquatic insect that is especially adapted to landing on water to feed, swimming underwater and flying in to the air, or that travels long distances. Ask the students to either construct or draw their imaginary aquatic insects, and then ask them to see if they can find a real aquatic insect that is similar to the invented one.

4. Make a list of amazing adaptations found in aquatic animals. Place the name of the animal and a description of the adaptation on a 3″ × 5″ card. Make at least 10 different cards. Have the students draw a card and role-play the animal. Have the rest of the group guess the animal and its adaptation.

5. Extend the concept of this activity to focus on adaptations of stream invertebrates. Consider factors such as swiftness of current, type of bottom material, feeding techniques, and locomotion.

## And the Wolf Wore Shoes

Establish categories of aquatic habitats or environments—for example, pond, stream, river, lake, ocean. Conduct this activity as described except classify the aquatic animals according to the aquatic environments in which they are supposed to live and then indicate whether the portrayal is real or make-believe.

## Animal Charades

Have the students list several types of aquatic environments: stream, lake, pond, river, estuary, ocean. Next, ask the students to select an animal to role-play as they determine the aquatic environment in which the portrayed animal could live. Have the students role-play the organism's characteristics. Those watching need to identify the aquatic animal being portrayed and match it to the appropriate aquatic environment in which it could live.

## Ants on a Twig

1. Have the students pick an aquatic insect, spider, bird, reptile, fish, amphibian, and mammal. List the common name for each organism; its typical habitat; and the food, kind of water, shelter, and space each needs to survive.

2. Many aquatic insects have fascinating means of locomotion. Have students find one, observe the locomotion strategy, and demonstrate its movement to the group.

# Bearly Growing

Have the students identify a variety of aquatic wildlife, the average life span of each organism, its weight at birth, and its weight at maturity.

# Can Do!

Have the students select a problem to solve that involves water as a component of habitat on the school grounds.

# Cartoons and Bumper Stickers

Have the students create bumper stickers or cartoons focused on important issues related to aquatic wildlife and aquatic habitats.

# Classroom Carrying Capacity

Ask the students to give examples of how the concept of carrying capacity might apply to aquatic environments—for example, to a pond or a stream.

# Color Crazy

1. Have the students create a colorful and wild aquatic animal.

2. A coral reef is one of the most colorful places in the world. Find pictures of reef fish or other reef animals, or have students look at tropical fish tanks in a pet store or aquarium to see the diversity of colors found in coral reef animals. Pick a picture of a colorful animal that lives in a coral reef. Think of at least one way this bright color might help the animal survive in its environment. Using bright-colored crayons or other art materials, create a colorful reef animal and draw a picture of it in its habitat.

# Drawing on Nature

1. Use the techniques in this activity for enhancing observations of aquatic wildlife and habitat. Include drawings of aquatic organisms in your own "Field Guide to Our School's Aquatic Wildlife" or "Field Guide to Our Community's Aquatic Wildlife."

2. Using an aquarium, have the students use these same techniques to record their visual observations.

3. While at an aquarium, pick one feature of aquatic organisms to investigate. Have the students make drawings of this feature in several different organisms, such as features used for locomotion in under-water animals.

# Enviro-Ethics

Ask the students to identify five actions they can take that represent responsible behavior related to aquatic species and aquatic habitats; ask them to put the behaviors into practice. Keep track of these new behaviors for a day, a week, a month. Are these responsible behaviors now a part of each student's daily life? If not, why not?

# Environmental Barometer

1. Ask the students to make observations concerning the availability, apparent quality, and suitability for wildlife needs of the water found in each of the habitats they investigate. Are there more wildlife species apparent in those areas where there is more water? If yes, what seem to be the contributing factors? If no, what seem to be the contributing factors?

2. Make a "wildlife barometer" comparing the quality of two different aquatic habitats as places in which a diversity of wildlife can successfully live. Explain the reasons for the differences in the two areas.

# Ethi-Reasoning

1. Ask the students to solve the two following dilemmas that involve aquatic wildlife. Have students consider these, as well as others, and follow the procedures outlined in the *Project WILD K–12 Curriculum and Activity Guide*.

*Situation A*

You are a homeowner in an area directly near a city. Local government officials have proposed the diversion of a small stream from the property of several homeowners near the city, including yours, to power a hydro-electric

*continued*

system that will benefit the entire city. As a homeowner, you are concerned with losing the aesthetic values of this stream from your property. You are also concerned about the effect the removal of this stream will have on the fish and aquatic habitat. Another concern is that your property may lose some of its value for resale. You realize that your city needs to supply electric power to all its citizens as cost-effectively as possible. Which would you do?

- Hire a lawyer and prepare to sue the city for loss of property value.

- Form a coalition of homeowners to meet with city planners and explore possible alternatives.

- Sell your property before the project begins.

- Decide the needs of the city are more important than either the consequences to you personally or the ecological costs.

- Do something else.

*Situation B*

Your family owns a 500-acre farm. A tributary to a high-quality fishing stream runs along the boundary of your property. The nitrogen- and phosphorous-based fertilizer that your family uses to increase crop production is carried into the stream by rain runoff. This type of fertilizer is increasing algae growth and adversely affecting the fish in both the tributary and the main stream. Your farm production is your sole source of income, but your family has always enjoyed fishing and does not want to lose the fish from the streams. Which would you do?

- Change fertilizers even though it may reduce crop yield.

- Allow a portion of your land along the stream to grow wild, thus establishing a buffer zone (riparian area).

- Investigate the possibility of gaining a tax exemption for the land you allowed for a buffer zone.

- Do nothing.

- Do something else.

2. Ask the students to list activities that are sometimes or always harmful to aquatic wildlife and aquatic habitats. Are these activities harmful or beneficial? How can these activities be prevented or increased? Identify at least five things people can do in aquatic environments that are not damaging to populations of aquatic animals or the long-term health of aquatic habitats.

## Everybody Needs a Home

Have the students draw the "homes" of some kinds of aquatic wildlife and discuss the species' needs for food, water, shelter, and space in a suitable arrangement.

## First Impressions

Prepare a series of large photos or drawings of a variety of aquatic animals. Select a range so that there are likely to be some that cause a fearful or negative first impression among some people. Do the activity as described in the *Project WILD K–12 Curriculum and Activity Guide*. Here are various aquatic animals as examples: mosquito, pelican, trout, frog, dragonfly, shark, dolphin, sea otter, seal, sea gull, manatee, catfish. Discuss how each animal has an important role to play in aquatic ecosystems.

## Flip the Switch for Wildlife

Conduct the activity examining the possible positive and negative consequences for aquatic wildlife and aquatic habitats because of energy-use practices and sources of energy used.

## Graphananimal

Pick two aquatic habitats—such as lake and river, pond and stream, or fresh water (lake) and salt water (ocean). On separate cards, have the students make a collection of animals for each habitat by listing, drawing or cutting out pictures of animals from magazines. Mix the cards. Have the students sort the cards by correctly identifying which animal lives in which aquatic habitat. Do any seem to live in both? If yes, which ones? Create a poster display to show the variety of animals living in each of these two aquatic environments.

## Grasshopper Gravity

Do this activity with a water-related insect. Adjust the specific questions as needed to suit the insect's characteristics, still using these general categories: Interesting Features, Legs, Wings, Head, Mouth, Antennae, Motion, Noise, Colors, Habitat, Conclusions.

## Habitat Lap Sit

Do a variation to "Habitat Lap Sit" as follows: Have the students form a circle, holding hands. Name one student as an animal in an aquatic ecosystem. Name the next four students in the circle as food, water, shelter, and space for that animal. Repeat the process until all the students are involved. That is, name another student as an animal in the same aquatic ecosystem, and then name the next four students in the circle as food, water, shelter, and space for that animal. Finish the procedure as described in the Variation section of the activity. Conduct the activity more than once, picking a different aquatic ecosystem each time to emphasize that all aquatic animals, in any aquatic ecosystem, need food, water, shelter, and space in a suitable arrangement in order to survive.

## Habitat Rummy

Make new cards specifically for aquatic species in aquatic ecosystems.

## Habitracks

Do Extension 1 in the *Project WILD K–12 Curriculum and Activity Guide*. Next, have a student pick an aquatic animal. Have the student stand in the middle of the other students who are labeled food, water, shelter, and space. The student representing the aquatic animal should touch or hold on to the yarn to connect with every other student. The connection indicates the importance of having a suitable habitat in which to live.

## Habitrekking

Adjust the "habitrekking" instructions to apply specifically to aquatic wildlife and aquatic habitats. That is, find evidence that humans and aquatic wildlife are subject to the same or similar environmental problems.

## Hazardous Links, Possible Solutions

1. Focus this activity on aquatic species by substituting squid for grasshoppers, fish for shrews, and pelicans for red-tail hawks.

2. Show how pesticides can enter aquatic environments and end up in the food chains of terrestrial environments (mosquito larvae—fish—birds) and how pesticides can enter the food chains in terrestrial environments and end up in aquatic environments (grasshoppers—small fish—large fish).

## Here Today, Gone Tomorrow

1. What habitats are aquatic species dependent upon? Have students find out more about the conditions affecting each of these aquatic species, their status, and projections for their likelihood of survival as a species.

2. Are factors affecting threatened and endangered aquatic species significantly different from those affecting terrestrial species? Have students respond and defend their answers. If yes, why? If no, why not?

## A History of Wildlife Management

1. In some states, fish populations are not managed by the same state agency that manages other wildlife species. In some states, one agency manages marine fish, while another manages freshwater fish. Which state agency is responsible for managing fish species in your state? Find out if this agency also manages all other aquatic species. If not, find out which agency does. Identify the major responsibilities of the state agencies responsible for managing fish and other aquatic wildlife in your state.

*continued*

2. Work with students to develop a summary of major laws and regulations affecting fish and other aquatic species of wildlife in your state.

3. Ask students to select an aquatic organism and to investigate the laws and management practices affecting that organism. Are the regulations local, state, national, global? Are they effective? Are there any areas in which improvements could be made? If yes, in which?

## Improving Habitat in the Community

Pick a habitat improvement project directly related to aquatic wildlife and aquatic habitats.

## Interview a Spider

Aquatic wildlife habitats occur in a variety of forms, colors, sizes, and adaptations. Conduct "Interview a Spider" with the students choosing an aquatic animal to research, interview, and report to the class.

## Know Your Legislation: What's in It for Wildlife?

Choose a key piece of legislation related to aquatic species or aquatic habitats and research its impact on aquatic species or aquatic habitats.

## Learning to Look, Looking to See

What is the closest water source? It might be a drinking fountain, a sprinkler hose, a pond, a stream, or the beach. Have the students imagine it clearly in their minds, and then have them draw a picture showing as much detail as possible of the water and its immediate environment. Include any wildlife and vegetation that may be in the environment near and in the water. Now, or as soon as possible, have the students go to the place in the picture, and have them make a written list of anything that was not included in their drawings. Ask the students to add the missing details to their drawings to make them complete.

## Litter We Know

1. Can litter be potentially harmful to aquatic wildlife? If so, how?

2. What happens when garbage is dumped into the ocean or other bodies of water? Where does this happen? Where does the garbage go? How does this affect communities and wildlife? Are there regulations affecting the dumping of garbage into the seas and other bodies of water? If yes, are they enforced?

## Lobster in Your Lunch

Be sure to include foods derived from aquatic environments in your study—for example, from rivers, streams, ponds, lakes, or oceans. Aquatic foods might range from fish to the kelp that is used as a stabilizer in many foods, including ice cream.

## Mircotrek Treasure Hunt

Adjust the "Wildlife Treasure Hunt" instructions to apply specifically to aquatic wildlife and aquatic habitats. For example, find evidence that humans and aquatic wildlife share environments.

## Museum Search for Wildlife

Have the students search through magazines or books for pictures of aquatic wildlife in art. How frequently is wildlife included in art that also includes water? Make a list of the kinds of aquatic habitats found in artwork and tally how many times each habitat is portrayed.

## Muskox Maneuvers

Many fish species also have effective adaptations that protect them from predator species. Have one student be a predator and all the rest of the students be prey. This time the predator is a tuna, and the prey are herring in a school of fish. (Educators can choose an example of predator and prey. Just pick a prey species that forms a school of fish.) Role-play the school of fish moving through waters with the predator trying to catch at least one to survive. In a large open area, have the students move as the school of

fish. Have three or four students inside the school of fish wear a bright-colored cloth or tie that the predator will try to remove in order to have successfully caught its prey. The school of fish must keep moving. See if the school of fish can successfully move the length of the open area at least once without any fish being caught by the predator. The predator may move in any direction and may stop and start moving at any time. The prey must move generally together and may not stop. For the sake of safety, no running allowed!

## My Kingdom for a Shelter

Have the students create models of shelters used by a variety of aquatic wildlife.

## No Water Off a Duck's Back

What are the consequences of oil spills on other species of aquatic wildlife (e.g., fish, marine mammals)?

## Oh Deer!

Conduct the activity in the same fashion, substituting an aquatic species of wildlife. Rather than assuming all the necessary space is available, assume all the water is available but space is needed, as are food and shelter. Hands on stomach signal food, hands together over head signals shelter, and arms out to the side signals space. Otherwise, conduct the activity in the same fashion.

## Philosophical Differences

Choose an issue directly related to aquatic species and aquatic habitats, and conduct the activity as outlined.

## Planning for People and Wildlife

Conduct the activity as outlined, with the following additions. Ten years have passed. Your community has doubled in size. What measures, if any, have you taken to protect the availability and quality of water in the community? What

impacts, if any, have there been to wildlife in the area as a result of this increase in population? What changes, if any, need to be made to protect the availability and quality of the water resources in this community for the next 25 years for both people and wildlife?

## Planting Animals

Focus this activity specifically on aquatic species. See what students discover—if not in your state, then in your region of the country.

## Power of a Song

Aquatic themes are abundant in traditional songs, as well as some contemporary songs. Sea chanteys and songs like "Oh, Shenandoah" and John Denver's song "Calypso" are examples. Have the students listen to a variety of songs with aquatic themes and analyze their lyrics. Look for examples of ecological concepts, historical information, political messages, and many ways that people value water and aquatic environments.

## Quick Frozen Critters

1. Conduct this activity using aquatic predator and prey species.

2. Have the students "swim" toward their food while portraying trumpet fish, flounder, stonefish, or other marine organisms that "freeze" as a defense mechanism.

3. If possible, conduct the activity in the shallow end of a real swimming pool. Hula hoops will float!

## Rainfall and the Forest

1. Following procedures in the activity, add major bodies of water, if any, to the map. Add ways to identify watersheds. Have the students discuss possible influences of these areas of water and watersheds on the vegetation and wildlife in the associated areas.

*continued*

2. After reviewing the interrelationships between the data and information the students have gathered, have the students generate a set of hypotheses about the factors that seem to directly affect the availability of suitable habitat for wildlife in your state. Ask the students to support their hypotheses with one or more paragraphs using their findings from this study.

## Riparian Zone

Conduct this activity in conjunction with other riparian activities from the *Project WILD Aquatic K–12 Curriculum and Activity Guide*, including "Blue-Ribbon Niche," "Riparian Retreat" and "To Dam or Not to Dam."

## Saturday Morning Wildlife Watching

Have the students look for any examples of aquatic wildlife portrayed in Saturday morning cartoons. Add these to the other examples of wildlife portrayed in cartoons, and do the activity as described in the *Project WILD K–12 Curriculum and Activity Guide*.

## Seeing Is Believing!

Compare the size of the eyes of a variety of different species of fish, aquatic mammals, aquatic insects, and aquatic birds.

## Shrinking Habitat

1. Have the students generate a list of possible human activities that can reduce or eliminate aquatic habitats (examples: draining wetlands; construction on shorelines; diversion of waters for agricultural, domestic, or business purposes). For every example given, identify possible reasons both for and against taking such action.

2. Have the students look at old and new maps of their area or state. Are there any locations where wetlands no longer exist? If yes, what happened to the wetlands?

## Smokey Bear Said What?

Investigate the potential effects from forest and grassland fires on watersheds.

## Stormy Weather

Storms can also affect aquatic wildlife. Discuss with students what happens to fish in a stream during heavy rains. (Many tend to seek shelter near rocks or among under-water plants. Sometimes the storm washes soil and rocks into the stream, making it difficult for the fish to breathe.) What happens to the fish and mammals in ocean waters during hurricanes? Have students imagine themselves as an under-water animal in a storm and describe what happens to the animal and its behavior.

## Thicket Game

1. Aquatic and terrestrial animals are adapted for survival in a variety of ways. Have the students imagine an under-water thicket. What would be the same, if anything, about predator and prey relationships in an under-water thicket? What would be different, if anything? Draw two under-water thickets: one in a pond and one in an ocean. Include pictures of fish and other aquatic life that are hardly visible because of adaptations that make them hard to see, plus pictures of others that are easy to see.

2. Ask the students to identify predators and prey in two or more aquatic environments.

## Too Close for Comfort

Because water is one of the essential components of habitat, areas where water is available in the natural environment are frequently visited by many species of wildlife. Some live in or near the water. Others come to the water as needed. As a result, ponds, lakeshores, river banks, ocean beaches, streams, reservoirs, canals, irrigation ditches, and even city fountains can sometimes be places where people get "too close for comfort" when it comes to wildlife. Ask students to think of three examples of situations where people can get "too close for comfort" in aquatic habitats, with possible negative consequences for wildlife. Then think of three examples of people and wildlife being able to coexist near and in water.

## Tracks!

Following the procedures found in the activity, display all the tracks according to the habitats in which students found them. How many of the tracks, if any, were found near water? If any were found near water, identify the kind of aquatic environments in which the tracks were found (e.g., pond, stream, lake, marsh, beach).

## Urban Nature Search

1. Make a map showing all the public water areas in your community. Streams, ponds, lakes, or rivers are all possibilities. If there are no such public areas of water in a natural or near-natural environment within your community, look next for water that people have introduced, but that is still accessible to the public. For example, count and map the location of the public water fountains in the community. Next, have students list and tally all the different kinds of wildlife that seem to depend on any single identified water source.

2. Have students look at urban ponds and lakes in parks. Compare those species living in concrete-bottomed ponds with those living in mud-bottomed ponds. What lives where? Where and how do they acquire their food?

## What Bear Goes Where?

1. Have the students look at pictures of three species of fish and discuss the similarities and differences among the fish. Next, have the students imagine the place where each fish lives. Then have them draw a picture of each fish in a place where they think it could live. Discuss whether their perceptions are accurate.

2. Find out more about the adaptations of different species of fish that make it possible for them to live where and how they do. See the Project WILD Aquatic Activity "Fashion a Fish."

3. Help make a bulletin board that shows "What Fish Goes Where?" Show fish that live in ponds, fish that live in lakes, fish that live in streams, fish that live in rivers, and fish that live in oceans. Include a picture of the appropriate habitat along with a picture of the fish. See the Project WILD Aquatic Activity "Fishy Who's Who."

## What Did Your Lunch Cost Wildlife?

Conduct this activity asking this question: "What Did Your Lunch Cost Aquatic Wildlife?" Ask students to think of whole populations of species of aquatic animals and aquatic habitats.

## What's for Dinner?

Create at least two food chains that involve people, aquatic wildlife, and plants.

## What's That, Habitat?

Ask the students to think of an aquatic animal and to draw a picture of the animal in a place where it lives. Make sure they include food, water, shelter, and space in an arrangement they think would make it possible for the animal to survive. Talk about their drawings, pointing out the habitat components included.

## What's Wild?

1. Aquatic wildlife occurs in a variety of forms. Have the students create a collage of many kinds of aquatic animals.

2. Have the students create posters or collages of aquatic wildlife according to the habitat in which it lives.

*continued*

## Who Fits Here?

Conduct this activity using only aquatic ecosystems, (e.g., pond, lake, stream, estuary, marsh, ocean, river).

## Wild Bill's Fate

1. Conduct this activity again by focusing on water-related legislation. Have the students identify any possible effects on aquatic wildlife and aquatic habitats if the legislation is passed.

2. Have the students write letters to a legislator expressing their opinions about proposed legislation affecting aquatic wildlife. They should include at least three statements that support with evidence their perspectives concerning the proposed legislation.

## Wildlife Issues: Community Attitude Survey

Follow the procedures for this activity with students picking an issue directly related to aquatic species and aquatic habitats.

## Wildlife Research

Conduct this activity again by focusing specifically on research related to aquatic wildlife and aquatic habitats.

## Wildwork

Conduct this activity again by focusing specifically on the variety of aquatic-related careers that are available.

## Wildlife Is Everywhere!

Have the students survey the school grounds or neighborhood for any possible aquatic habitats for wildlife. Check puddles, sprinkler systems, and, if possible, streams, beaches, ponds, and so forth. Look for evidence—direct or indirect—of any wildlife that lives in or near these water-related areas. Have the students share what they find taking care not to damage any wildlife they find, or its habitat.

# Outdoor Classrooms

Education places many demands on educators and students alike. In the urgency for educators to teach more and faster, there is a growing assumption that the classroom building is the only place where legitimate learning can take place. The result of this tendency is increasingly to abandon the outdoor world. The *Project WILD K–12 Curriculum and Activity Guide* and the *Project WILD Aquatic K–12 Curriculum and Activity Guide* both have numerous activities that are enhanced when conducted outside. Effective learning is often heightened in natural settings. The most fundamental reason for teaching outdoors whenever possible, when using Project WILD, is that nature itself is the subject. The natural context—the living world and people's interactions with it—is the subject for most Project WILD activities.

The school ground, a nearby park, a pond, a small stream, a vacant lot, and sites visited on extended field trips all may enhance learning when incorporated within instructional experiences. In this urbanized age in which much information comes to us vicariously and abstractly, it is increasingly important to make sure that students have meaningful, first-hand experiences with the living world. Another benefit gained from outdoor experiences is that they provide a foundation for lifelong learning and leisure pursuits. More and more leisure activities take advantage of outdoor settings. Bird watching, hiking, camping, photography, and drawing and sketching, plus sports such as skiing, snorkeling, and running are all popular. Students who are grounded in outdoor studies are more apt to continue outdoor active learning beyond their school years.

Getting outside does not require the capacity to drive distances to undeveloped forests and open spaces. Using the outdoors as a natural classroom can take many forms. It may be as simple as using the windows and windowsills of the classroom to observe what's outside, or using the school grounds as legitimate and appropriate places for study of concepts. Urban settings, such as city parks, can offer a variety of opportunities. Such natural explorations lead students to understand and remember important concepts. With confidence gained first hand in relatively small scale field experiences, students can more effectively embrace ideas that involve wildlife in the global ecosystem.

# Field Ethics

The question of whether to collect some objects from natural settings—either temporarily or permanently—is difficult to answer. Such decisions are left to individual educators and their students and are based on thoughtful decision making, caution, and respect for the living environment. In most cases, Project WILD urges no collecting at all—and recommends instead simply leaving the natural environment as it is found, with as little impact from students in the process of learning as possible.

There are times, however, when it may seem appropriate and so instructionally powerful that some limited forms of collecting are desired. Such collecting for instructional purposes can take a variety of forms. Sometimes it involves going outside and picking up fallen leaves on an autumn day. Sometimes it involves collecting litter from a park. Sometimes it involves using a net and examining organisms found in pond water.

If any collecting is to be done, it should begin with a respect for the environment. Educators should determine in advance what laws may apply. Then, involve students in deciding what, if anything, to collect and how much collecting is appropriate. By involving students in the process of deciding whether and what to collect, they are more likely to develop an ethic that considers the impact on ecosystems. This kind of thoughtful decision making about the consequences of our actions is an important, lifelong skill.

The following ethic was developed by a class of sixth graders in Illinois:

1. We should obey all laws protecting plants and animals.

2. We should ask the owner before we take anything.

3. We should collect an animal only if we know we can keep it alive long enough to learn from it.

4. We should not collect things that will hurt us.

5. We should collect something only if there are a lot of them in that place.

6. We should collect something only if we can learn something very important about it.

Obviously, any collecting for instructional purposes should alter the environment as little as possible and should not significantly damage wildlife or its habitat. Where possible, anything collected from the environment for instructional purposes should be returned to its original location at the conclusion of the activity.

Beyond the collecting issue, students must understand that humans can affect living things in other ways. For example, just by walking over fragile areas outdoors or observing animals under certain conditions, we can destroy or disturb organisms. Leaving a trail can injure or kill small plants and animals, just as walking along the banks of a stream can affect vegetation. Even walking on rocks can remove new soil and crush mosses and lichens if they are present. Students must pay attention to the consequences of their actions. Thoughtful decision making and responsible behavior are not just an outcome or goal of Project WILD, but a path to take in the process of learning.

# Observations and Inferences

Learning how to be observant and learning how to make inferences are two important skills. They are two skills that students can develop when participating in some of the Project WILD instructional activities. Because many students seem to confuse observations and inferences, this section is intended to help distinguish between the two.

Observations are descriptions of characteristics or attributes—for example, of objects, processes, or events. Inferences are judgments or interpretations about things such as objects, processes, or events.

If a student sees a fish in the water and describes the fish's coloration, length, width, thickness, mobility, fin pattern, scale configuration, and eye characteristics, that student is making an observation. A student who sees a fish darting about near some fish eggs in the water and says it is a female fish protecting a nest has made an inference.

Observations are objective in the sense that what is said about objects, processes, or events can usually be agreed upon by any observer. Descriptions of characteristics such as measurements, weights, color, fin patterns, and such, may usually be the same for any observer, while inferences—derived from judgments or interpretations—go beyond descriptions.

For many students, the act of labeling something becomes an end in itself. For example, a student may observe a fish and identify it as a trout. Observationally, the student may be seeing an animal of about 10 inches in length with a body 2 inches thick and 3 inches deep that lives in an aquatic environment. Inferentially, the student may decide that the fish is protecting a nest. Inferences go beyond objective information of the kind obtained by observation and involve efforts to determine cause-and-effect relationships with other elements. Inference requires students to use observations in combination with information they may be missing in order to establish what are intended to be informed cognitive leaps, or inferences.

In scientific study, observations typically are gathered. Later, when patterns begin to emerge, the process of inference begins. The distinction between these two modes of inquiry becomes especially important when we consider how willingly some tend to come to conclusions on the basis of inferences with no grounding in observational experience. At best, such inferences reflect guessing and, at worst, superstition and prejudice. Learning the skills of observation adds richness to the database from which inferences are made. As students learn these skills of observation, mature inferences tend to emerge, which in turn lead to hypothesis and theory in science.

# Interviewing People

To some extent, everyone in a community is an expert on something. Perhaps students will want to know what something in the community looked like 20 or 40 years ago. They may want to speak with some long-term residents of the area. An interview can provide a powerful piece of oral history, or it can be an intrusion into the life and privacy of a person. If students are encouraged to interview people, some guidelines are useful.

*Recommendation: Send an introductory letter on school stationery explaining the project and asking for cooperation and assistance—with thanks in advance.*

Plan interviews in advance, at least in terms of outlining major questions to be asked. Students need to be reminded to conduct themselves in a professional manner and to keep the interview focused on the purposes of the research. For example, have students listen and record their subject's responses. Rather than the students using the time of the interview to expound their own views on the topic, their task is to learn the subject's views. Treat the subject with dignity and respect at all times. If any form of recording is desired, ask the people in advance for their permission, and advise them how the information will be used. If a student wants to quote the person being interviewed by name, give the person the opportunity to see the written proceedings of the interview, review any excerpts to be used, or review the recording before any class or public use of the information takes place.

If any public opinion surveys or other forms of interviews in public places are planned, students should be supervised by adults. People who might be concerned (businessowners, mall managers, etc.) need to be asked in advance and informed about the project and its purposes. If people do not want to be interviewed, thank them politely for their time and allow them to proceed with their business. As a general principle, recommend that any interviews conducted by students be arranged in advance with the involvement of their teacher. An in-class trial run or practice session using role-playing techniques can be an effective preparation for actually conducting interviews. Students act the parts of interviewers and subjects while other students serve as constructive critics of their performances.

# Animals in the Classroom

## The National Science Teachers Association Position Statement

*The following is a portion of the NSTA Position Statement on "Responsible Use of Live Animals and Dissection in the Science Classroom." Please see the NSTA website www.nsta.org/positionstatement&psid=44 to view the entire statement which includes a section on dissection that is not represented below.*

NSTA supports the decision of science teachers and their school or school district to integrate live animals and dissection in the K-12 classroom. Student interaction with organisms is one of the most effective methods of achieving many of the goals outlined in the National Science Education Standards (NSES). To this end, NSTA encourages educators and school officials to make informed decisions about the integration of animals in the science curriculum. NSTA opposes regulations or legislation that would eliminate an educator's decision-making role regarding dissection or would deny students the opportunity to learn through actual animal dissection.

NSTA encourages districts to ensure that animals are properly cared for and treated humanely, responsibly, and ethically. Ultimately, decisions to incorporate organisms in the classroom should balance the ethical and responsible care of animals with their educational value.

While this position statement is primarily focused on vertebrate animals, NSTA recognizes the importance of following similar ethical practices for all living organisms.

## Including Live Animals in the Classroom

NSTA supports including live animals as part of instruction in the K-12 science classroom because observing and working with animals firsthand can spark students' interest in science as well as a general respect for life while reinforcing key concepts as outlined in the NSES.

NSTA recommends that teachers

- Educate themselves about the safe and responsible use of animals in the classroom. Teachers should seek information from reputable sources and familiarize themselves with laws and regulations in their state.

- Become knowledgeable about the acquisition and care of animals appropriate to the species under study so that both students and the animals stay safe and healthy during all activities.

- Follow local, state, and national laws, policies, and regulations when live organisms, particularly native species, are included in the classroom.

- Integrate live animals into the science program based on sound curriculum and pedagogical decisions.

- Develop activities that promote observation and comparison skills that instill in students an appreciation for the value of life and the importance of caring for animals responsibly.

- Instruct students on safety precautions for handling live organisms and establish a plan for addressing such issues as allergies and fear of animals.

- Develop and implement a plan for future care or disposition of animals at the conclusion of the study as well as during school breaks and summer vacations.

- Espouse the importance of not conducting experimental procedures on animals if such procedures are likely to cause pain, induce nutritional deficiencies, or expose animals to parasites, hazardous/toxic chemicals, or radiation.

- Shelter animals when the classroom is being cleaned with chemical cleaners, sprayed with pesticides, and during other times when potentially harmful chemicals are being used.

- Refrain from releasing animals into a non-indigenous environment.

- Adopted by the NSTA Board of Directors June 2005

Reference: National Research Council. (1996). National science education standards. Washington, DC: National Academy Press.

# Using Local Resources

In the course of conducting activities in Project WILD, educators may find that local resource people would be of great assistance. Some of the topics covered in Project WILD activities address areas in which many educators may not have extensive background experience. Various resource people in the community may be invited to share with students their special knowledge of wildlife, environmental, or natural resource topics. However, involving such resource people should be done in a manner that uses each expert's time effectively. Preparing in advance before inviting experts to speak to classes, sending students to interview them, or taking field trips to special facilities is important. Here are a few basic suggestions that may help you with this process.

***Have students explore the question of who might have special knowledge to contribute to a particular activity or topic.***

One of the important skills that students can learn is "How can we find out?" Part of this process may involve asking someone who knows more than we do. Students can conduct web searches for potential experts. Where could they find someone who knows about local water quality—in the local city health department? In the state water commission? In the Office of the Environment? Are any citizen groups interested in the topic? Do they publish any resource materials? Do local colleges and universities have people on their faculties with expertise in this area? Develop a list of "leads," possible avenues to explore in order to identify the experts on a topic in your area.

***Develop a plan for approaching the agencies or organizations where "experts" may be found.***

Once the students have decided where experts might be found, they will need to decide how to approach those institutions in order to actually acquire the names of some people who might be speakers, lead field trips, or be interviewed. Some governmental agencies, for example, have public affairs departments, and those departments might be the best place to start. Some public libraries have information librarians who specialize in that sort of task and may know whom to approach. Some universities and colleges publish speaker lists that include topics that faculty members are willing to speak about. Local businesses may also have people who are experts. Again, the public affairs departments may be good places to start. Sometimes you may be referred directly to the resource person. In case this happens, consider the next suggestion, found below, before you undertake this part of the search.

***Once you have identified potential resource people, develop a strategy for determining whether they would be willing to act as experts for your class and, if so, how they would like to work.***

As a teacher, you may want to speak with resource people before you actually have them come to your class (usually a good idea). Sometimes, when you explain the questions in which your class has an interest, or the topic of your study, the experts may suggest that they themselves are not the best choice to address the topic. They may suggest someone else. Some experts are not comfortable speaking to large groups of people, especially young students. They may want to talk to a small group, or even one student, who can take the information back to the rest of the class. Some may not be able to get away from their work to visit your school during the day. In that case, you may want to consider whether a field visit would be possible for the class. The expert may suggest other sources of information, such as books, magazines, or films.

If the resource person is willing to work directly with students, find out what advance preparation is needed and in what type of setting the expert would like to work. Would he or she like written questions from the class beforehand? Would he or she be willing to be recorded or videotaped or written up in the school or local newspaper? If the expert is coming to your school, what sort of special equipment will be needed (slide projector, overhead, etc.)? If the class will take a field trip to visit the resource person at his or her office, laboratory, business, or home, what should the class know in advance? Are any special clothes required? How long will the visit be? Where should the group report to start the visit? Attention to this kind of detail can make the trip more productive, effective, and appropriate.

### Decide who will act as interviewers, recorders, moderators, and hosts. Brief the class about the roles each of these students will serve, and the responsibilities and expectations for behavior of all students.

Resource people coming to a school for the first time may be quite uncertain about simple things, beginning with how to find the school. A letter to the resource person in advance will help to verify the details of the arrangements to which you have agreed, and you might include a map to the school. When a guest arrives at the school, a student can meet and escort the visitor to the classroom, asking if he or she wants assistance with any materials, and

so forth. If student interviewers will visit the resource person, they should have a letter of introduction, they should be briefed about how to interview the person, and they should operate in pairs or with adult supervision for personal safety. Students who leave the school grounds to interview people should see themselves as representing the school and your class in particular. They will want to leave a good impression. Whether guests come to school or students visit resource people in the community, the importance of courteous, considerate, and responsible behavior should be stressed.

### Do advance work on the topic.

Resource people usually do not mind giving their time to people they think can use it well. If you and the class have done some homework on the subject, you are more likely to ask intelligent questions and be able to understand what the expert has to offer. This advanced preparation is strongly recommended in any circumstance. It is especially important to make the best use of a field trip to a complex facility, such as, a community sewage treatment plant or a fish hatchery.

### Remember that a little consideration and hospitality go a long way.

Resource people can become lifelong supporters of your school and its programs, or lifelong critics. Which will happen depends not only on things such as the suggestions offered here, but also on small but important things such as thanking them at the time of their visit (or your visit) and following up with a letter. If the class uses the information from the resource person in some special way, send a picture or samples of the work to the resource person to show what was accomplished. If the local media produce an article, send along a copy to your expert. Do not expect or demand large amounts of additional time from the experts, but do let them know that their expertise was appreciated as well as how it was used.

# Simulated Field Trips

A simulated field trip is a powerful way for students to create vivid experiences in their minds. Many older people remember when the major form of entertainment was radio. With its absence of visual images, radio required its listeners to create mental pictures of the way various characters looked and acted. It was common for listeners to imagine landscapes, cities, and any number of exotic settings, thereby stretching their creativity.

Research has shown that with their eyes closed, people activate parts of their brain-mind systems that are not often stimulated. When we picture things in our minds, we call these parts of our brains into activity. Studies show skill in picturing things in our minds enhances our ability to enrich reading and to increase skill and imagination in writing. The capacity to remember concepts, words, names, and ideas is enhanced.

The following guidelines provide a basic, useful approach to simulated field trips as a teaching tool:

1. Ask the students to lay aside all pens, pencils, books, and such.

2. Instruct the students to sit in a comfortable and relaxed position with their eyes closed.

3. Wait until you see a general state of relaxation before beginning.

4. Using a steady and paced reading or speaking style, begin offering the students the narrative. Remember to speak slowly and steadily. If you want the students to create rich mental pictures, you must allow them time to do so. It takes about as much time to observe mental images as it does to carefully review actual physical settings.

5. Once the narrative is finished, invite the students to review all of the images they saw in their minds. Again, try to allow enough time for an adequate visual review— and remember, the review takes time.

6. After adequate time for mental review (at least 1 minute and possibly 2 minutes), ask the students to open their eyes.

7. Begin discussing the simulated field trip in terms of the instructional purpose for its use.

In some cases, the process serves simply to provide a visual review of some of the students' past experiences. At other times, you are providing stimuli for the students to create original images. In any case, it is important to realize that there are no mistakes in mental images. The images are data. If students create images that are consistent with what you expected, consider the images to represent differing perspectives rather than wrong answers. Try to honor and nourish variety as a means to add richness to the topics being explored. In addition to being a powerful and effective way to explore and remember concepts, regular use of simulated field trips also tends to relax students. When relaxed, they frequently will be more productive in all academic areas.

# Using Simulations for Instructional Purposes

An educational simulation is an instructional activity that models aspects of the real world to teach one or more concepts. Simulations—especially those that involve students in kinesthetic learning experiences—are used frequently in Project WILD.

In the *Project WILD Aquatic Curriculum and Activity Guide*, "Hooks and Ladders," a salmon simulation, and "Migration Headache," an activity about limiting factors affecting populations of migrating water birds, are examples. In conducting simulations for instructional purposes, you must remember that the activity can take on a life of its own. The students can become so involved in the role they are playing that they forget to relate the objects, events, and processes to what they represent in nature.

Students of all ages may tend to become competitive when they are responsible for capturing or escaping the animals depicted in an activity. Antic and energetic physical behavior often results. During such activity, the students identify subjectively with the role they are playing. This identification is important and should be encouraged as part of the powerful learning that is possible through simulations. Yet it also is important to link the subjective experience with the objective concepts that are central to each activity.

Distinguish between what is realistic and what is not realistic about the simulation. Simulations, by definition, are simple representations of more complex natural interactions. Teachers should point this out to students and help them understand how the simulation is like and unlike the real situation.

Simulations always leave out some elements that exist in nature. They simplify to make a point. Make sure that the students are clear about the point and the limitations of the activity in demonstrating the complexities of real-world situations.

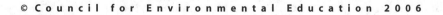

# A Guide to the Ecosystem Concept

Many hundreds of books and many thousands of research articles have been written in the field of ecology. There are also many fine textbooks. This short description of a complex and sophisticated field cannot, by its brief nature, do anything more than provide a summary of a few major concepts. However, the *Project WILD K-12 Curriculum and Activity Guide* and *Project WILD Aquatic K–12 Curriculum and Activity Guide* contain a number of activities that are designed to invite students of all ages to ask questions about how ecosystems work. To address these questions, educators need not be professional ecologists nor have extensive backgrounds in biology or wildlife management. This appendix is designed as a reference to help educators develop a few simple and powerful ecological concepts with students.

## The Ecosystem

The word ecosystem combines two words: ecology and system. It connects the idea of "eco," the household of nature, with that of "system," a set of interactions over time among living and nonliving elements of the household. Ecologists have offered a number of definitions of this concept. One of the problems that many educators encounter with the term is the question of size of an ecosystem. Some have seen photos of Earth from space and have heard the entire planet referred to as an ecosystem. This ecosystem is called the "global ecosystem" or "biosphere."

The term ecosystem is a convenience. We can draw an imaginary line around a section of the larger world, decide to treat its elements separately from the rest, and call it an ecosystem.

When we describe how the organisms in the system behave; how they interact, grow, adapt; what they eat; how long they live; what happens to them when they die; and what they require to stay healthy or to reproduce, we are dealing with the way in which the household system operates—and we are thinking SYSTEM-atically. We are finding connections.

Often the connections between elements of a system are subtle and hard to see or understand. Quite frequently, this is because they take a long time to happen. The life cycle of some organisms in North American west coast forest ecosystems is 300 to 500 years. In an average human life span, we might see little change in those forests. But the life cycle of an ecosystem in a pond that dries up during the summer and is frozen in the winter might be 12 months. Life cycles in a jar of microbes might be measured in hours.

Ecosystem is really a term that represents an idea more than a place or set of things. When children set up a wide-mouth jar in the classroom with pond water, a few small animals, and some plants in it, and then cap the bottle tightly, they have established an ecosystem. The jar contains biotic and abiotic elements. The biotic elements are all the living things in the jar: plants, snails, microbes, and so forth. The abiotic elements are the nonliving elements: air, water, rocks, and bottom debris. Even here it is often difficult to distinguish between living (biotic) and nonliving (abiotic) things. Some biologists would define the abiotic components as those elements in the system that are not of biological origin.

Problems arise when one considers that some of the carbon dioxide gas was produced by animals and some of the oxygen, if not all of it, by plants. This little ecosystem in a jar will quickly turn into a gooey mess unless the children place the bottle in the light—but not in direct sunlight. The system in the bottle is not going to operate without a source of energy, namely light energy. If there are not too many animals and other nongreen organisms in the jar, the bottle can be tightly sealed, even "air tight," and may operate as a self-contained environment for many years. It will slowly change over time. Some organisms will die and be decomposed. Slow hatching eggs or spores may develop and germinate. The acidity of the water may change. The color of the water may change and absorb more heat and light. The system will undergo a life cycle of its own, slowly aging and changing.

When the term ecosystem is used in Project WILD, it describes a system in which there are living organisms, nonliving components, and a primary source of energy interacting over time within a defined locale. In most systems, the primary source of energy is the sun. We could establish organisms in various environments, but unless there was an appropriate balance or set of relations among them, the system would quickly or slowly go into crisis and die. Many students and teachers have seen examples of changed systems when they have cleaned out refrigerators or discovered last month's uneaten lunch in the bottom of their lockers.

One ecosystem that is often studied in school is the pond. Pond is not a word that is typically used with a precise definition. It is like the word ecosystem in many ways. In some parts of the world, a pond is a small body of fresh water, usually a very small body of water. In other places, a pond can be a lake quite reasonable in size and depth. In some countries, ponds can be small bays with narrow entrances to the ocean. Here we use the term to refer to small, shallow, fresh-water bodies, of water.

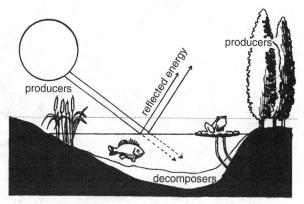

*Diagram A*

Diagram A shows a "typical" pond. While it is greatly oversimplified, it shows the basic elements of any ecosystem. There is the sun— the energy source. The sun is the "engine" driving the rest of the system. There are the green plants and animals. The green plants are direct "sun catchers." The wonderful process of capturing some of the sun's energy is known as photosynthesis—photo (light) and synthesis (assembly, connection, manufacture). The energy of the sun is stored in the form of chemical bonds in molecules. Photosynthesis magically stores solar energy by assembling complex molecules with six carbon atoms from building blocks of carbon dioxide ($CO_2$) and water. Animals are not capable of photosynthesis. They rely on green plants to catch solar energy and to use it to assemble food materials. Green plants are the food factories in natural systems. They are called producers. Plants also provide oxygen as a byproduct of this process.

Not all animals eat plants directly. Those that eat plants and only plants are known as primary consumers, or herbivores. They are one step away from being sun catchers. Animals that eat other animals are two steps away from the sun, so they are often called secondary consumers, or carnivores (meat eaters). The sequence becomes more complex if we add animals that prey on other meat eaters: tertiary consumers (three steps away from the sun). Diagram B on the following page illustrates some of those relationships.

*continued*

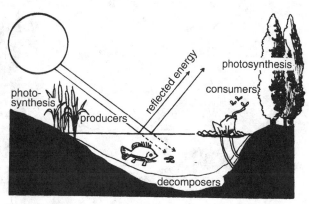

*Diagram B*

A diagram linking some of these organisms as producers and consumers is illustrated as a food chain. Diagram C shows a very simple food chain that might be associated with a pond. In this diagram, the eagle eats the fish that eats the frog. In turn, the frog eats spiders and the spiders eat insects.

*Diagram C*

But this food chain is not an ecosystem. Some things are missing. There are no direct sun catchers (producers)—no green plants capable of photosynthesis. The eagle cannot capture energy from the sun directly. It is at least three steps away from the sun's input of energy. In its tadpole stage, the frog eats plant material. The insect might feed on plant nectar, or its larval stage might eat leaves. The food chain describes only a portion of the connections in the pond ecosystem. If the diagram were more complex, then a food web would be produced. It would

include all the producers and consumers in the pond, or as many as we can identify. It would introduce a new set of special consumers, the decomposers. Decomposers are the garbage collectors of nature, however they do not trap solar energy directly because they are not green and, therefore, cannot perform photosynthesis. They break down a variety of materials into simpler compounds. Decomposers produce $CO_2$ and release needed elements into the system. Without these recyclers, the entire ecosystem gradually would run down. Imagine a forest in which none of the fallen trees, branches, dead animals, and leaves ever rotted. Soon it would be impossible to move through the debris and nothing new could grow. With-out some decomposition in ponds, the accumulation of materials falling to the bottom would result in the pond's rapidly becoming so shallow that it would no longer be a pond.

As a general principle, students need to understand that both energy and materials constantly circulate in all ecosystems. Plants, through the process of photosynthesis, are the major point of entry of the sun's energy into the natural system. However, that energy does work in ecosystems in other ways as well. Solar heating of the atmosphere and oceans produces the flow of winds and the great patterns of air circulation in the atmosphere. The absorption of solar energy in the oceans is expressed in the flow of ocean currents. In a way, the entire planet is a great solar-powered engine. All materials cycle— some slowly, some quickly.

Carbon dioxide, for example, is a byproduct of respiration in plant and animal cells. The carbon of $CO_2$ is used by green plants in photosynthesis and becomes the building block of many biological molecules, including sugars, proteins, and fats. Once assembled into these materials, the carbon may be taken in by animals when they eat food materials—whether from plant or animal sources. Food is both a source of energy and a source of raw materials for biological construction.

The carbon cycle is one of the great cycles in natural systems. Nitrogen, water, and elements such as phosphorus are also involved in cycles. The passage of materials along food chains and through cycles is responsible for the concentration of chemicals such as pesticides. Small amounts of pesticide molecules passed along a food chain may accumulate when they reach the top consumer, whether that be an eagle or a human. Sometimes animals like the humpback whale may "shorten" the steps between the input of solar energy and themselves by feeding directly on millions of small animals and plants that are closer to the source of solar energy. (See Diagram D.)

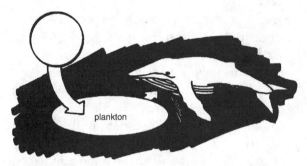

*Diagram D*

An ecosystem, therefore, may be viewed as a set of elements, living and nonliving, interacting over time within a defined locale. Ecologists attempt to define ecosystems in terms of sets of elements that normally interact with each other. At a global level, all the elements on the planet interact. The rain that falls today on the plains may have evaporated yesterday from the leaf of a tree in the coastal forest. But in practical terms, for studying and understanding the interactions among organisms in the environment, you will find it useful to draw boundaries around certain groups of organisms that are normally interacting in a relatively direct way, as a community or neighborhood grouping. This grouping may be considered an ecosystem.

Within these biological neighborhoods, it is possible to assign organisms both an "address," describing their typical location in space, and an "occupation," or role, that they play in the system. An organism's address is its "habitat."

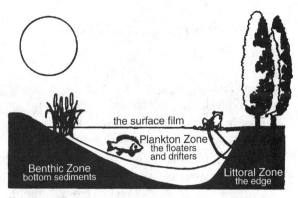

*Diagram E*

The occupation of an organism in an ecosystem is called its "niche." For many people, the term niche seems to describe a location, a type of space, but as the term is used by ecologists, it applies to the organism's roles or activities in the system. This definition has frequently been a source of confusion.

There are many different aquatic ecosystems. Within those systems are a variety of zones. Diagram E illustrates some of the zones that can be found in a typical pond ecosystem. There are organisms occupying the edge or margins of the pond. These are said to be in the littoral zone. There are others that float and drift in the water itself. These are planktonic organisms and may be plants or animals. There are still others that live on the bottom and in the sediments. And there are those, like water-striders, that inhabit the narrow zone composed of the actual water surface film. Sometimes organisms inhabit different zones at different stages in their lives.

It is important to explore a variety of zones in different habitats because students will encounter quite different sets of organisms in different zones. Often, people tend to overlook some zones—possibly because they do not seem very interesting or attractive. Who wants to spend time sifting through the muck on a pond bottom when the dip nets are filled with interesting things found in the water or on the rushes at the shore line? But, to develop an understanding of the diversity of life forms that inhabit an ecosystem, we need to explore the whole range of addresses where they might be found.

*continued*

# Tips on Studying Ecosystems

A major purpose in having students study ecology is for them to develop an awareness and understanding of relationships. This process entails developing the ability to see systems, or sets of interactions, and to think about how they have changed and still might change with time. It entails beginning to understand living systems as complex mosaics in which all the parts fit together to make a whole. The removal of one small, apparently unimportant component can often have major consequences.

It is convenient for teachers to start small with students. Making miniature ecosystems in jars and plastic bags can start students thinking about what elements are needed to keep an ecosystem healthy. Asking students to create drawings connecting things from nature to as many other things (themselves included) as they will promote thinking about interactions. A dead leaf floating on the surface of a pond might be seen as simple litter until—by drawing connections in as many directions and dimensions as possible—the student starts to see it as food, as a habitat, and as a former trap for the sun's energy. The student thus begins to appreciate the role of apparently inert and dead material.

At times, individual organisms can be strange, beautiful, or even humorous. The next step in developing ecosystemic thinking is to try to appreciate the role played by the organism in the community of which it is a part. Is this a predator, or is it prey? Ultimately, all organisms are "food," even if for microbes. Does one organism provide a home for other organisms? Is it a sun catcher, a trapper of solar energy? An important part of the debriefing of many of the activities in Project WILD is to ask students to think about these connections, and ultimately to connect themselves to the system as well.

Naming is often both an asset and an obstacle to the study of natural systems. When students go to a community, they want to know the names of the organisms they encounter. This is a good time to learn to recognize some plants and animals. But often it is enough to appreciate differences and similarities, and even for students to assign names of their own making to the things they see. Do not let a lack of detailed knowledge of names discourage study. Instead, use this opportunity to pose the "How can we find out?" questions. Emphasize the characteristics of plants and animals and their interactions, rather than losing sight of those attributes in a quest to label the parts.

Finally, it is often a powerful experience for students to visit and revisit a natural setting at various seasons of the year. Spring is an ideal season to study ponds and streams. But it is a mistake for students to think of nature as dead, or even as largely dormant, in the winter. Seasonal changes are important to the economy of nature. Ecosystems change over time. The changes of the seasons are an important expression of continuing natural change in natural systems. So, if the opportunity presents itself, have students follow an ecosystem—perhaps a pond, stream, lake, or river—through the seasons from late summer to fall, through winter and into spring and summer. School grounds can also provide useful opportunities of this kind. Some schools have adopted a local pond or stream and have made it the focus of studies by classes over many years. If the past data are saved, students can appreciate what is happening to their local ecosystems.

# Keeping Classroom Aquaria: A Simple Guide for Educators

Many resource books are available on the topic of keeping aquaria. These books provide a great deal of detailed information on aquaria of many different types including tropical freshwater, temperate fresh water, and marine aquaria. Many specialized aquaria require equally specialized equipment and a lot of care and attention to keep the animals and plants in them healthy. Most educators have neither the time nor the resources to do this but may want to maintain a simple aquarium. Some will want to use an aquarium as an object of interest and as a catalyst for classroom activities.

The following procedures are a very simple way to start a freshwater aquarium. It is suitable for the many species of hardy fish that are widely sold in pet shops. If educators or students are bitten by the "aquarium bug," a more detailed book will be necessary for additional guidance.

Some people will have ethical objections to keeping a classroom aquarium. Whether it is or is not appropriate to keep plants and animals in a classroom aquarium for instructional purposes will be left to individual educators and students to decide. If educators do decide that a classroom aquarium is appropriate, these procedures will help ensure that it is a healthy medium within which the plants and animals can live.

## Equipment

The following items will be needed to start an aquarium.

**A glass fish tank:** The size will depend on the number of fish you want to keep. A 5- to 10-gallon tank (19 to 38 liters) is recommended as a beginning size; however, this size will hold only a few fish. An aquarium can safely support about 1 inch of fish per gallon of water (10 inches of fish in a 10 gallon aquarium).

**Aquarium sand or gravel:** This item can be purchased in a pet shop. Natural sand, especially from a seashore or lakeside beach, will have to be carefully washed before use in your tank. It is easier to buy prewashed sand or gravel. Natural sand may also introduce unwanted organisms. A ratio of 1 pound of gravel for every gallon of water is recommended.

**Air pump with plastic tubing:** Tygon is a high-quality plastic tubing.

**Air stone:** This device is a porous, stone-like block of material that attaches to the end of the tubing and forces the air from the pump to spread into many small streams of bubbles.

**Water-filter system:** Many pumps are attached to a filter of some kind. Some filters hang outside the tank. Others are built into a plastic grid that is placed below the sand and gravel in the bottom of the tank. Sub-sand filters are often cheaper and are suitable for a general-purpose tank with a small number of fish or small animals.

**Nylon wool (glass wool) and charcoal granules:** These items are used in the air pump (See Step #6 on page 231). They help to reduce odors and discoloration and can be obtained at your local pet store.

**Foil wrap (aluminum cooking foil):** This item will prevent sand from being stirred up as water is poured into the tank (See Step #4 on page 231).

**Reagent grade salt:** This is noniodized or natural sea salt.

*continued*

**Crystals of potassium permanganate:** This chemical is available in many drug stores and is often found in school science storerooms.

**Aquarium hood or cover:** This item is necessary to keep fish from jumping out. Many hoods have built-in lights. Check standard hood sizes before constructing your own aquarium.

**Dried fish food:** This item can be purchased at your local pet or grocery store.

**Aquarium heater:** This equipment is optional for certain conditions.

## Constructing a Glass Tank

The funds to buy even a small, professionally made fish tank simply may not be available. You can make your own tanks if you want to save money. If so, you will need the following:

**Five pieces of glass:** One piece is needed for the bottom, and four pieces are needed for the sides (see Diagram A). You can get these at a hardware store or glass shop. Staff members will cut them from glass of the weight (thickness) you desire. Bigger tanks should be made from heavier glass, but normal window-grade glass is suitable for 5-gallon tanks. Have the glass shop polish all the edges of the glass pieces on their machines so that they are smooth and square. Ask them not to bevel the polished edges. Once you have the glass pieces, you are ready for the next step.

**Aquarium sealant:** Aquarium sealant is a glue for sticking pieces of glass together. It is usually a high-quality silicone sealant. Do not use ordinary silicone sealant for the aquarium because it contains a compound that is toxic to fish and other animals. The tube will say "aquarium sealant" on it. Most aquarium supply shops sell this material. Squeeze a wide line of the sealant out of the tube around the perimeter of the piece you are going to use for the bottom of your tank. Squeeze a line of the sealant around three sides of two of the other side pieces. Stand them up on top of the bottom piece so that their edges overlap at the corners. Repeat the process with the two other side pieces. The tank

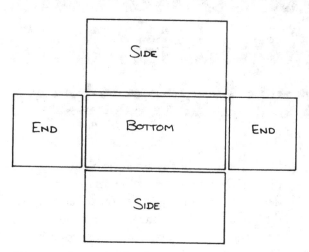

*Diagram A*

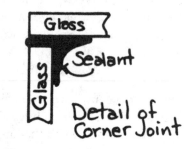

*Diagram B*

will now be formed from the bottom and the four sides. Make sure the sides are square at the corners and perpendicular to the bottom. Leave the tank where it was assembled until the sealant dries. Note that the sealant always stays somewhat soft or rubbery. This drying process will take 12 to 24 hours. Following the first drying period, go around the inside corners and the entire bottom inside where the sides join the bottom piece with another good line of sealant. Let it dry for an additional 24 to 48 hours. Fill your new tank with water, and let it stand to test that it is leak proof and that the sealant is secure.

NOTE: Diagram B is a detail of the corners, showing the fit of the glass and sealant. The end pieces will have to be shorter by two times the thickness of the side pieces of glass so that they will all fit inside the perimeter of the bottom.

CAUTION: Water is heavy! It is never a good idea to try to carry even a small aquarium while it is filled with water.

## Preparation of Tank for Animals

Once you have a tank and the other items mentioned above, follow these steps to get it ready for the fish or other animals.

**Step 1.** Set up the tank where it is not in direct sunlight. You may use a 25-watt bulb in a normal lamp for light if your room has little natural light.

**Step 2.** Put your aquarium sand in a bucket, and wash it with hot tap water. Swirl the water with the sand, and pour off the water and any fine debris. Repeat this process until the wash water is clear. New sand is usually dusty, and this process removes the dust.

**Step 3.** Pour the sand into the bottom of the tank, and smooth it until it covers the bottom. If you are using a sub-sand filter, you should place it on the tank bottom before you add the sand.

**Step 4.** Cover the sand with a sheet of the aluminum foil wrap. Slowly add hot tap water. The foil prevents the sand from being stirred up as you pour in the water, but pour quite slowly and gently. Once the water cools, remove the aluminum foil wrap.

**Step 5.** Add a teaspoon of the plain salt (noniodized). Add a few crystals of potassium permanganate. This step helps to maintain the chemical balance of the tank water. Instead of potassium permanganate, you can use some dechlorinator available from pet stores; use according to instructions provided at time of purchase.

**Step 6.** Set up your air pump, tubing, and air stone. If you are using a filter that hangs outside the tank or that is attached to the air pump, set it up now as well. (The charcoal and glass wool are for the pump.) If you are using a sub-sand filter, attach the tubing from the pump to the tube coming up from the sub-sand filter. (The booklets that come with the filters or pumps

usually will explain this arrangement.) Once your pump and filter are working and air is bubbling, let the system "age" for at least 2 days. Five days is better. Aging means letting the equipment operate with no fish or plants in the water.

**Step 7.** Add floating plants or the type that are planted in the sand. Make sure your hands are clean before you plant the bottom plants. Rinse your hands well to get rid of any traces of hand soap, hand lotion, etc. Be sure the plants are healthy before adding any animals.

**Step 8.** You are now almost ready to add the fish or other animals. Before adding the fish to the tank, float the bags containing the fish or other animals and the water from the pond or shop where you obtained them on the surface of your tank for 1 to 2 hours before opening them. This process allows the water from the pond or shop to come to the same temperature as that in your tank and reduces any stress to the animals. Add one-half cup of aquarium water to the bag of fish every 15 minutes for 45 minutes to 1 hour before adding any fish to the aquarium water. Begin by adding no more than two fish to the aquarium. Wait 3 to 5 days before adding any more fish.

**Step 9.** You may need a tank heater if you want to keep tropical freshwater fish, or if your tank gets cold because your school heat is turned off on weekends or overnight. Heaters for small tanks are fairly inexpensive and have built-in thermostats to maintain the temperature. You may want to set up the thermostat during Step 6 above. Install an aquarium thermometer to monitor and maintain recommended water temperature.

**Step 10.** Once the fish are in the tank and the aquarium is balanced, you should never have to change all the water. Every month, remove and replace 25 percent of the water. Remember that the water you use to replace the aquarium water should be "aged." Keep a supply of water that has been taken from the hot water tap and then allowed to stand for 2 days in a clean bottle, with salt and permanganate crystals or dechlori-

*continued*

nator added. If aquarium water is heated, add replacement water slowly to avoid shocking fish with cold water.

**Feeding:** Feed the fish lightly once each day. Do not feed more than the fish can eat in 2 or 3 minutes. Feeding on weekends may not be necessary. Never leave quantities of decaying food or any vegetable matter (dead plants, etc.) in the tank. Make or purchase a siphon, and "vacuum" your tank with it. If you are away for a long time, you can buy slow feeding tablets from pet supply shops. Make friends with the school custodians because they will often look after your tank on holidays. Some animals such as frogs, salamanders, dragonfly nymphs, and diving beetles require live food. Brine shrimp are good sources. You can set up and keep a brine shrimp colony in the classroom. You can also buy live brine shrimp in many aquarium-supply shops.

**Disease:** Many diseases can afflict aquarium fish but the two most common are fungus and ich. Fungus occurs after an injury or loss of the fish's protective mucous coating and appears on the fish as white, cotton-like patches. Ich usually occurs after a period of stress and looks like small grains of salt on the fish. Consult a pet shop for proper medications.

## Special Purpose Tanks and Aquaria

Aquaria can take many forms and shapes. You can make small aquaria from gallon jugs if they have clear glass. You can use a two-hole stopper on top so that the tube from an air pump can be let into the neck of the bottle. You will have to use a small air stone so that it can be slipped through the narrow neck into the bottle. If you have a special jar cutter (a tool for scribing around glass jars so that they can be cut to remove the neck), you can make a number of cylindrical tanks from scrap bottle jugs. Be

careful to avoid cutting yourself. Some local glass shops will do this job for you. Always have the newly cut surfaces polished because a freshly cut glass surface is very sharp.

You can use aquarium sealant and small pieces of glass to make mini-aquaria of special shapes so that you or the students can photograph fish and pond animals in a thin "sandwich" of water. Otherwise, the thickness of water in a normal tank allows the animal to turn away from the camera or to swim out of view, especially in close-ups. You can also adjust the lights on small tanks to get well-lighted photos. If you are studying special behaviors (e.g., egg laying or predation), then small, narrow tanks are often best.

Often, small aquaria and small animals are more useful for examination and observation than are big tanks, but big tanks can serve as long-term classroom learning centers by providing the focus for many instructional activities, including creative writing, drawing, painting, poetry, reading, and research, as well as science and mathematics activities.

# Taking Action

## Involving Students in Environmental Action Projects

The following excerpt has been adapted from Project WILD's *Taking Action: An Educator's Guide to Involving Students in Environmental Action Projects*, published by the Council for Environmental Education in cooperation with World Wildlife Fund. For more information or to order this guide, please contact Project WILD, Council for Environmental Education, 5555 Morningside Drive, Suite 212, Houston, TX 77005, Phone: (713) 520-1936, E-mail **info@projectwild.org**, or visit the Project WILD Website at **www.projectwild.org**.

### What Is an Action Project?

Project WILD has defined environmental action projects as any activities that get students involved in tackling an environmental issue or problem, or that aim at improving an environmental setting. Activities are often most successful when they're focused on the local community, such as the enhancement of outdoor habitats or the development of natural sites within a neighborhood or on the school grounds. Projects can also work on a much broader scope—raising money to adopt sea turtles, for example.

An action project can be simple or complex— as straightforward as putting up a community bulletin board of environmental current events, or as involved as developing and implementing a community plan for oil collection and recycling. However complex, most action projects will fit into a variety of educational settings. Many educators find that action education blends well with their regular teaching duties, while others choose to make it the basis for after-school sessions. Action learning is effective in nonformal settings, too, involving young people through nature centers, zoos, aquaria, and scouting programs.

### Who Can Do Action Projects?

Students of all ages can take part in environmental action projects, matching the complexity of the tasks to the abilities of students. Older students can get involved in issues that require research, issue analysis, in-depth discussion, careful planning, and follow-up. Students might establish river monitoring activities or conduct community education initiatives. Younger students can begin with projects that don't involve heated controversy, long-term commitments, or complex solutions. Picking up litter, writing a letter about an environmental concern, or planting a butterfly garden are excellent starting points for younger students.

## Some Tips to Keep in Mind

### Encourage student ownership and initiative.

The more students are involved in the project, the more they'll get out of it. To the extent possible, allow the students to make their own decisions on which problem to focus, how to conduct the project, and how to share results. Help the students chart their own course, evaluate the pros and cons of each choice, and then gauge how much direction is needed.

### Encourage parents and other community members to support the project.

Conflict sometimes can surface when students interact with community members who don't agree with a specific activity or who don't feel that action projects are an appropriate educational approach. In many cases, you can diffuse this response by discussing projects with parents and community members beforehand and by explaining how environmental action projects enhance educational goals.

*continued*

### Keep your opinions in perspective.

Allow the students to research material, discuss the issues, and form their own perspectives on the issues. Allow everyone the chance to openly express his or her opinions, no matter how different they may be. It is also critical to keep students on track and focused on the facts. Emotionally charged debate and hotly contested points of view can obscure the real facts and divert students' attention from the issue under scrutiny.

### Encourage student cooperation, compromise, and understanding.

Have the students work in small groups as much as possible. Besides the well-documented educational benefits of cooperative learning, group work offers a taste of real-life problem-solving. Teams of scientists, politicians, business people, and concerned citizens often arrive at a plan of action together. Ideally, each person brings his or her own perspectives and talents to the process, and the results reflect the strengths of those human resources. Multiple perspectives encourage thoughtful debate, boost critical thinking skills, and allow students to make informed choices—especially if opinions are accompanied by reliable information.

### Help students evaluate their methods and change their plans if necessary.

From time to time over the course of a project, have the students assess the overall scheme and evaluate their methods. Ask if they think things are running as smoothly as expected. If they think there's room for improvement, ask what might be done to adjust the situation. In some cases, problem-solving teams can brainstorm ways to deal with the snags and setbacks encountered along the way.

### Help students appreciate the value of their work.

It's important for students to know that their project, no matter how small, is significant. Assure students that every action counts. Even if the students' actions don't seem to have much effect right away, the long-term results can be very important.

## Approaches to Environmental Action

### Teach It!— The Educate and Inform Approach

Projects that focus on teaching others about environmental issues (These might include older students mentoring younger students, conducting community education programs, writing and performing songs and poems, or conducting workshops with school or community groups.)

### Make the Case— The Persuasive Approach

Projects designed to convince people to support a certain course of action or point of view (Activities include creating posters or brochures, conducting debates, writing letters to the editor, giving speeches, and distributing public service announcements.)

### Be on the Money— The Economic Approach

Strategies that encourage consumers to shop with the environment in mind, as well as projects that raise money to support specific organizations, programs, or individuals working on environmental issues (Activities might include promoting environmentally friendly products, asking for cash or in-kind donations of time and materials from businesses and community groups, or applying for grants.)

### Get Physical— The "Ecomanagement" Approach

Projects that physically improve the environment, such as planting trees, landscaping school grounds, cleaning up neighborhood parks or streams, or building bird and bat houses

### Make Decisions— The Political Action Approach

Projects focusing on political action that could include speaking at a public hearing, meeting with an elected representative to discuss specific legislation, testifying before lawmakers, circulating petitions and fliers, writing letters to the editor, or campaigning for candidates.

### Become Legal Eagles—
### The Courtroom Approach

Projects that attempt to create change through legislation, or that take legal action against an individual, corporation, community, or government agency (Although most projects that involve primary and secondary students will not involve actual legal action, many projects can educate youngsters about existing laws and the workings of the legal system.)

Source: "Approaches" adapted with permission from *Investigating and Evaluating Environmental Issues and Actions* by Harold R. Hungerford et al. (Champaign, IL: Stipes Publishing Co., 10–12 Chester St., 1992)

## Seven Steps to Action

Here are some basic steps that will help students get action projects off the ground. While the steps are listed in order, it's important to note that planning and implementing a project is not always a clear-cut, linear process. In some cases, students will investigate an issue, discuss it, begin to work on it, and then change their strategy as they use new information. They might decide to narrow their focus or switch projects after realizing that the potential solutions are beyond their capabilities. Such adjustments are a normal part of the learning process.

### 1. Get Informed

Before students decide which environmental projects to pursue, they need to become informed about the possibilities. Students may collect a pool of information from newspapers and magazines, interview community members and parents, or contact organizations and government agencies that focus on environmental issues.

Another important step in this initial process, if it can be arranged, is for students to get out and see local environmental problems firsthand. A field trip to a stream in need of cleanup is much more powerful than reading about water pollution. Even if the students eventually select a problem that's occurring thousands of miles from their community, the exposure to concerns in their own backyard will be an important learning experience.

### 2. Create a List of Possibilities

Once the students' search has highlighted a number of potential topics, have them work in groups to develop a list of the most interesting or worthwhile ones. Then have the students draft a list of projects to address all or part of each topic.

Environmental topics can be very broad and there are almost always several project possibilities for each topic. For example, water quality in the community might encompass pollution in a local river, lead in the city water system, or leaks in a landfill. Projects might include monitoring the pollution levels in the river over time and presenting data to the city council, conducting an education campaign about lead in the city's drinking supply, or developing a recycling plan to reduce the pressure on a landfill. Have students list the topic they most want to tackle, then they can brainstorm specific projects that might help the situation, listing any additional information they'll need to evaluate each project.

### 3. Narrow the Choices

Once the groups have selected the issues and projects they are most interested in, they need to evaluate and narrow their choices. For each project listed, the groups need to realistically address what they might accomplish and what problems the project might solve.

Encourage students to discuss the feasibility of each possibility by asking specific questions that help them think about the details of accomplishing certain tasks. Students may want to develop criteria to help them first select a project and then decide how they will determine the most appropriate solution. How much time will the project take? How complex is it? What resources are needed? Whom will they need to talk to?

*continued*

Sometimes it's difficult for students to decide among local, national, and global projects. Although each will provide learning opportunities, an advantage of a local project is that students will learn more about how their own community works. They'll also be more likely to see real results.

### 4. Select a Project

By this point, students should have narrowed the list to the top three to five projects. Give them adequate time to research. Then encourage the use of libraries, interviews with experts, surveys, newspaper articles, local TV news, and so on. Invite experts or resource people in to discuss problems, find potential solutions, and help evaluate students' ideas. The more your students know about specific possibilities, the better equipped they'll be to develop a realistic action plan.

As students approach their final decision, have each group present a case for one or more of the projects that the group feels strongly about. Then hold a group vote or have a large group discussion to reach consensus. The important thing is to let students have as much say in the decision-making process as possible, choosing a project that they think is both interesting and achievable.

### 5. Create an Action Plan

Once students have done their research and selected a project, help them get started on their action plan by asking, "What do you hope you'll be able to accomplish by doing this project?" After students share their answers, guide them in developing a goal for the project and specific, concrete objectives that need to be accomplished along the way.

Remind students to keep the goal and objectives in mind as they work to complete a planning sheet that includes the following:

1. What environmental problem or issue will the project address?

2. How would you briefly describe the goal of the project and the strategy to accomplish this goal?

3. What are the specific objectives that will help the group reach its overall goal?

4. What are the approximate starting and ending dates of the project?

5. Did you list the tasks to accomplish to meet each objective? Include a tentative completion date for each task, the names of people responsible, the supplies and equipment needed, any funding needed, and ideas of where to get materials and funding.

6. Did you write down the names of people and organizations that may be able to provide useful information, specific skills, or expertise, or other help?

7. Did you list ideas on how to publicize and generate support for the project?

8. Did you describe how your success will be measured?

A large-format task and time line chart may help the groups keep track of responsibilities and deadlines. As the students work on their action plan, guide them toward realistic objectives. One of the most common problems for students is thinking too big. Help them focus and simplify the project by discussing the responses to the questions on their planning sheet and by asking them to really consider hard questions. How will the funds be raised? Can the problem be tackled on a smaller scale?

### 6. Put the Plan into Action

Students' projects will work best if they keep careful records of what they've done, when they did it, whom they've contacted, and so on. They'll also need to keep track of who's doing what to make sure crucial tasks are being completed and to avoid duplicating efforts. It's important that students take stock of the project periodically to see if they're on target and to make modifications, if necessary. Remind them that it's acceptable to rethink their goals and objectives and to revise their plan of action in light of new information or unexpected obstacles.

To build support for action projects, publicize any successes and showcase the ways that action learning promotes educational goals and addresses community priorities. There are many ways to let others know what students have done—holding a community awards event, getting a reporter from the local newspaper or television station to cover a project, or sending out public service announcements (PSAs). Have the students brainstorm ways to publicize their work.

### 7. Assess, Generalize, and Apply

Taking time to reflect upon and evaluate an action project helps students understand what they've accomplished and allows them to recognize how their project has facilitated their personal growth. As a project nears completion, guide students in assessing the project itself, as well as their feelings about the experience. It's important for students to evaluate the success of each project and to think about improvements for the next time. It's also important that they look beyond the immediate impact to more long-term, broad-scale gains—skills, knowledge, and attitudes that they can apply to other aspects of their lives.

## Ideas for Measuring Success

### Assessing Student Knowledge

- Keep a video or photo log of project highlights. After the project is completed, use the video or photo scrapbook as a springboard for discussions in which students share what they learned and their feelings about the experience.

- Collect memorabilia (articles about the project, newspaper photos, students' own photos, planning schedules, and so on) to create an action project scrapbook that students can sign and write comments in.

- Ask the students whether they've changed their thinking or behaviors as a result of the project. Have the students write essays describing what those changes are and what students think prompted them.

- Have the students keep a journal to record feelings about the project, its progress, and its setbacks, and to keep notes about working with others. After the project, students share parts of their journals with the group and discuss their perceptions.

- Have the students evaluate other members of their group, as well as themselves. Before they do, give students pointers on positive, constructive feedback. Focus the session on specific points, such as contribution to the project, effort, conflict resolution approach, and so on.

- Have the community members who were involved in the project assess student performances. Educators can develop an assessment form or have students conduct short interviews.

### Assessing Project Success

- Have the students describe how well they think their project accomplished the objectives they outlined at the start.

- Have the students conduct surveys, field studies, or interviews to assess the success of their completed project. What worked? What didn't? Why?

- Evaluate how the students planned for ongoing maintenance and sustainability of the project.

- Have the community members and others who were involved in the project assess project outcomes.

# Evaluating and Assessing Student Learning

As the nation moves toward educational reform and literacy in all subject areas, standards in assessment become vital. The National Research Council suggests that the following assessment standards be used with students:

- Assessment Standard A: Assessments must be consistent with the decisions they are designed to inform.

- Assessment Standard B: Achievement and opportunity to learn science (or other subject areas) must be assessed.

- Assessment Standard C: The technical quality of the data (or other information) collected is well matched to the decisions and actions taken on the basis of their interpretation.

- Assessment Standard D: Assessment practices must be fair.

- Assessment Standard E: The inferences made from assessments about student achievement and opportunity to learn must be sound.

Source: *National Science Education Standards* (Washington, DC: National Research Council, National Academy Press, 1996)

Project WILD is designed to assist teachers as they assess student learning. Each activity has an evaluation section that suggests at least one way to evaluate students' work, accomplishments, or performance. This section correlates directly with the stated objectives. Some of the suggested evaluations assess student understanding of factual information. Many of them ask students to demonstrate a theoretical or applied conceptual understanding.

Exemplary practice outlines the following strategies when assessing students' learning. Project WILD encourages educators to incorporate some of these methods when using this guide.

### Educator-Generated Tests

Unlike commercially produced tests, educator-generated tests are created by the instructor. They can be multiple choice, fill-in-the-blank, true/false, or essay type tests. Project WILD recommends that this type of evaluation be used on a regular basis for ongoing evaluation rather than as a cumulative tool.

### Portfolios

A portfolio is a collection of class or project work chosen to specifically address a student's progress. Portfolios usually include examples of student work, reflections, self-evaluations, and goal-setting items. The purpose of a portfolio is to document what has been taught and the national standards that have been met. It also allows subject area assessments to be integrated and student growth to be charted.

### Performance Tasks

A performance task is an assessment tool (generally chosen by the student) that demonstrates an understanding of concepts and processes as they apply to everyday life. The task is usually meant for a larger audience rather than for the educator alone. It is carefully planned and evaluated with detailed scoring. Performance tasks can range from solving a real-life problem to preparing a speech or project, demonstrating a specific skill, or writing a paper or report.

### Journals and Learning Logs

Journals and logs are tools for students to use to record their own learning in a less-formal manner. Journals are usually a subjective account of a student's perspective on what has been learned. Logs are more detailed and give a direct account that follows a given format.

### Visual Vocabulary

An alternative method of assessment for the expression of learned concepts is through pantomime and creative movement. Students review vocabulary they have researched and then select specific terms that demonstrate their understanding of the activity's concepts.

### Observation Checklists

Educators may use observation checklists to monitor whether a student has mastered a specific skill. This type of checklist is a useful tool to address specific skills.

### Graphic Organizers

Web diagrams, charts, and other forms of graphics can be generated by students to demonstrate what they have learned and how it has been organized into their thought process.

### Interviews and Conferences

Educators can assess learning by interviewing and conferencing with students using a systematic approach. When discussing a topic, students can clarify their thinking and educators can gather information on how students are processing what they have learned.

### Rubrics

Rubrics are used for any of the assessment strategies outlined above. A rubric is a set of scoring criteria against which a product/activity is evaluated. Generally, rubrics identify levels of quality (such as "Excellent, Good, Needs Improvement" or numeric scores "4, 3, 2, 1," which can be added for a total score). A rubric allows students and educators to know specifically what is expected and how each student has measured up to those expectations; they can also be used in self-evaluation or evaluation by peers or educators.

# Skills Index

Below is an alphabetical listing of all activities found in the *Project WILD Aquatic K–12 Curriculum and Activity Guide*. Also listed are the page numbers, suggested grade levels, settings (indoor or outdoor), and skills addressed for both cross discipline and subject-specific areas. Under Grade Level, an **E** indicates that the activity correlates to national learning standards for grades K–4, an **M** for grades 5–8, and an H for grades 9–12. The specific skills for each subject area can be found on the Project WILD website at **www.projectwild.org**.

SYMBOL NOTE: The dot and triangle symbols are of equal value. They were used to help distinguish between the Cross-Discipline Skills and the Subject Area Skills.

| Activity Name | Page Number | Grade Level/National Learning Standards Correlation | Indoors (I) or Outdoors (O) | Cross-Discipline Skills | | | | | | | | | | | | Subject Area Skills | | | | | |
| --- | --- | --- | --- | --- | --- | --- | --- | --- | --- | --- | --- | --- | --- | --- | --- | --- | --- | --- | --- | --- | --- |
| | | | | Analysis | Application | Classification | Comparison | Construction | Description | Evaluation | Generalization | Observation | Problem-solving | Research | Synthesis | Science | Math | Social Studies | Language Arts | Environmental Education | Expressive Arts |
| Alice in Waterland | 151 | M | I,O | | | | | • | • | • | • | • | • | | | ▲ | ▲ | ▲ | | ▲ | ▲ |
| Aqua Words | 29 | E | I | • | | | | | | | | | • | | | | | | ▲ | ▲ | |
| Aquatic Roots | 163 | M | I | • | • | • | | • | • | • | • | | | • | • | ▲ | | ▲ | | ▲ | |
| Aquatic Times | 188 | M | I | • | • | | | • | • | | | | • | • | • | | | | ▲ | ▲ | |
| Are You Me? | 2 | E | I | • | • | • | | | | | | | | | | ▲ | | | | ▲ | |
| Blue-Ribbon Niche | 52 | M | I,O | • | • | | | • | • | • | | • | • | | • | ▲ | | | ▲ | ▲ | |
| Dam Design | 193 | H | I | • | | | | • | • | • | | | | | | ▲ | | ▲ | ▲ | ▲ | |
| Designing a Habitat | 19 | M | I | • | • | • | • | | • | | • | • | • | • | • | ▲ | | | ▲ | ▲ | ▲ |
| Dragonfly Pond | 198 | M | I | • | • | • | • | | • | • | • | • | • | | • | | | ▲ | | | |
| Eat and Glow | 69 | M | I | • | | • | | • | • | • | • | • | • | • | • | ▲ | ▲ | | | ▲ | |
| Edge of Home | 75 | M | I,O | • | | • | | | • | | • | • | | | • | ▲ | | | | ▲ | |
| Facts and Falsehoods | 124 | H | I | • | • | • | | | • | • | • | | • | | • | | | | ▲ | ▲ | |
| Fashion a Fish | 56 | E | I,O | • | • | | | • | • | | • | | | | | ▲ | | | | ▲ | ▲ |
| Fishable Waters | 158 | M | I | • | • | | • | | • | • | • | • | | | • | ▲ | | ▲ | | | |
| Fishy Who's Who | 8 | M | I | • | • | • | • | • | | | | | | • | | ▲ | | ▲ | ▲ | ▲ | ▲ |
| Hooks and Ladders | 43 | M | I,O | • | | | | • | | • | • | • | | | • | ▲ | | ▲ | | ▲ | ▲ |
| How Wet Is Our Planet? | 121 | M | I | • | | | | • | | | • | • | | | • | | ▲ | ▲ | | ▲ | |
| Kelp Help | 195 | M | I | • | • | | | • | | | | | • | | • | ▲ | | | | ▲ | |

| Activity Name | Page Number | Grade Level/National Learning Standards Correlation | Indoors (I) or Outdoors (O) | Cross-Discipline Skills | | | | | | | | | | | | Subject Area Skills | | | | | |
|---|---|---|---|---|---|---|---|---|---|---|---|---|---|---|---|---|---|---|---|---|---|
| | | | | Analysis | Application | Classification | Comparison | Construction | Description | Evaluation | Generalization | Observation | Problem-solving | Research | Synthesis | Science | Math | Social Studies | Language Arts | Environmental Education | Expressive Arts |
| Living Research: Aquatic Heroes and Heroines | 204 | H | I | ● | ● | | | ● | | | | | | ● | ● | | | ▲ | ▲ | ▲ | |
| Marsh Munchers | 34 | E | I,O | ● | | | | ● | | ● | | ● | | | ● | ▲ | | | | ▲ | ▲ |
| Mermaids and Manatees | 80 | M | I,O | ● | ● | ● | | ● | | | ● | | | ● | ● | | | ▲ | ▲ | ▲ | ▲ |
| Micro Odyssey | 49 | M | I,O | ● | | ● | ● | | | | | ● | | ● | ● | ▲ | | | | ▲ | |
| Migration Headache | 15 | M | I,O | ● | | ● | | | ● | ● | ● | ● | | | ● | ▲ | | | | ▲ | ▲ |
| Net Gain, Net Effect | 85 | M | I,O | ● | | ● | | | | | ● | ● | | | ● | ▲ | ▲ | ▲ | | ▲ | |
| Plastic Jellyfish | 128 | E | I,O | ● | | | | | | | ● | ● | | | ● | ▲ | ▲ | ▲ | | ▲ | |
| Pond Succession | 66 | M | I | ● | | ● | | ● | | | | ● | | | ● | ▲ | | ▲ | | ▲ | ▲ |
| Puddle Wonders! | 114 | M | I,O | ● | | ● | | ● | | | ● | ● | | | ● | ▲ | ▲ | | | ▲ | |
| Riparian Retreat | 118 | M | I,O | ● | | ● | | ● | | | ● | ● | | | | | | | ▲ | ▲ | |
| Sea Turtles International | 98 | H | I | ● | | | | | ● | ● | ● | | | | ● | | | ▲ | | ▲ | |
| Silt: A Dirty Word | 190 | E | I,O | ● | | ● | | ● | | ● | ● | ● | | | | ▲ | | | | ▲ | |
| Sockeye Scents | 61 | E | I,O | ● | | ● | | | ● | | | ● | ● | | | ▲ | | ▲ | ▲ | ▲ | ▲ |
| Something's Fishy Here! | 145 | M | I | ● | | | | ● | ● | ● | ● | | ● | | ● | | | | ▲ | ▲ | |
| The Glass Menagerie | 155 | H | I,O | ● | | ● | | ● | | | ● | ● | | | ● | ▲ | | | | ▲ | |
| To Dam or Not to Dam | 184 | M | I | ● | ● | | ● | ● | ● | ● | ● | ● | | | ● | | | ▲ | | ▲ | |
| Turtle Hurdles | 172 | M | I,O | | | | | ● | ● | ● | ● | ● | | | ● | ▲ | | ▲ | | ▲ | |
| Water Canaries | 24 | M | O | ● | | ● | | ● | ● | ● | ● | ● | ● | ● | ● | ▲ | | | | ▲ | |
| Water Plant Art | 31 | E | I | ● | | ● | ● | ● | | | | | | | | ▲ | | | | ▲ | ▲ |
| Water We Eating? | 83 | E | I | ● | | | ● | ● | | | ● | ● | ● | ● | ● | ▲ | | ▲ | | ▲ | |
| Water Wings | 110 | M | I,O | ● | ● | | | ● | | ● | ● | ● | | | ● | | | ▲ | ▲ | ▲ | ▲ |
| Water's Going On? | 149 | M | I | ● | | | | | | | | | | | | ▲ | ▲ | ▲ | | ▲ | |
| Watered-Down History | 91 | M | I,O | ● | ● | ● | ● | ● | | | ● | | ● | ● | ● | | | ▲ | | ▲ | |
| Watershed | 132 | M | I,O | ● | | | ● | ● | ● | ● | | ● | | | ● | | ▲ | | | ▲ | |
| Wetland Metaphors | 39 | M | I,O | ● | | ● | | ● | | ● | ● | | | | ● | | | | ▲ | ▲ | |
| Whale of a Tail | 10 | M | I,O | ● | | ● | ● | ● | | | | ● | ● | ● | ● | | | ▲ | | | ▲ |
| What's in the Air? | 136 | M | I | ● | | ● | | ● | | | ● | ● | | | ● | ▲ | ▲ | ▲ | | ▲ | |
| What's in the Water? | 140 | M | I | ● | | ● | ● | ● | | | ● | ● | | | | ▲ | ▲ | | | ▲ | |
| When a Whale Is Right | 94 | H | I | ● | | | | ● | ● | | | | | | ● | | | ▲ | | ▲ | |
| Where Does Water Run? | 21 | M | I,O | ● | | | | ● | | | ● | | | | | ▲ | ▲ | | | ▲ | |
| Where Have All the Salmon Gone? | 180 | M | I | ● | | ● | ● | ● | | | ● | | | | | ▲ | ▲ | ▲ | | ▲ | |

# Topic Index

Below is an alphabetical listing of all of the activities found in the *Project WILD Aquatic K–12 Curriculum and Activity Guide*. Also listed are the page numbers, the approximate duration of the activity, and the broad topic categories for each activity.

GRADE LEVEL NOTE: An **E** indicates that the activity correlates to national learning standards for grades K–4, an **M** for grades 5–8, and an **H** for grades 9–12.

DURATION NOTE: The length of the activity is listed by a letter code: **A** = up to 45 minutes, **B** = 45 to 60 minutes, **C** = 60 to 90 minutes, **D** = 90 minutes to 3 hours, **E** = over 3 hours, and **V** = variable length.

TOPIC NOTE: Many of the topics listed incorporate important subtopics. For instance, *Biodiversity* includes *Endangered, Invasive,* and *Exotic Species; Change* includes *Succession; Environmental Quality* includes *Pollution, Acid Rain, Erosion,* and *Eutrophication; Population Dynamics* includes *Predator and Prey Relationships* and *Limiting Factors; Sustainability* includes *Conservation;* and *Food Chains* includes *Food Webs, Energy Transfer,* and *Trophic Relationships.*

Additional topics are indexed in the Expanded Topic Index on pages 244–250.

SYMBOL NOTE: The dot and triangle symbols are of equal value. They are placed in alternating columns for ease of tracking down the column.

| Activity Name | Page Number | Grade Level/National Learning Standards Correlation | Duration (A,B,C,D,E,V) | Adaptations | Biodiversity | Change | Consumptive Use | Culture | Economics/Commerce | Environmental Quality | Food Chains | Habitats | Interdependence | Issues | Land Use | Ocean/Marine | Political Processes | Population Dynamics | Resource Management | Responsible Action | Sustainability | Urban | Values |
|---|---|---|---|---|---|---|---|---|---|---|---|---|---|---|---|---|---|---|---|---|---|---|---|
| Alice in Waterland | 151 | M | D | | | ● | | ● | | ● | | ● | | | | | | | | ● | ▲ | ● | |
| Aqua Words | 29 | E | V | | | | | | | | | | ▲ | | | | | | | | | | ▲ |
| Aquatic Roots | 177 | M | D | ▲ | ● | | | | ▲ | | | | ▲ | ● | | | ▲ | | ▲ | | | | |
| Aquatic Times | 188 | M | V | | | | | | | | | | | ● | | | | | | | | ● | ▲ |
| Are You Me? | 2 | E | A | | | ● | | | | | | | | | | | | | | | | | |
| Blue-Ribbon Niche | 52 | M | D | ▲ | ● | | | | | ● | ▲ | ● | ▲ | | ▲ | | | | ● | | | | |
| Dam Design | 193 | H | E | | | | | | | ▲ | | | ▲ | ● | ▲ | | ▲ | | | ▲ | ● | ▲ | ● |
| Designing a Habitat | 19 | M | D | | | | | | | | | ● | ▲ | | | | | | | | | | |
| Dragonfly Pond | 198 | M | D | ▲ | ● | | | ● | ▲ | ● | | ● | ▲ | ● | ▲ | | ▲ | | ▲ | ● | ▲ | | ▲ |
| Eat and Glow | 69 | M | E | ● | | ● | | | | | | ● | | | | | | ● | | | | | |
| Edge of Home | 75 | M | C | ▲ | | | | | | | | | ▲ | | | | | | | | | | |
| Facts and Falsehoods | 124 | H | D | | | | ● | | | | | | | ● | | | | | | ● | | | |
| Fashion a Fish | 56 | E | V | ● | | | | | | | | ● | | | | | | | | | | | |
| Fishable Waters | 158 | M | C | | ▲ | ● | ▲ | | ▲ | ● | | ● | | ● | ▲ | | | | ▲ | ▲ | ● | | ● |
| Fishy Who's Who | 8 | M | D | | ▲ | | | | | | | | | | | ● | | | | | | | ▲ |
| Hooks and Ladders | 43 | M | B | ● | ▲ | ● | ▲ | | ▲ | | ▲ | ● | ▲ | ● | | | | ● | ▲ | | | | |

**DURATION:** A = up to 45 minutes, B = 45 to 60 minutes, C = 60 to 90 minutes, D= 90 minutes to 3 hours, E = over 3 hours, V = variable length

| Activity Name | Page Number | Grade Level/National Learning Standards Correlation | Duration (A,B,C,D,E,V) | Adaptations | Biodiversity | Change | Consumptive Use | Culture | Economics/Commerce | Environmental Quality | Food Chains | Habitats | Interdependence | Issues | Land Use | Ocean/Marine | Political Processes | Population Dynamics | Resource Management | Responsible Action | Sustainability | Urban | Values |
|---|---|---|---|---|---|---|---|---|---|---|---|---|---|---|---|---|---|---|---|---|---|---|---|
| How Wet Is Our Planet? | 121 | M | B | | | | | ● | | | | | ▲ | • | | ● | | | | | ▲ | ● | |
| Kelp Help | 195 | M | D | | | | | ● | | | ● | | ▲ | | | ● | | | | ● | | | ▲ |
| Living Research: Aquatic Heroes and Heroines | 204 | H | V | | | | | ● | | | | | | | | ● | | | | ● | ▲ | ● | |
| Marsh Munchers | 34 | E | B | ● | | | | | | | ▲ | ● | ▲ | | | ● | | ● | | | | | ▲ |
| Mermaids and Manatees | 80 | M | C | ● | ▲ | | | ● | | | | ● | | | | | | | | | | | |
| Micro Odyssey | 49 | M | D | ● | | | | | | | ▲ | ● | ▲ | | | | | ● | | | | | |
| Migration Headache | 15 | M | A | | ▲ | | | | | ● | | ● | ▲ | ● | ▲ | | | | ● | ▲ | ▲ | | |
| Net Gain, Net Effect | 85 | M | B | | ▲ | ● | | ● | ▲ | | | | ● | | | ● | ▲ | ● | ▲ | ● | ▲ | | |
| Plastic Jellyfish | 128 | E | B | | | | ▲ | ● | ▲ | ● | | | ● | | | ● | ▲ | ● | | ● | ▲ | | |
| Pond Succession | 66 | M | B | | ▲ | ● | | | | | | | ● | ▲ | | | | | | | | | |
| Puddle Wonders! | 114 | M | V | ● | | ● | | | | | | | ● | ▲ | | | | | | | | ● | |
| Riparian Retreat | 118 | M | A | | | | | | | | | | ● | ▲ | | | | | | | | | ▲ |
| Sea Turtles International | 98 | H | C | | | | ▲ | ● | ▲ | | | | ▲ | ● | ▲ | ● | ▲ | | ▲ | ● | ▲ | ● | ▲ |
| Silt: A Dirty Word | 190 | E | B | | | | | | | ● | | | ● | ▲ | ● | ▲ | | | | ● | ▲ | ● | |
| Sockeye Scents | 61 | E | D | ● | | | | | | | | ● | | | | | | | | | | | |
| Something's Fishy Here! | 145 | M | D | | | ● | | ● | ▲ | ● | | | | ● | | | | | | ● | ▲ | ● | |
| The Glass Menagerie | 155 | H | E | | ▲ | ● | | | | ● | | | ● | ▲ | | | | | | | | | |
| To Dam or Not to Dam | 184 | M | V | | ▲ | ● | ▲ | ● | ▲ | | | | ● | | ● | ▲ | | ▲ | | ▲ | | | |
| Turtle Hurdles | 172 | M | A | | ▲ | ● | ▲ | | ▲ | | ▲ | ● | | ● | ▲ | ● | ▲ | ● | | ● | ▲ | | ▲ |
| Water Canaries | 24 | E | C | | ▲ | | | | | ● | | | ● | ▲ | | | | | | | | | ▲ |
| Water Plant Art | 31 | E | A | | | | | | | | | | ● | ▲ | | | | | | | | | ▲ |
| Water We Eating? | 83 | E | V | | | | | ● | ▲ | | ▲ | | | | | | | | | ● | | ● | |
| Water Wings | 110 | M | V | | | ● | | | | | | | ● | ▲ | | ● | | | | | | | ▲ |
| Water's Going On? | 149 | M | C | | | | | | ▲ | | | | | | | | | | | | ● | ▲ | | |
| Watered-Down History | 91 | M | D | | | ● | | ● | | | | | ● | ▲ | ● | ▲ | | | | ● | | | |
| Watershed | 132 | M | V | | | | | | | ● | | | ● | ▲ | | | | | | ● | | | |
| Wetland Metaphors | 39 | M | V | | ▲ | ● | | | | ● | | | ● | ▲ | | | | | | | | | ▲ |
| Whale of a Tail | 10 | M | V | | ▲ | | | | | | | | | | | ● | | | | | | | |
| What's in the Air? | 136 | M | V | | | ● | | | | ● | | | ● | ● | | | | | | | | | |
| What's in the Water? | 140 | M | A | | ▲ | ● | | ● | ▲ | ● | ▲ | ● | ▲ | ● | | | | ● | | ● | ▲ | ● | ▲ |
| When a Whale Is Right | 94 | H | D | | | | | | | ▲ | | | ● | | | ● | | | | ▲ | ● | ▲ | |
| Where Does Water Run? | 21 | M | D | | | ● | | | | | | ● | ● | ▲ | | | | | | | | ● | |
| Where Have All the Salmon Gone? | 180 | M | D | | | | ▲ | ● | ▲ | | | ● | | | ● | | ● | ▲ | ● | ▲ | | | |

**DURATION:** A = up to 45 minutes, B = 45 to 60 minutes, C = 60 to 90 minutes, D= 90 minutes to 3 hours, E = over 3 hours, V = variable length

# Expanded Topic Index

The following is an alphabetical listing of topics included in Project WILD Aquatic activities. This is not a comprehensive listing; that is, it does not list every possible topic. It does, however, include topics that might be included in an elementary or secondary course of study in a variety of subject areas.

Activities are listed alphabetically, not according to the degree to which they emphasize the topic. We hope this serves to assist in your curriculum planning as you integrate Project WILD Aquatic activities into exis-ting courses of study and other instructional programs.

## Acid Percipitation or Rain

What's in the Air?

## Actions

Alice in Waterland; Dragonfly Pond; How Wet Is Our Planet?; Living Research: Aquatic Heroes and Heroines; Net Gain, Net Effect; Plastic Jellyfish; Something's Fishy Here; Turtle Hurdles; Water We Eating?; Water's Going On?; Watered Down History; Watershed; What's in the Water?; When a Whale Is Right

## Adaptation

Eat and Glow; Fashion a Fish; Hooks and Ladders (indirect); Marsh Munchers (indirect); Mermaids and Manatees (indirect); Micro Odyssey (indirect); Puddle Wonders (indirect); Sockeye Scents

## Amphibians

Are You Me?; Blue-Ribbon Niche; Puddle Wonders

## Animals

Are You Me?; Blue-Ribbon Niche; Fishable Waters; Fishy Who's Who; Hooks and Ladders; Marsh Munchers; Mermaids and Manatees; Micro Odyssey; Migration Headache; Net Gain, Net Effect; Puddle Wonders; Riparian Retreat; Something's Fishy Here; To Dam or Not to Dam (indirect); Turtle Hurdles; Water Canaries; Water Wings; Watered Down History; Whale of a Tail; When a Whale Is Right

## Awareness

Aqua Words; Aquatic Times; Are You Me?; Edge of Home; Fishy Who's Who; How Wet Is Our Planet?; Kelp Help; Marsh Munchers; Puddle Wonders; Riparian Retreat; Something's Fishy Here; Water Canaries; Water Plant Art; Water We Eating?; Water Wings; Water's Going On?; Wetland Metaphors; Whale of a Tail; When a Whale Is Right; Where Does Water Run?

## Birds

Are You Me?; Blue-Ribbon Niche (indirect); Migration Headache; Plastic Jellyfish; Riparian Retreat; To Dam or Not to Dam (indirect)

## Change

Alice in Waterland; Aquatic Roots; Are You Me?; Blue-Ribbon Niche; Dragonfly Pond; Eat and Glow; Fishable Waters; Glass Menagerie; Hooks and Ladders; Net Gain, Net Effect; Pond Succession; Puddle Wonders; Something's Fishy Here; To Dam or Not to Dam; Turtles Hurdles; Water Wings; Watered Down History; Wetland Metaphor; What's in the Air?; What's in the Water?; Where Does Water Run?

## Communications

Aquatic Times; Facts and Falsehoods; Living Research: Aquatic Heroes and Heroines; Mermaids and Manatees

## Community (cultural)

Alice in Waterland; Dragonfly Pond; Facts and Falsehoods; How Wet Is Our Planet?; Living Research: Aquatic Heroes and Heroines; Plastic Jellyfish; Something's Fishy Here; To Dam or Not to Dam; Water We Eating?; Water's Going On?; What's in the Water?; Watered Down History; When a Whale Is Right; Where Does Water Run?

## Community (ecological)

Blue-Ribbon Niche; Dragonfly Pond; Fishable Waters; Fishy Who's Who; Glass Menagerie; How Wet Is Our Planet?; Kelp Help; Marsh Munchers; Micro Odyssey; Migration Headache; Puddle Wonders; Riparian Retreat; Water Canaries; Watershed; Water Wings (indirect); Watered Down History; Wetland Metaphors; What's in the Water?; Where Does Water Run?

## Conflicts

Dragonfly Pond; Hooks and Ladders; Net Gain, Net Effect (indirect); Plastic Jellyfish; Sea Turtle International; Something's Fishy Here; To Dam or Not to Dam; Turtle Hurdles; What's in the Water?; When a Whale Is Right

## Conservation

Alice in Waterland; Dragonfly Pond; How Wet Is Our Planet?; Living Research: Aquatic Heroes and Heroines; Migration Headache; Net Gain, Net Effect (indirect); Plastic Jellyfish; Something's Fishy Here; Turtle Hurdles; Water's Going On?; Watershed; What's in the Water?; When a Whale Is Right

## Culture

Alice in Waterland (indirect); Dragonfly Pond; Facts and Falsehoods; How Wet Is Our Planet?; Kelp Help; Living Research: Aquatic Heroes and Heroines; Mermaids and Manatees; Net Gain, Net Effect; Plastic Jellyfish; Sea Turtle International; Something's Fishy Here; To Dam or Not to Dam; Water We Eating?; Water's Going On?; Watered Down History; What's in the Water?; When a Whale Is Right ; Where Have All the Salmon Gone?

## Dams

Blue-Ribbon Niche (indirect); Fishable Waters; Hooks and Ladders; To Dam or Not to Dam; Where Have All the Salmon Gone?

## Diversity

Are You Me?; Blue-Ribbon Niche; Edge of Home; Fashion a Fish; Fishable Waters; Fishy Who's Who; Mermaids and Manatees; Micro Odyssey; Puddle Wonders; Riparian Retreat; Water Canaries; Wetland Metaphors; Whale of a Tail

## Ducks

Are You Me?; Migration Headache

## Ecological Systems

Aquatic Roots; Blue-Ribbon Niche; Designing a Habitat; Dragonfly Pond; Fishable Waters; Fishy Who's Who; Kelp Help; Marsh Munchers; Migration Headache; Pond Succession; Puddle Wonders; Riparian Retreat; Water Canaries; Water Wings (indirect); Watered Down History; Watershed; Wetland Metaphors; What's in the Water?; Where Does Water Run?

## Economics

Aquatic Roots (indirect); Dam Design; Dragonfly Pond; Hooks and Ladders (indirect); Net Gain, Net Effect; Plastic Jellyfish; Sea Turtle International; Something's Fishy Here; To Dam or Not to Dam; Turtle Hurdles; Water We Eating?; Water's Going On?; What's in the Water?; When a Whale Is Right; Where Have All the Salmon Gone?

*continued*

## Ecosystem

Blue-Ribbon Niche; Dragonfly Pond; Edge of Home; Fishy Who's Who; Glass Menagerie; Marsh Munchers; Puddle Wonders; Riparian Retreat; Water Canaries; Water Wings (indirect); Watered Down History; Watershed; Wetland Metaphors

## Edge Effect

Edge of Home

## Endangered Species

Aquatic Roots (indirect); Blue-Ribbon Niche (indirect); Dragonfly Pond (indirect); Glass Menagerie (indirect); Hooks and Ladders (indirect); Mermaids and Manatees (indirect); Migration Headache (indirect); Net Gain, Net Effect (indirect); Plastic Jellyfish; To Dam or Not to Dam (indirect); Turtle Hurdles; Whale of a Tail; What's in the Water?; When a Whale Is Right

## Erosion

Fishable Waters; Watershed; What's in the Water?; Where Does Water Run?

## Estuary

Dragonfly Pond (indirect); Marsh Munchers; Wetland Metaphors; What's in the Water?

## Eutrophication

Fishable Waters; Glass Menagerie

## Exotic Species

Aquatic Roots

## Fish

Aquatic Roots; Are You Me?; Blue-Ribbon Niche (indirect); Fashion a Fish; Fishable Waters; Fishy Who's Who; Hooks and Ladders; Marsh Munchers; Net Gain, Net Effect; Plastic Jellyfish; To Dam or Not to Dam (indirect); Where Have All the Salmon Gone?

## Fishing

Fishable Waters; Hooks and Ladders; Net Gain, Net Effect; To Dam or Not to Dam (indirect); Turtle Hurdles (indirect); When a Whale Is Right; Where Have All the Salmon Gone?

## Food Chains, Food Webs

Blue-Ribbon Niche; Fishable Waters; Hooks and Ladders (indirect); Marsh Munchers; Micro Odyssey; Plastic Jellyfish (indirect); Turtle Hurdles; Water We Eating?; What's in the Water?

## Government

Aquatic Roots (indirect); Dragonfly Pond (indirect); Fishable Waters; Net Gain, Net Effect (indirect); Plastic Jellyfish (indirect); To Dam or Not to Dam (indirect); When a Whale Is Right

## Groundwater

Alice in Waterland; Dragonfly Pond (indirect); How Wet Is Our Planet?; Water Wings; Water's Going On?; What's in the Water?; Where Does Water Run?

## Habitat

Alice in Waterland; Blue-Ribbon Niche; Designing a Habitat; Dragonfly Pond; Eat and Glow; Fashion a Fish; Fishable Waters; Fishy Who's Who; Hooks and Ladders; Kelp Help; Marsh Munchers; Mermaids and Manatees; Micro Odyssey; Migration Headache; Puddle Wonders; Riparian Retreat; Silt is a Dirty Word; Sockeye Scents; To Dam or Not to Dam; Turtle Hurdles; Water Canaries; Water Wings; Watered Down History; Watershed; Wetland Metaphors; What's in the Air?; What's in the Water?; Where Does Water Run?; Where Have All the Salmon Gone?

## Insects

Are You Me?; Blue-Ribbon Niche (indirect); Riparian Retreat; Water Canaries

*continued*

*continued*

## Values of Aquatic Species and Environments

Aquatic Times (indirect); Aqua Words; Dragonfly Pond; Fishy Who's Who; Kelp Help; Marsh Munchers; Riparian Retreat; Sea Turtle International; Turtle Hurdles; Water Canaries; Water Plant Art; Water Wings; Wetland Metaphors

## Water Cycle

Alice in Waterland; Dragonfly Pond (indirect); How Wet Is Our Planet?; Water Wings; What's in the Water?; Where Does Water Run?

## Water Quality

Alice in Waterland; Dragonfly Pond; Fishable Waters; Glass Menagerie; Something's Fishy Here; Water Canaries; Wetland Metaphors; What's in the Air?; What's in the Water?; Where Does Water Run?

## Watershed

Alice in Waterland; Dragonfly Pond (indirect); How Wet Is Our Planet? (indirect); Watershed; What's in the Water?; Where Does Water Run?

## Wetland

Dragonfly Pond; Marsh Munchers; Migration Headache; Wetland Metaphors; What's in the Water?

## Whales

Plastic Jellyfish; Whale of a Tail; When a Whale Is Right

## Zoos and Aquaria

Designing a Habitat

# Metric Conversion Chart

**Approximations**

| Symbol | When You Know | Multiply By | To Find | Symbol |
|---|---|---|---|---|
| | **Length** | | | |
| in | inches | 2.5 | centimeters | cm |
| ft | feet | 30.0 | centimeters | cm |
| yd | yards | 0.9 | meters | m |
| mi | miles | 1.6 | kilometers | km |
| cm | centimeters | 0.4 | inches | in |
| m | meters | 3.3 | feet | ft |
| m | meters | 1.09 | yards | yd |
| km | kilometers | 0.6 | miles | mi |
| | **Area** | | | |
| $in^2$ | square inches | 6.5 | square centimeters | $cm^2$ |
| $ft^2$ | square feet | 0.09 | square meters | $m^2$ |
| $yd^2$ | square yards | 0.84 | square meters | $m^2$ |
| $mi^2$ | square miles (640 acres) | 2.6 | square kilometers | $km^2$ |
| acre | acre (43,560 $ft^2$) | 0.4 | hectares | ha |
| $cm^2$ | square centimeter | 0.16 | square inches | $in^2$ |
| $m^2$ | square meter | 10.8 | square feet | $ft^2$ |
| $m^2$ | square meter | 1.2 | square yards | $yd^2$ |
| $km^2$ | square kilometer | 0.4 | square miles | $mi^2$ |
| ha | hectare | 2.5 | acres | acre |
| | **Mass** | | | |
| oz | ounces (avoirdupois) | 28.0 | grams | g |
| lb | pound | 0.45 | kilograms | kg |
| t | short tons (2,000 lb) | 0.9 | tonnes (metric ton) | t |
| g | grams | 0.035 | ounces (avoirdupois) | oz |
| kg | kilograms | 2.2 | pounds | lb |
| t | tonnes (metric tons) | 1.1 | short tons (2,000 lb) | t |
| | **Volume** | | | |
| tsp | teaspoons | 5.0 | milliliters | ml |
| Tbs | tablespoons | 15.0 | milliliters | ml |
| fl oz | fluid ounces | 30.0 | milliliters | ml |
| c | cups (liquid) | 0.24 | liters | l |
| pt | pints (liquid) | 0.47 | liters | l |
| qt | quarts (liquid) | 0.95 | liters | l |
| gal | gallons | 3.8 | liters | l |
| $ft^3$ | cubic feet | 0.03 | cubic meters | $m^3$ |
| $yd^3$ | cubic yards | 0.76 | cubic meters | $m^3$ |
| ml | milliliters | 0.2 | teaspoons | tsp |
| ml | milliliters | 0.07 | tablespoons | Tbs |
| ml | milliliters | 0.03 | fluid ounces | fl oz |
| l | liters | 4.2 | cups (liquid) | c |
| l | liters | 2.1 | pints (liquid) | pt |
| l | liters | 1.06 | quarts (liquid) | qt |
| l | liters | 0.26 | gallons | gal |
| $m^3$ | cubic meters | 35.0 | cubic feet | $ft^3$ |
| $m^3$ | cubic meters | 1.3 | cubic yards | $yd^3$ |
| | **Temperature** | | | |
| °C | degrees Celsius | $(9/5 \times °C) + 32$ | degrees Fahrenheit | °F |
| °F | degrees Fahrenheit | $5/9 \times (°F-32)$ | degrees Celsius | °C |

© Council for Environmental Education 2006

# Glossary

This is a limited glossary. It does not duplicate terms that are found in the glossary of the *Project WILD K–12 Curriculum and Activity Guide*. It does include some of the terms that are specifically helpful when studying water resources and aquatic environments.

**acid precipitation:** all forms of precipitation that have an acidity lower than normal rainfall (pH 5.6)

**acre-foot:** the amount of water needed to cover 1 acre of surface area to the depth of 1 foot (12 inches)

**adaptation:** an alteration or adjustment in structure or habits by which a species or individual improves its condition in relationship to its environment

**aerate:** to supply with air or oxygen; to supply the blood with oxygen as in the function of lungs; to supply running water with additional oxygen as when a stream runs over falls or rapids or when wind creates waves on a lake

**alevin:** a young salmon during the first 2 weeks after hatching until the yolk sac has been absorbed

**algae:** simple one-celled or many-celled plants capable of photosynthesis; usually aquatic

**algin:** any hydrophilic, colloidal substance found in or obtained from various kelps

**amphibian:** an animal that typically lives in an aquatic habitat breathing by gills as young, and primarily in a terrestrial habitat breathing by lungs and through moist glandular skin as an adult (e.g., frog)

**anadromous:** species of fish that live their lives in the ocean and migrate to fresh water to spawn

**aquaculture:** deliberate growing of plants and animals in freshwater environments

**aquatic:** growing, living in, or frequenting water

**bag limit:** the maximum number of animals allowed to be taken by an individual in regulated fishing or hunting

**biodegradable:** capable of being decomposed by biological agents, especially bacteria

**biodiversity:** a term used to represent the variety of life forms in a given area

**bog:** a wetland formed where low oxygen levels and soil temperature cause incomplete decomposition and limited drainage, and an accumulation of fibrous peat

**catadromous:** a species of fish that begins its life in the ocean, lives most of its life in fresh water, and returns to the ocean to spawn

**coloration:** a genetically controlled pattern or markings that protects an individual organism

**condensation:** the process of a substance changing from a gas to a liquid, usually as a result of cooling

**conservation:** the use of natural resources in a way that ensures their continuing availability to future generations; the wise and intelligent use or protection of natural resources

**consumer:** the first part of an ecosystem is the nonliving substance; the second part consists of those organisms that are called "producers," or food makers; the third part of this system is called the "consumer" because it uses the producer for its food; it may in turn be used as food by a secondary consumer

**control:** to verify a scientific experiment by conducting a parallel experiment or by comparing with another standard

**decomposer:** those organisms (e.g. bacteria, fungi) that convert dead organic materials into inorganic materials

**detritus:** dead plant, animal, and other organic matter

**dissolved oxygen:** molecules of oxygen gas dissolved in water

**ecology:** the study of the relation of organisms or groups of organisms to their environment; the science of the interrelations between living organisms and their environment

**ecosystem:** a natural unit that includes living and nonliving parts interacting to produce a stable system in which the exchange of materials between the living and nonliving parts follows closed paths

**edge effect** the tendency of wildlife to use the areas where two vegetative types come together forming an edge

**effluent:** any matter that enters the environment from a specific source; the term generally refers to waste water from a sewage treatment or industrial plant

**endangered:** a species that is in danger of extinction throughout all or a significant portion of its range

**environment:** the circumstances and conditions surrounding an organism that influences its existence, including physical, biological, and all other factors

**environmental issue:** a situation in which there is disagreement about solutions to an environmental problem, often because of differing values and beliefs

**environmental problem:** a difficult situation involving the interaction between people and the environment

**erosion:** the removal or wearing away of soil or rock by water, wind, or other forces or processes

**estuary:** a site where the sea and river meet and mix fresh water and salt water

**eutrophication:** enrichment of soils and water resulting from fertilization, sewage, effluent, or other waters that carry a high plant-nutrient component

**evaporation:** the process of a substance changing from a liquid to a gas by exposure to air, heat or both

**evapo-transpiration:** the process of transferring moisture from the ground to the atmosphere by evaporation of water and transpiration from plants

**exotic:** a plant or animal that is not native to a habitat

**extinction:** the condition of having been removed from existence

**fish ladder:** a series of ascending pools of water constructed by humans as mechanisms to enable salmon or other fish to swim upstream around or over a dam

**fishery:** a system that includes: fish or shellfish populations; the habitats and communities of species in which those populations live; and the people who affect and use those populations

**food web:** an interlocking pattern of food chains

**fresh water:** clean, unpolluted water without salinity

**freshwater marsh:** a wetland where standing fresh water exists year-round in most conditions

**fry:** small young fish that have recently hatched

**gill net:** a curtain-like fishing net, suspended vertically in the water, with meshes of such a size as to catch a fish by the gills when it has thrust its head through the mesh netting

**ground water:** water found under the Earth's surface between saturated soil and rock supplying wells and springs

**habitat:** the arrangement of food, water, shelter, or cover and space suitable to animals' needs

**harvest:** the intentional gathering of plants, animals, and other natural resources for use

**hatchery:** a place where fish eggs are hatched and raised

**hydrology:** the study of the properties, distribution, and effects of water of the Earth and in the atmosphere

**international agency:** an agency that has representation from more than one nation

**introduced species:** a non-native species that is intentionally or accidentally brought into an ecosystem

**inventory:** a detailed, itemized list used in the process of identifying and counting animals

*continued*

**isolated ecosystems:** an ecosystem that is separated from another ecosystems **land use:** usually refers to how the land is used by people

**life cycle:** the continuous sequence of changes undergone by an organism from one primary form to the development of the same form again

**limiting factors:** influences in the life history of any animal, population of animals, or species (e.g., food, water, shelter, space, disease, predation, climatic conditions, pollution, hunting, poaching, and accidents)

**limnology:** the area of science dealing with the study of fresh water aquatic ecology

**litter:** (1) carelessly discarded garbage; (2) the number of young born per birthing to a mammal

**mariculture:** deliberate cultivation of plants and animals, including fish and kelp, in estuarine, coastal, and other marine areas

**microorganism:** an organism microscopic in size, observable only through a microscope

**migration:** the periodic movement of animals from one area to another and back again as a natural part of their lives.

**mitigate:** to make up for; to substitute some benefit for losses incurred

**native:** a plant or animal species that was produced, grew, or originated in a certain region

**needs:** in biological terms, the things that a plant or animal needs to survive

**niche:** the function or position of an organism or a population within an ecological community

**organic matter:** chemical compounds of carbon combined with other chemical elements and generally manufactured in the life processes of plants and animals

**pH:** a measure that indicates the relative acidity or alkalinity of a substance (The pH scale ranges from 0 (most acid) to 14 (most basic), with a pH of 7 being neutral.)

**plankton:** those organisms suspended in an aquatic habitat that controls their movements; usually microscopic, including bacteria, algae, protozoan, rotifers, larvae, and small crustaceans (Phytoplankton are the plant plankton; zoo-plankton are the animal species.)

**plastic:** (1) a petroleum-based product; (2) capable of being formed or shaped

**political process:** the process relating to the study, structure, or affairs of government or politics

**pollution:** contamination of soil, water, or atmosphere by the discharge of harmful substances

**population:** the number of a particular species in a defined area

**predator:** an animal that kills and eats other animals

**prey:** animals that are killed and eaten by other animals

**producer:** a green plant or bacterium that uses photosynthesis or chemosynthesis; constitutes first trophic level in food chain

**riparian:** located or relating to the banks of a stream, river, or other body of water

**runoff:** water that drains or flows off the surface of the land

**salt marsh:** a marshy land area that is wet with salt water or flooded by the sea

**scavenger:** an organism that habitually feeds on refuse or carrion

**scent:** a smell and odor

**seine net:** a fishing net that hangs vertically in the water, with floats at the upper edge and sinkers at the lower

**shelter:** cover for natal activity or bedding and for protection from weather

**silt:** the fine-grained sediment carried by water

**slough:** a hollow filled with mud and water (e.g., an inlet from a river, backwater, or tidal flat)

**smolt:** a young, silvery salmon migrating to the sea

**solubility:** the capacity to be dissolved or liquefied

**spawning:** to produce and deposit eggs

**species:** a population of individuals that are more or less alike and that are able to breed and produce fertile offspring under natural conditions; a category of biological classification immediately below the genus or subgenus

A p p e n d i c e s

. . . . . . . . . . . . . . . . . . . . . . . . . . . . . . . . . . . . . . . . . . . . . . . . . . . . . . . . . . . . . . . . . . .

G l o s s a r y

**state wildlife agency:** the state agency that has the legal responsibility for management of some or all wildlife, including habitat protection, restoration, and alteration; planning; land acquisition; research; education; information; endangered species; consumptive uses; nonconsumptive programs; and regulations and usually law enforcement

**subsistence:** the act or means to exist; to find ones supply of food from hunting and fishing

**succession:** the orderly, gradual, and continuous replacement of one plant or animal by another

**sustainability:** maintaining resources in such a way to be able to renew themselves over time or to keep in existence and supply with necessities

**swamp:** a type of wetland where the soil is saturated and often inundated with water and trees as the dominant cover vegetation

**terminal blade:** the last blade to grow on a kelp frond nearest to the surface

**threatened:** in wildlife terms, a species present in its range but in danger because of a decline in numbers

**tolerance:** the ability to deal with an adverse environmental condition; the amount of variance from a standard that is allowed

**treatment:** the act, manner, or method of handling a situation

**trophic level:** a group of living things that share the same level in the food chain

**variable:** the part of an experiment that can be changed or manipulated

**vegetation:** the mass of plants that covers a given area

**wants:** those things that are not considered a need to survive but are desirable

**water cycle:** the continuous circulation of water in systems throughout the planet, involving condensation, precipitation, runoff, evaporation, and transpiration

**waterfowl:** water birds, usually ducks, but including shore and wading birds, geese, and so forth

**waterway:** a river, canal or other body of water used as a route or way of travel or transportation

**wetlands:** any land area that tends to be regularly wet or a lowland area that is saturated with moisture, such as a marsh or swamp

**wild:** not tamed or domesticated, living in a basically free condition (A wild animal provides for its own food, shelter, and other needs in an environment that serves as a suitable habitat.)

**wildlife:** animals that are not tamed or domesticated and includes, but is not limited to, insects, spiders, birds, reptiles, fish, amphibians, and mammals, if nondomesticated

**zooplankton:** plankton that is composed of tiny animals and animal matter

This glossary is designed primarily for reference and background information. Occasionally, terms are defined within an activity and are not repeated here. Key vocabulary for activities is usually defined here, especially if it is specific to wildlife and understanding of natural systems. This glossary is compiled from four principal sources. The majority of the terms and definitions are reprinted with few changes from Multidisciplinary Wildlife Teaching Activities, developed and edited by William R. Hernbrode. (Columbus, OH: ERIC Clearinghouse for Science, Mathematics, and Environmental Education, 1978). The next largest group of entries is derived from the glossary that appears in the Project Learning Tree Environmental Education PreK–8 Activity Guide. (Washington DC: American Forest Foundation, 1993). A number of entries are adapted or reprinted from Wildlife Aid No. 2. (Portland, OR: U.S. Forest Service, R-6, June 1965). Additional entries are based on the contributions of our Committee, members, staff, and reviewers. All glossary materials derived from previously published sources are adapted or reprinted with the permission of the copyright holder.

. . . . . . . . . . . . . . . . . . . . . . . . . . . . . . . . . . . . . . . . . . . . . . . . . . . . . . . . . . . . . . . . . . . . . . . . . . . . . . . . . .

© C o u n c i l   f o r   E n v i r o n m e n t a l   E d u c a t i o n   2 0 0 6

**269**

# Agencies and Organizations

The following federal agencies and organizations are involved in wildlife education. State wildlife agencies may be contacted directly in each state. Project WILD encourages educators and students to contact a range of organizations so they can make informed decisions. We recommend that requests be as specific as possible; mailed on behalf of a class or group rather than each individual student; and sent with a stamped, self-addressed envelope for return of requested materials.

## Federal Agencies

Bureau of Land Management
Office of Public Affairs
1849 C Street, NW, Room 406-LS
Washington, DC 20240
(202) 452-5125
www.blm.gov

United States Department of Agriculture
Cooperative State Research, Education, and
Extension Service
1400 Independence Avenue, SW, Stop 2201
Washington, DC 20250-2201
(202) 720-7441
www.csrees.usda.gov

National Marine Fisheries Service
NOAA Fisheries
1315 East-West Highway, 9th Floor
Silver Spring, MD 20910
(301) 713-2379
www.nmfs.noaa.gov

National Park Service
1849 C Street, NW
Washington, DC 20240
(202) 208-6843
www.nps.gov

Natural Resources Conservation Service
U. S. Department of Agriculture
PO Box 2890
Washington, DC 20013
(202) 720-7246
www.nrcs.usda.gov

U.S. Army Corps of Engineers
Public Affairs
441 G Street, NW
Washington, DC 20314
(202) 761-0011
www.hq.usace.army.mil

U.S. Department of Agriculture
1400 Independence Avenue, SW
Washington, DC 20250
(202) 720-4623
www.usda.gov

U.S. Environmental Protection Agency
Environmental Education Division
1200 Pennsylvania Avenue, NW
Washington, DC 20460
(202) 272-0167
www.epa.gov

U.S. Fish and Wildlife Service
Department of Interior
1849 C Street, NW
Washington, DC 20240
(800) 344-WILD
www.fws.gov

U.S. Fish and Wildlife Service
Reference Center
5430 Grosvenor Lane, Suite 110
Bethesda, MD 20814
(301) 492-6403
http://federalaid.fws.gov

USDA Forest Service
Natural Resource Conservation Education
1400 Independence Ave., SW
Washington, DC 20250-0003
(202) 205-8333
www.fs.fed.us

# Regional Offices
## *U.S. Environmental Protection Agency*

U.S. EPA Region 1
Environmental Education Program
1 Congress Street, Suite 1100
Boston, MA 02114-2023
(617) 918-1111
**www.epa.gov/region1/**

U.S. EPA Region 2
Environmental Education Program
290 Broadway, 26th Floor
New York, NY 10007-1866
(212) 637-3000
**www.epa.gov/region2/**

U.S. EPA Region 3
Environmental Education Program
1650 Arch Street (3CG00)
Philadelphia, PA 19103-2029
(215) 814-5000
**www.epa.gov/region3/**

U.S. EPA Region 4
Environmental Education Program
Atlanta Federal Center
61 Forsyth Street, SW
Atlanta, GA 30303-3104
(404) 562-9900
**www.epa.gov/region4/**

U.S. EPA Region 5
Environmental Education Program
77 West Jackson Boulevard (PI-19J)
Chicago, IL 60604-3507
(312) 353-2000
**www.epa.gov/region5/**

U.S. EPA Region 6
Environmental Education Program
1445 Ross Avenue (6XA), Suite 1200
Dallas, TX 75202-2733
(214) 665-2200
**www.epa.gov/region6/**

U.S. EPA Region 7
Environmental Education Program
901 North Fifth Street
Kansas City, KS 66101
(913) 551-7003
**www.epa.gov/region7/**

U.S. EPA Region 8
Environmental Education Program
999 18th Street, Suite 300, OC
Denver, CO 80202-2405
(303) 312-6312
**www.epa.gov/region8/**

U.S. EPA Region 9
Environmental Education Program
75 Hawthorne Street
San Francisco, CA 94105
(415) 947-8000
**www.epa.gov/region9/**

U.S. EPA Region 10
Environmental Education Program
1200 Sixth Avenue (EXA-142)
Seattle, WA 98101
(206) 553-1200
**www.epa.gov/region10/**

# Organizations

American Cetacean Society
National Headquarters
PO Box 1391
San Pedro, CA 90733-1391
(310) 548-6279
**www.acsonline.org**

American Fisheries Society
5410 Grosvenor Lane
Bethesda, MD 20814-2199
(301) 897-8616
**www.fisheries.org**

American Humane Association
63 Inverness Drive East
Englewood, CO 80112
(303) 792-9900
**www.americanhumane.org**

American Sportfishing Association &
 Future Fisherman Foundation
225 Reinekers Lane, Suite 420
Alexandria, VA 22314
(703) 519-9691
**www.asafishing.org**

Animal Protection Institute
PO Box 22505
Sacramento, CA 95822
(916) 447-3085
**www.api4animals.org**

Animal Welfare Institute
PO Box 3650
Washington, DC 20027
(703) 836-4300
**www.awionline.org**

*continued*

Association of Fish and Wildlife Agencies
444 North Capitol Street, NW, Suite 725
Washington, DC 20001
(202) 624-7890
**www.iafwa.org**

Bear Trust International
P.O. Box 4006
Missoula, MT 59806-4006
(406) 523-7779
**www.beartrust.org**

Cetacean Society International
PO Box 953
Georgetown, CT 06829
(203) 770-8615
**csiwhalesalive.org**

Cousteau Society
710 Settlers Landing Road
Hampton, VA 23669
(757) 722-9300
**www.cousteau.org**

Defenders of Wildlife
1130 17th Street, NW
Washington, DC 20036
(800) 385-9712
**www.defenders.org**

Ducks Unlimited
1 Waterfowl Way
Memphis, TN 38120
(800) 45-DUCKS
**www.ducks.org**

Earth Island Institute
300 Broadway, Suite 28
San Francisco, CA 94133
(415) 788-3666
**www.earthisland.org**

Fund for Animals
200 W. 57th Street, Suite 705
New York, NY 10019
(888) 405-FUND
**www.fundforanimals.org**

Greenpeace
702 H Street, NW
Washington, DC 20001
(202) 462-1177
**www.greenpeace.org/usa**

International Whaling Commission
The Red House
135 Station Road
Impington, Cambridge CB4 9NP, UK
England
+44(0)1223-233971
**www.iwcoffice.org**

Izaak Walton League of America
707 Conservation Lane
Gaithersburg, MD 20878-2983
(301) 548-0150
**www.iwla.org**

National Association for Humane
   and Environmental Education
Humane Society of the United States
2100 L Street, NW
Washington, DC 20037
(202) 452-1100
**www.hsus.org**

National Association of Conservation Districts
509 Capitol Ct., NE
Washington, DC 20002
(202) 547-6223
**www.nacdnet.org**

National Audubon Society
700 Broadway
New York, NY 10003
(212) 979-3000
**www.audubon.org**

National Rifle Association
Wildlife Management Division
11250 Waples Mill Road
Fairfax, VA 22030
(703) 267-1500
**www.nra.org**

National Wildlife Federation
11100 Wildlife Center Drive
Reston, VA  20190-5362
(800) 822-9919
**www.nwf.org**

The Nature Conservancy
4245 North Fairfax Drive, Suite 100
Arlington, VA 22203
(703) 841-5300
**www.nature.org**

New England Aquarium
Central Wharf
Boston, MA 02110
(617) 973-5200
**www.neaq.org**

The Ocean Conservancy
2029 K Street, NW
Washington, DC 20006
(800) 519-1541
**www.oceanconservancy.org**

Provincetown Center for Coastal Studies
115 Bradford Street
Provincetown, MA 02657
(508) 487-3622, ext. 101
**www.coastalstudies.org**

Safari Club International
4800 West Gates Pass Road
Tucson, AZ 85745-9490
(520) 620-1220
**www.safariclub.org**

Sierra Club
85 Second Street, 2nd Floor
San Francisco, CA 94105
(415) 977-5500
**www.sierraclub.org**

Whale Center of New England
P.O. Box 159
Gloucester, MA 01931-0159
(978) 281-6351
**www.whalecenter.org**

The Wilderness Society
1615 M Street, NW
Washington, DC 20036
(800) 843-9453
**www.wilderness.org**

Wildlife Management Institute
1146 19th Street, NW, Suite 700
Washington, DC 20036
(202) 371-1808
**www.wildlifemanagementinstitute.org**

The Wildlife Society
5410 Grosvenor Lane, Suite 200
Bethesda, MD 20814-2144
(301) 897-9770
**www.wildlife.org**

World Wildlife Fund
1250 24th Street, NW
P.O. Box 97180
Washington, DC 20090-7180
(202) 293-4800
**www.worldwildlife.org**

# Evaluation of Project WILD Materials

Project WILD meets the international criteria for environmental education and provides educators with materials that support national, state, and district standards in science, mathematics, language arts, social studies, and expressive arts. Project WILD curriculum materials undergo a thorough review, testing, and evaluation process. The purpose is to develop well-conceived, tested, current, and effective instructional resources of the highest quality that meet the needs of educators and students.

## Expert Review

All of the instructional activities in Project WILD, as well as the conceptual framework, have been reviewed for educational soundness, balance, and content accuracy. Primarily classroom teachers, often in cooperation with non-formal educators and wildlife specialists, wrote the initial instructional activities. Reviewers throughout each stage of Project WILD's development have included classroom teachers, university faculty, resource agency personnel, wildlife biologists, representatives of private conservation groups, public wildlife and natural resource agency personnel, representatives of animal welfare organizations, spokespersons for environmental organizations, school administrators; curriculum developers, environmental education specialists, representatives of private industry, citizen volunteers, and others. Results of this review process have been used in editing and improving the Project WILD instructional materials throughout the history of the program.

## Pilot Test

This entire pilot testing and revision process was developed and implemented by a respected team of independent researchers for the initial version of the *Project WILD Elementary and Secondary Activity Guide*, first introduced in 1983. Each of the instructional activities that appear in the Project WILD materials was tested by educators to ensure its quality and appropriateness. Revisions—from major to minor—were made in each of the activities tested, and a few activities were discarded entirely following the testing process.

The same process for pilot testing was used with the aquatic education activities. Therefore, each of the activities in the *Project WILD Aquatic Curriculum and Activity Guide* has been determined to be effective in accomplishing its stated objectives with the age level of students indicated.

## Field Test

Following the year of the pilot test of the *Project WILD Elementary and Secondary Activity Guides*, a major field test was designed and conducted to determine the effectiveness of the materials when used by teachers with their students. Again, this study was developed and implemented by a knowledgeable and esteemed team of independent researchers. The field test was conducted in three states, in three demographic areas (urban, suburban, and rural), and across all elementary and secondary grade levels during a full school year. Two hundred fifty-nine teachers and more than 6,000 students were involved.

The results indicate that Project WILD has a definite impact on teachers and students. Students showed significant gains in learning, and developed attitudes toward wildlife that are consistent with the goals of Project WILD. Educators generally found the activities stimulating and worthwhile in their classes and were able to integrate the activities into their curricula. A direct relationship was evidenced between the number of Project WILD instructional activities used by teachers and the students' gains in knowledge and attitudes. Statistical significance was found where teachers used seven or more Project WILD instructional activities. Project WILD was shown to be effective in urban, suburban, and rural areas.

## Continuing Evaluation

Project WILD continues to be monitored and evaluated on an ongoing and long-term basis to ensure its quality and effectiveness, as well as to make revisions and additions to the program as needed. Those involved with Project WILD welcome additional independent studies. Funding is not typically available to assist; however, Project WILD can provide other assistance.

## Additional Studies

A study similar to the major field test of Project WILD was conducted in Lee County, Florida, with comparable results. Several master's theses and doctoral dissertations, both quantitative and qualitative, have focused on or included Project WILD throughout the United States. Program assessment is also being conducted internationally. For example, a controlled study in Taiwan in 1996 focused on the impact of the Project WILD curriculum on student learning, attitudes, and behavior. Project WILD was shown to be most effective on positive, long-term behavior related to stewardship of the environment.

In 2001, a study conducted by Ohio State University measured the impact of Project WILD on student learning and attitudes. The results confirmed that Project WILD has a positive impact on student knowledge and attitudes about wildlife and constructs about wildlife. For more details on the results of this study, visit: www.projectwild.org.

Various surveys have been conducted to determine actual use of the Project WILD materials following Project WILD workshops. Additional studies related specifically to the Project WILD Aquatic materials are anticipated and encouraged.

## For Additional Information

Visit **www.projectwild.org** for more information on Project WILD evaluations and to download "Project WILD: A Summary of Research Findings 1983-1995 and 1996-2003."

# Acknowledgements

Project WILD was developed and sustained through the efforts of literally hundreds of thousands of talented and dedicated people throughout the United States and Canada. Most of this effort is entirely volunteer. The Council for Environmental Education would like to take this opportunity to thank everyone who has assisted—and who continues to help—in this effort to improve education about wildlife, people, and the environment.

It is not possible to individually thank and credit all of those who have assisted with the development of the Project WILD Aquatic Education materials—including the thousands of students in kindergarten through high school classrooms who participated in the formal pilot testing of these instructional activities. The Council for Environmental Education acknowledges the generous support by the U.S. Fish and Wildlife Service through the use of funds from the Wallop-Breaux Amendment to the Sport Fish Restoration Act, and we thank the International Association of Fish and Wildlife Agencies for recommending this funding. The Council for Environmental Education thanks the Western Association of Fish and Wildlife Agencies, as well as all of the Associate Sponsors and Contributors to this project. We thank the many patient, creative, and constructive professionals who helped to review and test these materials.

**FY 2006–2007 Council for Environmental Education Board Members**
Harold Aiken, Bill Futrell, Josetta Hawthorne (*ex officio*), Steve Huffaker, Dwight Landreneau, Barbara Price, Rudy Schafer, Rudi Thompson

**FY 2006–2007 Project WILD Program Committee Members**
Bill Andrews *(ex-officio)*, Tuss Erickson, John Gahl, Nancy Herron, Josetta Hawthorne (*ex-officio*), Jake Hohl, Steve Huffaker, Irene Pickhardt, Barbara Price.

## Third Edition: 2006 Update

**Project Oversight**
Josetta Hawthorne

**Project Supervisor**
Jennifer Paschke

**Editorial Coordinators**
Bill Andrews, Jennifer Paschke

**Writer**
Kelly Matthews

**Copy Editing**
Ted Smith

**Graphic Design and Layout**
Jennifer Paschke

**Prepress Assistance**
Hal Hammond Graphics, Sacramento, CA

**Professional Reviewers**
Doug Darr, Nancy Herron, Lisa Jones, Brenda Justice, Amy Parrish, Kate Skowron, Mark Stephens, Bobbie Winn

**Field Testers**
Marcia Bisnett, Barbara Devie, Rosemary Drummond, Roger Ellingson, Anne P. Green, Victoria Jordan, Jeff Laughlin, Laura Olson, Beverly Owens, Mack Tobias, Jennifer Webb, Cherie Wyatt

## Third Edition: 2001 Reprint

**Project Oversight**
Josetta Hawthorne

**Project Supervisor**
Suzy Sanders

**Editorial Coordinator**
Barb Pitman

**Copy Editing**
Barbara Hart, Publications Professionals, LLC

**Graphic Design and Layout**
Pam Cullen, Page Productions

**New Artwork**
Great Blue Heron by Cindie Brunner, page 39

We also would like to express our appreciation to the Project WILD State Coordinators, who provided feedback and suggestions during the process of updating the guide for reprints.

## Third Edition: 2000 Update

**Project Oversight**
Donna Asbury, Kelly Schaefer

**Project Supervisor**
Dr. Barbara Bonsall Wood

**Managing Editor and Format Supervisor**
Gwyn Rowland Rozzelle

**Copy Editing**
Steve Harding, Lily Auliff

**Graphic Design and Layout**
O'Conner Group
Pam Cullen, Page Productions

**Contributing Ideas and Field Testing for New and Revised Activities**
Sockeye Scents," "Dam Design," and "Silt: A Dirty Word," ©1999 Idaho Department of Fish and Game and Idaho Project WILD. Adapted with permission from *WILD About Salmon Activity Guide.*

Other new and revised activities developed, tested, or adapted by the following educators: Lisa Anderson, Jennifer Coggins, John Gahl, Suzie Gilley, Gwyn Rowland Rozzelle, Kelly Schaefer, Shirley Sypolt, Molly Tkacik, Barbara Bonsall Wood, Dell Young

**Draft Reviewers**
Lisa Anderson, Bill Andrews, Sarah Armstrong, Donna Asbury, Lily Auliff, Steve Bates, Karina Blizzard, Mendy Boyce, Shannon Caldwell, Laura Carey, Robin Dublin, Mimi Dunne, Dan DuPre, Connie Elpers, Dale Elshoff, Susan Eschbach, Lisa Evans, Bill Futrell, John Gahl,

Rusty Garrison, Warren Gartner, Barbara Gigar, Suzie Gilley, Sylvia Gude, Maggie Hachmeister, Carrie Hamby, Casey Harris, Josetta Hawthorne, Cheryl Hayes, Jake Hohl, Kevin Holliday, Dave Jensen, Valerie Keener, Burnie Kessner, Frank Knight, Pat Knighten, Chuck Kowaleski, Pam Landry, Lonnie Nelson, Bruce Palmer, Connie Rasmussen, Sandy Reith, Jennifer Richards, Christina Rolka, Nancy Rolli, Gwyn Rowland Rozzelle, Jeffrey Rucks, Gretchen Sanford, Kelly Schaefer, Rudy Schaefer, Elsie Sellars, Bob Sepanik, Art Shomo, Georgia Spencer, Charlotte St. Romain, Roland Stein, Al Stenstrup, Shirley Sypolt, Bryan Thompson, Margaret Tudor, Jackie Urband, Laurie Usher, Janet Vail, Diana Vos, Audrey Walker, Sharon Walker, Jay Webb, Colleen Welch, Bobbie Winn, Randy Wiseman, Barbara Bonsall Wood, Dell Young

## Second Edition: 1992 Update

**Editorial Staff**
Cheryl Charles, Judy Dawson, Janet Rasmussen, Dan Shaw, Mary Stuever

**Small Group Reviews**
Dr. Hans Anderson, Louise Ashman, Richard Baumfalk, Susan Beck, Mark Bennett, Nancy Brown, Becky Brown, Nancy Caldwell, Sam Carmen, Amy Chandler, Laurie Christie, Barbara Church, Jane Cleaves, Rodger Coombs, Phil Cooper, Randy Cotten, Clif Daniels, Shelly Davis, Jerry deBin, Elizabeth DelVerne, Alvin Diamond, Jo Dodds, Ed Donovan, Carolyn Dunmore, Miriam Dunne, Linda Eastwood, Mary Beth Eberwein, Jim Edwards, Kathy Farr, Beth Fasnacht, Jack Finger, Carl Finstad, TC Floy, Susan Foote-Martin, Terri Franklin, Nancy Franz, Connie Gahl, John Gahl, Warren Gartner, Rick Gilchrist, Susan Gilchrist, Alan Gray, Robert Griffin, Corey Hall, Lynn Haralson, Kerry Harkins, Bonnie Helzer, Mel Hickman, Earl Hodil, Carol Holden, Jean Holland, Douglas Housskeeper, Susan Ilgner, Elizabeth Javrin, Jan Jose, Twila Kadel, Michael Kamen, Marti Kane, Michael Karmen, Jeff Kiefer, Julie King, Judy Klippel, Sherry Klosiewski, Bill Koehler, Jackie Lane, Tim Lemon, Chris Martin, Jim McCollough, Jack

*continued*

McNeel, Cathy Meyer, Brenda Miller, Carrie Morgan, Tim Morgan, Margha Mulling, Stu Murrell, Jim Nelson, Deb Neuenschwander, Rod Nichols, Mike Overton, Rod Parker, Deborah Patton, Barbara Pietrucha, Mark Pochon, Polly Powell, Teresa Prather, Christine Raabe, Anna Radue, Barbara Reed, Marian Rendall, Ken Riddleberger, John Russell, Dave Sanger, Nancy Schneider, Ann Seppenfield, M. Sharp, Art Shomo, James Slater, Theresa Stabo, Caroline Sweigart, Jean Terry, Tracey Thompson, Mary Todd, Barbara Tucker, Kenneth Uhlhorn, Al Van Hoey, Karen Van Norman, Linda Walbruch, Bob Waller, Dave Wanisko, Jennifer Warwick, Luann Waters, Linda Watters, Brenda Weiser, Donna White, Frank Williams, Don Winslow, Shirley Wright, Julie Yamamoto, Dr. Dennis Yockers, Kathie Zager, Dean Zimmerman, Darci Zolman

### Draft Reviewers

Miriam Dunne, John Gahl, Barbara Gigar, Suzie Gilley, Maggie Hachmeister, Ellie Horwitz, Dr. Cliff Knapp, Don MacCarter, Chris Martin, Colleen Matt, Cheryl Mollohan, Ken Riddleberger, Larry Sarner, Nancy Schneider, Daphne Sewing, Art Shomo, Dr. Cindi Smith-Walters, Heidi Solper, Jo Temte, Brenda Weiser, Carl Wolfe, Dr. Dennis Yockers

### Independent Comments

Elaine Almeida, Bette Anderson, Paul Beckwith, Carol Beyna, Judy Binger, Sue Bogacz, Evelyn Bologna, Evelyn Boring, Gail Bouslog, Gerry Bryan, Sandra Buck, Sara Campbell, Susan Chambers, Rick Chase, Dorothy Chavez, James Colman, Michael Countess, Kelly Countouris, Ellen Cunningham, Jan Davis, Patrick DeSantis, Barbara Dunbar, LuAnne Folks, Janene Fowler, J. Frey, Sharon Giza, Jim Goodwin, Andy Greif, Karen Grimes Cooper, Linda Gruberski, Karen Hangrove, Linda Harris, Jean Harris, Bob Hernbrode, Earl Hodil, Kathie Holden, Mary Jane Holmes, Bonielee Hooper, Karen Hostetter, Mary Hurst, Jodi Jenkins, Laura Jodice, Jeffrey Keidel, Janice Kesler, Pat Knighten, Pat Lang, Mickey Larkins, Gretchen Leuenberger, Haile Macurdy, Barbara Marshall, Roy Martin, Dale Mason, Beth McCanley, Shalon McCart, Jim McCullough, Terry

McLaughlin, Mary Melican, Justine Menci, Patricia Mercker, Cathy Meyer, Debra Miller, Suzanne Miller, Susan Miller, Matt Miller, Sterling Miller, Gerald Mohr, Marie Monfredo, Fran Morris, Jane Moynihan, Kim Mumper, Tom Nelson, Dorcas Newkirk, Connie O'Brien, Helen Panagiotopoulos, Lynette Parkhurst, Deborah Poti, Earl Richardson, Dolores Ringdahl, Wanda Rowland, Linda Sand, Larry Sarner, Rachel Schneider, Mary Shapiro, Art Shomo, Lisa Silverman-Gent, Rick Sinnott, Lucy Slinger, Marlies Smith, Cecil Buckey Smith, Dean Smith, Jacquelyn Sparrow, David St. Clair, Paula St. Clair, Catherine Stefanides, Michael Stephan, Regina Stovall, Jack Turner, Dennis Unkenholz, Larry Vanderlinden, Jane Vollmer, Mary Frances Wagner, Dave Walters, Arthur Washburn, Kenneth Watkins, Elizabeth White, Ellen Wilken, Debbi Wilkinson, Tim Williams, Laurie Woodall, Jill Yeager, Eileen Yost, Janice Young, Cathy Zazanis, Judy Zeider, Sue Zimmerman, Nancy Zuschlag

### Artwork

Bob Samples: all diagrams unless otherwise acknowledged or public domain.

Susie Duckworth: illustrations for "Sockeye Scents," "Dam Design," and "Silt: A Dirty Word."

## First Edition Aquatic Guide

### Members of WREEC Ad Hoc Committee on Aquatic Education

John Gahl, Chairman; Suzie Gilley, Luba Mycio-Mommers, Don MacCarter, John Alderman, Sharon Fitzgerald, Kathy Johnson, John McMahon

### Editorial Staff

Cheryl Charles, Judy Dawson, Lyn Fleming, Bob Samples

### Project WILD Aquatic Writing Conference Participants

*Northwest Region:* Steve Andrews, Larry Broder, Peggy Cowan, Debra Faast, Patty Farthing, Kate Ferschweiler, Sheri Fetherman, John Gahl, John Garner, Paul Gregory, Cliff Hamilton, Bill Hastie, Ann Hymel, Dennis L. Lee, Rick Lemon, Neal Maine, Mike Mercer, Jake Nice, Rod Nichols, Vicki Osis, Susan K. Parker,

Marian Rendall, Mike Schaadt, Dolores Scott, Kathy Shaw, Bob Stewart, Jill Thayer, Marta Turksel, Laurie Usher, Joe Vogler, Scott Wolf, Shirley Wright, Kathie Zagner, Ernie McDonald, Environmental Education Association of Oregon. *Southeast Region:* John Alderman, Laura Jackson, Dell Young, Wendy Allen, Jay H. Davies, Marti Kane, Art Shomo, Tamsey W. Ellis, Ken Manuel, Jim Armstrong, Suzie Gilley, Rick Estes, Pat Sumner, Betty Ann Welsh, Mary Sutherland, Tracy Drury, Leroy Smith, Jr., Bill Martin, Roy King, Lundie Spence, Mary E. Sparrow, Hal Brown. *Northeast Region:* Bill Einsig, Mary Sue Topper, Marlena Campbell, Sharon Fitzgerald, Susan Wolf, Anita Sanchez, Karl Toft, Pat Kane, Dot Coates, Marylyn Locandro, Sarah Orleans, Patrice Wyzga, Robin Anderson, Loretta Pisani, Kathleen Dilger, Jeanette Gifford, Rene Kochenberger, Kim Contini, Cleti Cervoni, Alberto Mimo, Steven Fish, Kevin Kopp, Edward Morrows, Jerry Schierloh, Wayne DeFeo, Bruce Marganoff, Fred C. Lapse, Sr., David Grant, Frank Gallagher, Mike Kendall, Robert Sousa. *Midwest Region:* John Alesandrini, Merilyn Bohm, Susan Cook, Christine Dixon, Pat Fry, Anne Hallowell, Liz Hammerman, Keith Holtzman, Kathy Johnson, Larry Lane, Kathy Luczynski, Bruce Munson, Dennis Nelson, Peter Paladino, Nan Peters, Patricia Riggins, Doug Ehorn, Dave Jensen, Carl Strang, Elma Tuomisalo, Don Roderick, Dan Sivek, John T. Thompson, Dennis Yockers, Clifford Knapp. *Florida Review Conference:* Dale Crider, Roy King, David LaHart, Eileen Tramontana, Mark Robson, Sande Ross, Jo Ellen Kessler, John S. Street, Jan Kurke, Peggy Kinder, Marie Rocheleau, Carol Houck, Connie Bersok, Judi Breuggeman, Debbie Fritz-Quincy, Debbie Dorsett Hanson, Keith Hanson, Bill Hammond, Bill Haynes, Judy Gillan, Duke Hammond. *Southwest Region:* George Ek, Richard Larson, Tom Powell, Carol Jones, John Goettl, Tana Baldwin, Maureen Wilson, Dolores Varela-Phillips, Bill Kinman, Carolyn W. Zaugg, Sara Stokes, Mary Shanks, Dan Shaw, Flint Swerdfeger, Bob Hayes, Dan Smith, Joanna Lackey, Don MacCarter, Gerald Jacobi, John D. Leppink, Bob Hernbrode, Ellen Petrick-Underwood, Susan McLane, Norma Livo, Rosalie Bock, Bill Watt, Brenda Schussman, Kerry Baldwin, Jane S. MacCarter, Bob Stack, Trish Jahnke, Carol

Bergevin, Cheryl Mollohan, Kay Langstaff

**Additional Special Assistance**

Dick Myshak, Rick Lemon, Don Friberg, Bob Jantzen, Frank Dunkle, Rolf Wallenstrom, Mike Spears, Conley Moffett, Jim Pulliam, Gene Stephenson, Carl Sullivan, Gill Radonski, Jack Berryman, Bob Brantly, Harold Olson, Jim Flynn, Bill Morris, Della Haig, Pat McQuown, Linda Haschke, Jan Woodhouse, Jan Rensel, Dale and Linda Crider, Stician Samples, Tom Charles, Russ Cookingham, David Kennedy, Jean-Michel Cousteau

**Reviewers of Pilot Materials**

Rudy Schafer, Cliff Knapp, Conley Moffett, Don MacCarter, John Alderman, Miriam Dunne, Darleen Stoner, Bob Hernbrode, Milton McClaren, Peter Croskery, Joe Vogler, Dan Sivek, Gene Allen, Rhonda Reed, Craig Thompson, Steven N. Moyer, Suzie Gilley, Mary Sutherland, Dolores Scott, Ellie Horwitz, Roy King, Duke Hammond, Judy Gillan, Dennis Yockers, Sara LaBorde, George Ek, Dave Jensen, Elena Scofield, Bev Graham, Tom Peterson, Marnie Miller, Don Newberry, John Nickum, Anita Sanchez, Mark Osokow, Mike Conlin, Ray Tamppari, Linn Montgomery, Joanna Lackey, June McSwain, Suzette Woods, Neil Armantrout, Donald Martin, Art Shomo, Brenda Schussman, Rich Larson, Steve Andrews, John McMahon, Cheryl Mollohan, Bill Watt, Rick Estes, Patricia Sumner, Catherine Quinn, Kerry Baldwin, Susie Gwen Criswell, Andrea Shotkin, Donna Nye, Connie Coutellier, Kathleen Rude, P. Stewart, Carol Kaney, Jo Ellen Kessler, Keith Hanson, Daniel A. Poole, Tom Flatt, Paul Cuplin, Louise Belnay, Ilo Hiller, Steve Richardson, Cliff Hamilton, Ken Manuel, Jan Woodhouse, Diane Jacobson, Jim Black, Corinne Clay, Sherrie Wren, James Cole, Linda Falk, Valerie Silva, Nigel Lock, Paula Davenport, Sara Blanchard, Wendy Allen, Lundie Spence, CeCe Forget, Yolanda Orozco Juarez, Henry Neufeld, Pat Bower, Barry Sheehan, Chuck Clark, Richard Moats, Mark Johnson, Doug Buettner, Daniel Jeung, Bill Finch, Kathleen Drake, Peter Sherrill, Jeffrey Hodges, Marilyn Wein, Edward Pimentel, Jane Okada, Joel Wiens, Barbara Fujimoto, Gene Gabriel, Rhonda Reed, Sandra Diamond, Meryl Sundove, Ronald Fritzsche, Daniel R. Baker, Dave Patterson, Nancy

*continued*

Belmont, David E. James, Peter Stekel, Joy Grijalva, Ken Hashagen, James E. Hardwick, Doris Morris, Daniel Skanson, Jeffrey Keidel, Barbara Berka, L. Janet Lee, Patty Farthing, Karen Monteil, Patricia Zalo, Penney M. Hall, Robert Matheson III, Pat Ryan, Jim Bennett, Robin Knox, John Woodling, Dave Sanger, Carol Jones, Bill Hammond, Jan Rensel, Chuck Roth, Tim Manolis, Steve Sawyer, Pat McQuown, Carl Strang, Dave Grant, Bill Hastie, Sharon Fitzgerald, Karen Olin Johnston, Luba Mycio-Mommers, Laura Key, Alice Cyr, Joanna Bertolucci, Gary Hudson, John Miller, Bambi Fisher, Keith Hanson, Janet Posch, Margie Prickett, Toni Rumsey, Carole Sharo, Jeannie Wood, Jerry Blackard, Joseph W. Artmann, Howard N. Larsen, Sheri Fetherman, Elma Tuomisalo, Jim Allen, Carl Becker, Art Whitney, Willis Evans, Annette Dray, Janet Sheldon, Carroll Henderson, Robert Rawstron, Beth Huning, Pam Armstrong, Richard Klingbeil, D. Maxwell, Pam Stacey, Della Haig, Kathy Johnson, Ed Chiosso, Gene Stephenson, Mary Gilbert, Tony Angell, Stan Williamson

## Project WILD Aquatic Education
## Pilot Test Teachers

Bess Marie Adams, Judith Allard, Eileen Allen, Connie Alley, Debbie Alvey, Barbara Armentrout, Wilma Baker-Nelson, Howard Barbour, Jean Bateman, Ingeborg Baxter, Beverly Beard, Sue Beck, Irene Begay, Louise Belnay, Carol Bergevin, Paul Bixler, Gary Bloemker, Pat Bower, Steve Brandt, Kathleen Brian, Roxanne Brickell, Sharon Broguard, Daniel Brown, Anna Brown, Ann Bryan, Beverly Calloway, Carolyn Cannava, Daniel Capuano, Beth Ann Carnes, Judi Chandler, Betty Jo Collins, Sue Confer, Dianne Corneau, Patricia Currence, Atwood Curtis, Meg Davis, Marilyn Delaney, Michael Demchik, Lynn Dunn, Doug Emery, Denice Erb, William Evans, Patty Farthing, CeCe Forget, Pete Fortune, Lucille Fortune, Brad Frohloff, Jim Fugate, Liz Fulton, Connie Gahl, Amelia Garcia, Carol Gatzke, Lucille Gertz, Celia Graham, Stanley Griffin, Loraine Gustafson, Penney Hall, Raydel Hall, Rita Hall, Roberta Harlow, Pearlie Harris, Nancy Harte, Bob Hayes, Jan Hayes, Jodi Heath, Lin Heinrich, Sara Hepner, George Herrera, Carolyn Hill, Eric Hoeppner, Charlotte Hughes, Catherine

Isham, Carol Jackson, Dean Jamason, Sheri Jeter, Andrew Joachim, Ruby Johnson, Cydney Jones, Jeff Keidel, Carol Kelley, Lois Kenney, Mike Kersten, Carolyn Kirk, Sandy Klein, Mary Ann Kobayashi, Larry Langstaff, Floyd Larson, Janet Lee, JoAnn Loersch, Mrs. Lovett, Renee Mabry, Dotty MacVeigh, Gary Mason, Jack Massie, Robert Matheson, Gladys May, Kim McColman, Roberta McFarland, Mary McIlwain, Kathy McLean, Paul Mitschler, Jan Moberly, Jeanne Monteau, Karen Monteil, Miriam Moore, Doris Morris, Dalton Moultrie, Debbie Mues, Pat Naccarato, Robert Nappi, Midge Michelason, Brenda Niese, Barbara Oestreich, Russell Otto, Phyllis Parker, Dennis Pelletier, Nancy Peterson, Michelle Phillips, Linda Pils, Christine Raab, Sharon Richards, LaVonne Roll, Jane Rossman, Margery Salmon, Suzanne Sanchez, Kay Sanders, Ned Serleth, Mary Shanks, Nancy Schlietz, Peggy Shelton, Linda Sherman, Richard Simpson, Daniel Skanson, Jim Slaughter, Gloria Small, Linda Smith, Karen Snavely, Caroline Snow, Charles Soria, Carol Spangler, Michael Stewart, Roberta Stewart, Wanda Stinson, Larry Stonecipher, Brenda Stonecipher, Susan Streb, Pat Sullivan, Pamela Swearingen, Linda Turnborn, Rick Veatch, Marianne Webster, Cathy Ann Welch, Amy Welden, Susan Wells, Joyce Whittet, Andy White, Dean Williams, Ruth Windmuller, Twyla Wofford, Helen Woody, Lynn Worch, Barry Worczak, Jeff Wymer, Bonnie Yeager, Lee Young, Patricia Zalo, Carolyn Zaugg, Bill Zeller, Kathy Zentmyer

# Project WILD®

Project WILD National Office
Council for Environmental Education
5555 Morningside Drive, Suite 212
Houston, TX 77005
Phone: (713) 520-1936
Fax: (713) 520-8008
E-mail info@projectwild.org
Web www.projectwild.org

## Council for Environmental Education Staff

Josetta Hawthorne
Executive Director

Bill Andrews
Director, Project WILD

Mary Ford
Sr. Manager, Project WILD

Jennifer Paschke
Manager, Program Communications

Marc LeFebre
Sr. Coordinator, Flying WILD

Jeff Dornbos
Coordinator, Water Education Programs

Beshka Candelaria
Coordinator, Water Education Programs

Angee Austin
Business Administrator

Lanese Bush
Administrative Assistant CEE

Leslie Sun
Intern

Sara Yerger
Intern

# Project WILD Supplementary Resources

## Resources Available for Purchase

The following resources may be purchased from the Project WILD National Office. An order form may be obtained by accessing the Project WILD website at **www.projectwild.org** or by contacting the National Office by phone at (713) 520-1936 or by fax at (713) 520-8008.

### *Taking Action: An Educator's Guide to Involving Students in Environmental Action Projects,* 74 pages, 1995.

Developed in cooperation with the World Wildlife Fund, *Taking Action* inspires ideas and provides models for conducting effective environmental projects. From adopting species to protecting habitats to saving energy, this guide will help educators plan, implement, and evaluate environmental action projects. Samples of more than 30 projects from around the country provide a glimpse of how groups of students have recognized a need in their community and successfully worked together to implement change.

### *WILD School Sites: A Guide to Preparing for Habitat Improvement Projects on School Grounds,* 56 pages, 1993.

This guide helps students and teachers learn about the importance of biodiversity, understand the basic steps of creating a wildlife habitat, develop a plan for action, and gain community support. The purpose of this guide is to assist educators and their students in taking responsible action to improve their communities for people and wildlife, beginning on their school grounds.

### *"Exploring School Nature Areas,"* Video, 1994.

Produced in cooperation with St. Olaf College's "School Nature Area Project," this video is designed to demonstrate the value of school sites and school nature areas. The video, targeted for teachers and administrators, provides examples of outdoor classrooms around the country and shows students in action at school sites. The purpose of the video is to motivate educators and students to initiate environmental action projects that will improve habitats for wildlife and people.

### *WILD About Elk: An Educator's Guide,* 80 pages, 2003.

This guide is a product of the Rocky Mountain Elk Foundation and CEE. *WILD About Elk* provides a summary of the biology and ecology of elk. Topics addressed include elk's physical characteristics and adaptations, habitat and historical range, behavior, life cycles, social structure, migratory patterns, and the present and historical relationships between elk and humans. A primary message woven throughout the guide is the importance of habitat to the elk's survival. Activities in the guide assist educators in helping their students learn about elk and their habitat.

### *Correlations to the National Science Education Standards,* 36 pages, 2002.

To meet the demands of education reform, Project WILD has developed a correlation of the *Project WILD K–12 Curriculum and Activity Guide* (2nd Edition) and *Project WILD Aquatic K–12 Curriculum and Activity Guide* (2nd Edition) to the *National Science Education Standards* (the *Standards*). This document is divided into three sections: K–4, 5–8, and 9–12. Each of the activities has been correlated to an assessment rubric that indicates the fundamental concept taught in each activity. Using this document, educators can easily fit Project WILD activities into their lesson plans by following the user-friendly format for each section of the *Standards*.

*Correlations to Excellence in Environmental Education: Guidelines for Learning,*
72 pages, 2002

To meet the demands of education reform, Project WILD has developed a correlation of the *Project WILD K–12 Curriculum and Activity Guide* (3rd edition) and *Project WILD Aquatic K–12 Curriculum and Activity Guide* (3rd edition) to the *North American Association of Environmental Education's Excellence in Environmental Education: Guidelines for Learning.* Each of the activities has been correlated to an assessment rubric that indicates the fundamental concept taught in each activity. Using this document, educators can easily fit Project WILD activities into their lesson plans by following the user-friendly format for each section of the *Guidelines.*

*Proyecto WILD: Traducción en Español de Las Guías del Plan de Estudios y Actividades del Jardín de Niños Hasta La Preparatoria,*
240 pages, 1998.

This guide contains 34 translated activities taken from *Project WILD K–12 Curriculum and Activity Guide* and *Project WILD Aquatic K–12 Curriculum and Activity Guide.* The Spanish supplement introduces Project WILD to new audiences—teachers; scout leaders; school volunteers; parks and recreation staff members; and nature center, zoo, and museum staff members—who live and work in primarily Spanish-speaking communities. Project WILD hopes that these materials will open the outdoors to a new generation of students and volunteers.

*Water Watchers: Conserving Water at Your School and Home*
104 pages, 2005.

*Water Watchers* is an additional resource offered for purchase by the Council for Environmental Education. It is designed to provide educators with a framework for mentoring a student-driven audit of water use–and waste–at school and in their homes. Lessons in the guide are arranged to lead students from awareness of basic conservation concepts and issues to responsible action and stewardship of their water environment. Visit **www.wetcity.org** for more information.

## Resources Available through Workshops

The following resources may be obtained by attending a workshop. For information on workshops in your area, please contact your state Project WILD Coordinator. Contact information can be found on the Project WILD website at www.projectwild.org or by contacting the National Office by phone at (713) 520-1936 or by fax at (713) 520-8008.

*Science and Civics: Sustaining Wildlife,*
300 pages, 2005.

Supported by the National Environmental Education and Training Foundation (NEETF), Environmental Protection Agency, and ConocoPhillips, this guide is designed to meet the expressed need of secondary educators and administrators for materials that will prepare students to select and implement environmentally focused service learning projects. The program will also help teachers and students meet state course requirements by using the environment as a means to apply science, social studies, and other disciplines to real-world situations. This curriculum guides students in the investigation of wildlife concerns and encourages them to collaborate their findings in responsible action projects that benefit wildlife, people, and the environment.

*Flying WILD: An Educator's Guide to Celebrating Birds,* 358 pages, 2004.

As a companion program to Project WILD, Flying WILD provides cross-curricular activities for learning about birds and their conservation needs. The guide provides a complete set of guidelines and resources for implementing a bird festival, a key component of Flying WILD, in which students take a leading role. Three activity sets include those led by teachers prior to a festival, festival activities led by adult volunteers, and festival activities designed for middle school students (grades 6-8) to teach. While focusing on subjects involving migratory birds, Flying WILD complements and supports many of the concepts presented through Project WILD program publications.

# Alphabetical Listing

## Notes